The **BABY**
MACHINE

The BABY MACHINE

Reproductive Technology and the Commercialisation of Motherhood

Edited by
Jocelynne A. Scutt

GREEN PRINT

This edition first published in 1990 by
Green Print
an imprint of The Merlin Press
10 Malden Road, London NW5 3HR

Original edition first published 1988 by McCulloch Publishing,
Australia

ISBN 1 85425 053 1

Cover design by William Webb.
Typesetting reproduced from the Australian edition.
Printed in England by Biddles Ltd., Guildford, Surrey on recycled
paper.

Contents

ACKNOWLEDGMENTS

A strong memory of the early 1970s is reading Schulamith Firestone's (now classic) *Dialectic of Sex*. Agreeing with many of her propositions and particularly, with her, that women's liberation will not be achieved until children's liberation advances — indeed, that the two must go hand in hand — I was yet unable to empathise with Firestone's view that test tubes and glass wombs would free women from childbearing, and thus would women become 'free'. My misgivings — more, profound disagreement — crystallised when Dianne Wyndham and others published a discussion paper in 1982 on behalf of the Women's Electoral Lobby in Sydney, calling for a moratorium on reproductive engineering programmes. Later, the work of Robyn Rowland and Ramona Koval, amongst others, in publishing the negative features of *in vitro* fertilisation and other new reproductive technologies, and their profound effects and potential effects on the humanness and humane-ness of the world led me, as it has led many other women, to recognise the need for being outspoken about these new forms of human (and other primate) exploitation.

I am grateful to the foregoing and to the women attending the Emergency Conference on the New Reproductive Technologies held in Vallinge, Sweden in 1985 (particularly Gena Corea, Jalna Hanmer, Renate Klein, Janice Raymond and Maria Mies) for the consciousness raising which led to the production of *The Baby Machine — The Commercialisation of Motherhood*.

For their support and good work in the production of the book I appreciate Beth Wilson (for comment), Margaret Boundy (for editorial work), Deborah Barnes (for editing), and Elizabeth Wood Ellem (for indexing). For ever-continuing support I thank Robin Joyce, Felicity Beth, Di Graham, Kerry Heubel, Jennifer Aldred, Lesley Norris and Yvonne Carnahan (Burman), and Fleur Joyce, Kate McMullen and Bob McMullen. To my publisher, Susan McCulloch, special thanks.

JOCELYNNE A. SCUTT
Melbourne, Australia
May, 1988

Foreword

This volume documents the time in which we live; one characterised by increasing scientific and medical intervention in women's bodies. Today women in the South and East of the world are sterilised and given dangerous contraceptives in order to restrict child-bearing while women in the West and North are manipulated technologically in order to encourage child-bearing. Within industrialised countries the same pattern exists between ethnic and racial groups, so that for example in Britain it is easier to obtain an abortion if a woman is black and working class and much more difficult if she is white and a university student.

Today skin colour and social class converge to weight women's chances of being selected as a 'fit' or 'unfit' reproducer and a range of new techniques, including the selection of 'perfect' embryos, are being utilised to ensure the appropriate outcomes. Tomorrow the range of techniques to more closely control these processes will be greatly extended. Thus issues that at first glance may appear unrelated – IVF, surrogacy, biotechnology, genetic manipulations, interventions in conception, embryo research, eugenics, infertility, pregnancy, childbirth, motherhood, fathers' rights, women's reproductive choice and rights, law and commerce, and the relations between science, technology and society – take on a coherence when examined from the position of women in society.

The title of this book is taken from a woman's description of how the new reproductive technologies made her feel; dehumanised, a baby machine, but – more than that – at the same time blameworthy if she did not fulfil her machine status. In the destruction of her self-esteem and the confirmation that she does not count for anything in her own right lies the anger that fuels resistance; if not by this woman, then by others who believe she is neither to blame nor only a womb with eggs to develop. This perspective informs the contributions to this collection.

The division of women into body parts, objectified, reduced to the carriers of male genetic material, the beneficiaries of male largesse, is epitomised by the smiling white coated 'father' of hundreds of IVF babies that regularly grace our daily newspapers and television sets. But this is not simply a male professional take-over of women's biological activities moving smoothly from tradi-tional forms of conception, pregnancy and birth into those involving further commerce and the legal and ethical restructuring that is required when women's bodies are commercially developed to the full. Current commercial developments include obtaining material from women's bodies for experimentation in order to devise new interventions into life processes; acquiring the products of women's reproductive labour – that is, children – for commercial transaction; and correcting reproductive 'defects' for commercial gain.

We need to listen to those whose bodies constitute the prime experimental matter for the control and replication of life processes in order to further our understanding of both potential and current social transformations that are deeply affecting women. Australian women, who form the majority of contributors to this volume, were amongst the first to recognise the implications for women as Aus-tralia is a world-leader in the scientific, technological and commer-cial development of genetic and reproductive engineering. World leadership is, of course, contested terrain as scientific and medical teams and commercial developers jostle in the global arena. This volume offers a view from women, both as objects of these interven-tions and as critical protagonists.

The campaigns to improve the civil status of women in the nineteenth century made lasting improvements in women's lives, particularly in relation to our status as wives. The struggle to improve the status of women as biological producers of new life is with us today. But what to defend and how? As our biological selves are progressively destabilised, we are inevitably drawn into a painful reassessment of old certainties. Recognising the subjectivity of women in theory and in life is an obvious bottom line and one that challenges abstract statements of principle, whether in the language of rights, of choice, or of 'helping' women. By starting from the experiences of women and analyses of the social processes in which women's experiences are embedded, we can demystify the question of who benefits and how from reproductive and genetic engineering.

There is an urgency about this work that emotionally enlivens the text as an acceptance of women's experiences and analyses as socially legitimate is essential in order to further the well-being of all women. The empowerment of women in relation to reproductive and genetic engineering cannot proceed as long as women's voices continue to be excluded from public debate and understanding. But just as the issues for women are not confined within specific countries, neither are the critiques and analyses. *The Baby Machine* is a welcome addition to a very necessary expanding international literature.

JALNA HANMER
Senior Lecturer in Social Work
Co-ordinator, MA/Dip Women's Studies (Applied)
University of Bradford

Introduction

Jocelynne A. Scutt

The major slogan of the women's liberation movement is a demand
for control over our own bodies.

Jalna Hanmer, 1985*

In 1971 the American feminist Schulamith Firestone prophesied
that when women's reproductive function is taken over by technology— with children being conceived in test-tubes and nurtured
in glass wombs housed in medical laboratories—women's potential
for 'true' liberation will be met. Once women no longer produce
babies, asserted Firestone, women will automatically be equal with
men, liberation assured. Yet well on the way to twenty years after
Firestone wrote her influential book, *The Dialectic of Sex*,[1] the
reality is shaping up differently. In the years since she formulated
her thesis, changes have come about in reproductive technology
which might not have been thought possible (at least by the general
public) back in the early 1970s. Today it is a relatively usual event
to read of a new born child, conceived by artificial insemination,
brought to life in a petri dish or, sometimes, carried to term by a
'surrogate' mother. Talk abounds of genetic screening for detecting
and correcting perceived flaws in fetuses, of gene therapy 'around
the corner' (or even here). But are women better off?

In many analyses, women's oppression has been laid at the door
of child-bearing. Yet to assume that the biological function of procreation is solely the cause of women's oppression is evidently
wrong: prepubescent women, infertile women, childless women
and women after menopause all suffer sex-based discrimination as
do mothers rearing children produced from their own wombs. The

---

*"Transforming Consciousness: Women and the New Reproductive Technologies"
in Gena Corea, Duelli Klein, Jalna Hanmer, Robyn Rowland. *Man-Made Women—
How New Reproductive Technologies Affect Women* (editors/contributors) 1985,
Hutchinson, London, p. 93.

argument that women will become 'free' through handing over the reproductive function to test-tubes and laboratories assumes that traditional mothering—child-care and child-rearing—either does not in itself oppress women, or that children brought to term in artificial wombs will be equally likely to be cared for, on 'birth', by men as by women; and that this non-sex linked mode of bringing up children will in fact occur. But without massive social and political change, it is futile to assert that child-care and child-rearing will become non-sex based responsibilities.

To assume that freedom from nurturing during gestation and from giving birth, through the intervention of technology, should grant women freedom and equality also assumes that technology is not patriarchal—or at least that women will control (or be in equal control of) biological technology. Both assumptions are incorrect. Genetic and reproductive engineering exist in a world where women and men are not equal; genetic and reproductive engineering arise out of and are incorporated into that reality. As Robin Burns says:

> Science does have an implicit worldview of the human being and of society as technically manipulable objects; this is translated into an ideology for socio-political practice through the application of empirical or pseudo-empirical techniques to the solution of social problems. Because of the power and interest structure in science as a sub-culture, and because it contains in itself no adequate means for evaluation of its normative aspects, its myths and applications become self-perpetuating.[2]

Women scientists and medical practitioners are not produced in equal numbers with men; where they exist, they do not have equal power with their male colleagues. Men dominate, too, in the world of agricultural and veterinary science, where genetic and reproductive engineering technologies have their origins. In nursing, where women predominate—at least in numbers—little control is exercised over reproductive technology or genetic engineering. Technological reproduction programmes and genetic engineering teams are fostered, run and controlled by male scientists, male practitioners, and male veterinary surgeons. Certainly women may 'profit' from advances in genetic and reproductive engineering, 'fulfilling' themselves by becoming mothers, or being future mothers of 'perfect' children, yet women will not truly benefit from this research.

In vitro programmes are projected as a boon for infertile women.

Yet, as Gena Corea points out in *The Mother Machine* (dealing in the main with the United States' scene):

> . . . the vast majority of women enrolled in in vitro fertilization programs have not been helped and . . . many have suffered during the experimentation on their bodies. This fact has not surfaced. What has been allowed to surface is that a (white) woman in this city or that has had a baby through IVF and is extremely happy.[3]

She goes on to say that rather than bringing new and real hope to women unable to bear children, the programmes may well bring new despair:

> A few years earlier, a woman could at some point, however painfully, come to terms with her infertility, go on with her life, find a way to live it fully. Now there is no easy way off the medical treadmill. She may now spend a major part of her adult life in debilitating treatment in experimental programs. There is always a promising new program to enrol in, its low success rate played down, its 'hope' played up. The years roll on.[4]

The situation in the United States of America is replicated in Australia and elsewhere. As Ramona Koval and Jocelynne Scutt point out in Chapter 2, 'Genetic and Reproductive Engineering—All for the Infertile?' it is untrue that IVF and other reproductive programmes service only those who have never before borne children. On the contrary, many provide the technology to women who have previously given birth and to men who have fathered children, and who wish to add to their already established family, or parent children in a new marriage. 'Success' rates are low. Those running the programmes give statistics for 'pregnancy rates' not for live births. Pregnancy rates are calculated to include changes in hormonal levels which, though not resulting in a pregnancy and live birth, are described as having been early pregnancies resolved by spontaneous miscarriage. Millions of dollars are spent on reproductive technology and genetic engineering, yet little is spent on researching the causes of infertility and endeavouring to eliminate those causes, so that artificial reproduction methods become unnecessary.

Are women passing through *in vitro* fertilization programmes really able to resolve their feelings about being infertile? Are the pictures of proud mothers holding babies produced through reproductive engineering techniques typical? Christine Crowe talked with women on IVF programmes in New South Wales, over three years. Not all the women with whom she spoke were overtly critical, but all had doubts, fears and anxieties about participating in these technological 'advances'. Once in a programme, the women's lives become caught in a whirlpool of doctors' appointments, hospital visits, tests, invasive examinations, surgery, disappointment, hope, despair—with only the very occasional birth of a child. (Even then, as Koval and Scutt explain, the pregnancy and birth might well have occurred without the technological invasion—and that invasion may itself have delayed the pregnancy!) In Chapter 3, 'Bearing the Consequences—Women Experiencing IVF' Crowe discloses the real feelings of women who have become statistics in a battle for greater funding and higher recognition, clinics committed to making a name for 'making babies'—and reputations of those running the 'teams', with more fêting, more funding.

Women entering the programmes, or tempted to enter them, are not necessarily women who have been brought to see their only or major identity in terms of pregnancy, childbirth, mothering. In 'Off the Treadmill—Leaving an IVF Programme Behind' Chapter 4, Isobel Bainbridge, interviewed by Anna Murdoch, comments on her confrontation with infertility and the belief that she wanted to bear 'a child of her own'. She began a programme in Victoria—but after seven attempts decided to abandon the venture and regain fulfilment through her work, and by coming to terms with her life as a full human being.

Another perspective of women involved in the new reproductive technologies is given by Terese McFadden in 'Surrogate Motherhood—Refusing to Relinquish a Child', at Chapter 5. She was interviewed by the husband of a couple seeking a woman to bear a child for them—the wife was infertile. She agreed and went through the procedure, the pregnancy and the birth—finally deciding to keep the child. (Her husband agreed.) One clause of her 'contract' provided that she should not 'attempt to form a parent/child relationship' with the child she agreed to bear. As she writes: 'Those having had a child will realise the parent/child relationship begins long before birth.'

Australia is recognised as pre-eminent in genetic and reproductive engineering. This fact has been used to lobby governments for extra funding, and for legislative recognition of the procedures. In the current economic climate, where there is a struggle for the development and support of profitable and productive industries, reproductive and genetic engineering may be viewed as an ideal 'sunrise industry'—an opportunity to develop and commercially exploit a new Australian based industry. It is almost inevitable that governments will support these programmes rather than less glamorous programmes based on preventive health measures.

Why is Australia in the forefront of genetic and reproductive engineering? Marion Brown, Kay Fielden and Jocelynne A. Scutt point out in Chapter 6, 'New Frontiers—Or Old Frontiers Recycled? New Reproductive Technologies as Primary Industry', it surely has a connection with the long-existing 'populate or perish' syndrome peculiar to Australia, in combination with Australia's primary producing role. The development of genetic engineering in the plant world, for example rust resistant wheat and artificial insemination of cattle and other farm animals in the agricultural business, has long been known. Developments in human medicine often follow developments in the plant and animal world, and this is nowhere more evident than in the world of reproductive technology.

Who is gaining from the development and support of these programmes? A number of medicos (and at least one veterinary surgeon) involved with the programmes appear to have gained a deal of ego boosting from the publicity and adulation of those involved in the programmes (although that adulation may be tenuously held, as the reports of women subjects reveal). In Chapter 7, 'The Commercialisation of Reproductive Technology', Ramona Koval describes the quest for a child through reproductive technologies, and the quest for the 'perfect' product—the perfect embryo, fetus and child—through genetic engineering. She points out that these quests are big business in the making. Alliances are developing between business and universities in this new growth area. Australia has been faced with commercialisation of these reproductive technologies in the example of Monash University approving the establishment of a commercial venture, organised to sell the technology overseas. This new development came about disturbingly—little information was made available to the Monash University council (although it approved the venture), and even less to the public (which, after all, funds the university). Koval writes of attempts to keep research 'under wraps', away from possible competitors. This has serious implications for academic research—which traditionally has been 'open', without the secrecy so often found in research funded by industry.

The world of big business is being served not only through the development of reproductive and genetic technologies and their exploitation, but through the necessary intervention of the legal profession. Patent lawyers, lawyers involved in trade practices, commercial lawyers, family law practitioners, and lawyers involved in medical negligence are now presented with new fields. To leave the law as it was and develop these new technologies, means lawyers are provided with an area ripe for application of common law and existing statutory law. But changing the law to accommodate the technologies, as is now occurring, means lawyers have an area equally ripe for litigation, particularly as the laws vary from state to state and country to country.

The law is a two-edged sword, not least where women's rights are concerned. As Jocelynne A. Scutt points out in 'Disturbing Connections—Natural and Artificial Conception and the Right to Choose', Chapter 9, no sooner had women begun to gain some reproductive rights and freedoms in the more ready availability of safe, legal abortion, than laws were being drafted to cover new reproductive technologies—laws which may well threaten those hard won gains. Just as medicine is becoming 'fetal centred' with the expected child being viewed as 'the patient', the mother only as patient-carrier, is the law edging toward a concept of fetal rights which endangers women's rights? And are we now in a position of having to endorse access to *in vitro* programmes on the basis of the cry that it's 'a woman's right to choose'? Or is choice an empty word where these developments are concerned?

Once the child is born, custody battles may be fought out in courtrooms. Legal battles may erupt over who owns the technology, who owns the inventions, and whether trade secrets in genetic engineering or reproductive technologies have been stolen. Lawyers will be necessary to sort it out. There will be battles if the child is born 'defective'—when the parents expected a 'perfect' embryo. What if the 'surrogate' mother smoked or drank through the pregnancy, in contravention of contractural terms, and the intending parents now want to absolve themselves from responsibility for the child's custody and welfare, fearing the child has somehow become harmed? And does the child created through the new technologies, who is born blind or deaf, or suffering from some genetic disease, have an action against the doctor? The parents against the mother who refused to undergo prenatal testing? As Scutt writes in Chapter 10, 'Women's Bodies, Patriarchal Principles—Genetic and Reproductive Engineering', even if no one else wins through litigation, the lawyers will!

Although some would like the law not to be involved, this is impossible. The law already holds principles applicable to the new reproductive technologies and to circumstances arising out of their application, or the application of genetic engineering techniques. The laws exist. The question is, what new laws are being devised, and how will they operate? Scutt points out that the legal systems existing in the United States, Britain, Canada, Australia and New Zealand—possibly the world over—are based in patriarchal notions of child ownership, motherhood and paternity. These laws are little concerned with women's strivings for autonomy, or women's right to recognise not our ownership of our bodies, but our bodies as ourselves; and children's rights not to be property, not to be trammelled in notions of ownership.

These notions have a long history, in law and in medicine. In 'Women, Pregnancy and Childbirth—Plus ça change encore la même chose', at Chapter 1, Joanne Finkelstein traces the wresting of healing and childbirth out of the hands of women into the hands of professionals—mostly (and for a long time only) men. Midwifery was gradually down-graded until it became a second class or outlawed vocation, in the face of the licenced (male) medical practitioner, the obstetrician and gynaecologist. 'Care' can be taken of women's bodies, of women in pregnancy and childbirth. And money can be made. The very nature of professionalism is its money base. 'Formal medicine is instrumental in confining women to the relatively restricted social role of mother', writes Finkelstein. It is also a means of extracting larger and larger sums of money for medical intervention on all sorts of grounds.

Although some—such as Edward Shorter in *The History of Women's Bodies*[5]—would act as advocates for the medical profession, arguing that women's lives and health have been greatly improved by the coming of the male medico, others—such as Barbara Ehrenreich and Deidre English in *For Her Own Good*[6]—would contend that male intervention has led to women's confinement. 'Improved medical conditions' have too often come about to remedy problems caused by earlier 'improvements' in the world of pregnancy and childbirth. Rather than removing the causes of those problems, yet another form of male technology is used to 'correct' the first. The layer upon layer of technology, technology 'correcting' technology, 'correcting' technology endlessly, costs money. As Finkelstein says, 'lying flat on the back with knees bent, legs in stirrups, increases a woman's sense of exposure and degree of passivity, as well as preventing her from adopting a position of greatest natural leverage to ease birth'. This 'creates conditions in which the woman requires further interventions and assistance, such as drugs for augmenting contractions, and episiotomies'. Episiotomies are not costless. Drugs are not free.

The women's movement has worked hard to regain for women some control over conditions of pregnancy and birthing. The homebirth movement has forced hospitals to reduce their clinical outlook, introducing birthing centres in hospitals and encouraging fathers (and sometimes older children of the family) to be present at the birth. Yet simultaneously there has been a greater acknowledgement by the medical profession that where pregnancy and childbirth are concerned, the fetus and newborn infant hold their attention. 'Care' for the mother-to-be has been replaced by concern for the well-being of the child-to-be. The woman's body is seen as a container or receptacle, holding the baby. In reproductive technologies the woman's role in procreation is considered as secondary to the role of the 'medico-father', creator of the technology, and to the child resulting from it.

Finkelstein's analysis of the history of pregnancy and childbirth and its links to the new reproductive technologies and genetic engineering connects with Koval and Scutt's exposure of the great infertility debate, male technologies in the area of health, and male interventions in the environment, frequently lead to infertility. Ironically, male interventions of this nature do not result in infertility in women alone. Thus, although it seems apparent that pesticides such as 2,4,5-T and 2,4-D may have a strong link with birth defects[7] and possibly infertility, and that the use of Agent Orange and other chemicals during warfare harmed not only 'the enemy', but also United States, Australian and New Zealand military in Vietnam[8] the longterm damaging effects may be 'corrected' with reproductive and genetic engineering. So prevention, through not resorting to chemical warfare, and the search for other ways to maintain the ecological balance, retreat in the face of the 'technological fix'. Bad technology is matched with 'corrective' technology. More money, more harm. Women (and men) remain infertile, but (male) technology produces—wham!—the longed-for baby (but only sometimes). Male technology distorts nature, then (expensively) beats nature at her own game.

Meanwhile, those who are least able to pay are those who bear the greatest burden. Gena Corea writes in Chapter 8, 'Women, Class and Reproductive and Genetic Engineering—The Effect of New Reproductive Technologies on All Women', of the class bias of male technological developments in pregnancy and childbearing. This bias may divide women, yet leave us all, ultimately, disadvantaged. Does patriarchy govern the reality of choice for all women? Is 'choice' real for women married to middle class men, living in a sexist society? Women with working class husbands are patently vulnerable, their 'choice' even more problematic. Women in the lower socio-economic levels are, where necessary, used for experimentation when new reproductive technologies are devised, just as they have always been used when new contraceptive measures have been introduced. But if those women *want* new reproductive procedures they cannot have them—they do not have the money with which to make their choice felt.

Perhaps it is significant that the first mother of a 'test tube' baby, Lesley Brown, faced with a possible life-time career on the factory floor, was not middle-class. But neither was she the 'lucky' recipient of largesse of the doctors involved in producing the technology. Rather, she was the unrealising subject of an experiment. As she was reported to have said after the birth, she had not known that she was destined to be the first such mother. She had believed that there were many others. She was not told she was participating in an experiment. Little wonder she was not a member of a socio-economic level where, had there been errors, complaints might have been felt more bitterly by the medicos concerned—through loss of custom, or even damages suits through the courts. How many other women were used in the experiment before the successful birth? How many were failures? How many depressed or distraught women were in those clinical trials?

It is time for all women to fight back. Renate D. Klein writes in 'Genetic and Reproductive Engineering—The Global View', Chapter 11, of international alliances favouring the new exploitation of women, women's bodies, and the reproductive function; and those international alliances of women fighting to regain our bodies for ourselves, and our own control over our reproductive abilities. She recounts the efforts of the masculine world to exercise some control over technologies produced by their male colleagues—such as setting up ethics committees in hospitals, research bodies and universities—and pinpoints their failure to exhibit any real concern for women, or for children as autonomous beings.

Fighting back, women have held state, provincial, national and international conferences in Britain, the United States, Sweden, Australia, Canada, Europe, Japan, and elsewhere in the world. Women are planning further international action. But, Klein concludes, women cannot just be *against*. Women must produce constructive alternatives and new ideas for science, for women's health and for the social and medical problems of infertility.

Women and the world have a right to see the underlying background to the new reproductive technologies and genetic engineering. Far from being designed to give women more choices about reproduction and life styles, these techniques are designed to bring to their male inventors glory, (misplaced) gratitude, and recognition in the marketplace. This is done only through experimentation and surgical intervention on women's bodies. The commercialisation of motherhood is now a global industry, based on seemingly sophisticated technology. It satisfies masculine demands for economic development, ego boosting, and control of reproduction. As the United Nations revealed in 1980:

> Women constitute half the world's population, perform nearly two-thirds of its work hours, receive one-tenth of the world's income and own less than one-hundredth of the world's property.[9]

At least two-thirds of the world's production is created and performed by women, yet men control production. The world's human reproduction is created and performed almost 100 per cent by women. Yet men, too, aim to control reproduction.

In *The Mother Machine*, published in 1985, Gena Corea writes:

> The issues surrounding the new reproductive technologies are confusing. Sometimes our heads spin. The benevolent rationales for the technologies and images of kindly, smiling pharmacrats* swirl around in our brains along with our sense that when we are called 'living incubators' and 'oocyte [egg] donors', all is not well. We are *supposed* to be confused. The confusion keeps us speechless and powerless. It is as a Native American friend once told me: Confusion is a tool of oppression.
>
> While we are struggling out of our confusion and into speech, we must stubbornly stay with our sense of uneasiness and think it through. We cannot allow ourselves to be bullied into acquiescence with a 'tolerant' view of the technologies simply because we are not yet able to fully articulate why the benevolent rationales for these technologies clash with our sense of our own dignity and worth. We can stand stubbornly and say: 'Something is wrong here', and explain that 'something' to the best of our ability. Each time we do it, we will get better at it.
>
> When many women break the silence, when many women finally speak the truth, and speak it again and again and again, the world will have to change.[10]

*"Pharmacy" comes from the Greek root *pharmakon* for "medicine" and is analogous to "theocracy", rule by God or priests, and "democracy", rule by the people. Corea refers to physicians, embryologists and others involved in professional reproductive and genetic engineering as pharmacrats. See Gena Corea, *'The Mother Machine'*, 1985, Harper and Row, New York, p. 2.

The Baby Machine—The Commercialisation of Motherhood uses Corea's urging as its guide. Our contributions have developed out of a sense of our own dignity and worth, and the profound clash with that sense of the 'advances' described in *The Baby Machine*, is another break in the silence. It joins with the voices of women in Australia and abroad; speaking our truth, to join with their truth—again and again, so the world *must* change.

Endnotes

1. Shulamith Firestone, *The Dialectic of Sex: The Case for Feminist Revolution*, 1971, Jonathan Cape, London.
2. Robin Burns, *Science, Values and Education* unpublished paper, 1985 School of Education, La Trobe University, Victoria, Australia.
3. Gena Corea, *The Mother Machine—Reproductive Technologies from Artificial Insemination to Artificial Wombs*, 1985, Harper and Row, New York, at p.6.
4. Gena Corea, 1985, at p.6.
5. Edward Shorter, *A History of Women's Bodies*, 1982, Allen Lane, London.
6. Barbara Ehrenreich and Deidre English, *For Her Own Good: 150 years of the Experts' Advice to Women*, 1978, Anchor Press/Doubleday, Garden City, New York.
7. For example, in Coffs Harbour, New South Wales, women have been concerned about the number of births taking place where the children are genetically affected—for example, with hare lips and other such defects. They have attributed it to the heavy use of pesticides in the area, where various crops are grown—for example, Kiwi fruit or Chinese Gooseberries, bananas and so on. Research has been carried out which appears strongly to confirm this. See Coffs Harbour Women's Health Centre, *The Bulletin—Bush Telegraph of the Coffs Harbour Women's Health Centre*, April/May 1986, at p. 7.
8. Evidence to the Royal Commission on Agent Orange, conducted in Australia (established by the federal government) over the years 1984-1986. It should be noted that the Report of the Royal Commission absolved Agent Orange from any involvement in the defects listed by veterans and others giving evidence as to research and surveys, however the results of the Commission have caused some controversy in this regard. See Jock McCulloch, *The Politics of Agent Orange*, 1984, M.I.T., Ma. (distributed in Australia by Heinemann).
9. *United Nations Report*, 1980. See generally Robin Morgan, *Sisterhood is Global, The International Women's Movement Anthology*, 1984, Penguin Books, Harmondsworth, England.
10. Gena Corea, 1985, at pp.322-323.

1 Women, pregnancy & childbirth

Joanne Finkelstein

Plus ça change encore la même chose*

Women's relationship with scientific medicine has long been unhappy. It has been shaped by a belief that biology is destiny, that women are principally childbearers because females are capable of gestation and birth. Whilst women are therefore seen as crucial to the survival of society, the childbearing role has also been a source of women's constraint and containment. Women's other activities, such as participation in society at large, have been contingent upon female capacities as childbearers. Throughout history, the status of women has been made relative to their biological capacity to reproduce and, in the twentieth century, the historical contingency is still much in evidence.

In all societies control over the size and growth of the human population has been vitally important. In this way it has been necessary to control the female's capacity for birth. Such controls have been internally exercised through taboos of infanticide and incest, and externally apparent through the provision of health care and birth control, such as the availability of contraception, abortion, sterilisation, and fertility treatment. Those with control over these regulations, for example medical practitioners who supply birth technology, have immense power over the realm of individual experience, as well as over long term historical changes.[1]

*The more things change, the more they remain the same.

The history of women has been that the more things have changed with regard to reproductive procedures, the more women's social position has remained the same: that is, contingent upon biological capacities.

Formal medicine has been instrumental in confining women to the relatively narrow social role of mother. Reproductive control is irreducibly social and individual. Individual women must, for future generations, learn to value pregnancy, birth, children and family in ways that are fully compatible with wider social needs. Formal medicine has played an important part in promoting these views. Through its long history of increasingly invasive physical incursions into the female body, medicine has reinforced the belief that biological reproduction is woman's destiny. In turn, the expectation of and desire for motherhood amongst women has been a boon to medicine. It has brought women to the doctor requesting assistance in the fulfillment of that particular social expectation. At every stage of medicine's advance into women's reproductive capacities, greater control is gained over women's social future. This incremental control over women can be seen in the history of women and medicine, and in the current developments in birth technology labelled 'the new reproductive technologies'.

MEDICAL CURES FOR THE FEMALE CONDITION

For as long as women have been seen primarily through the reproductive function, any anomalies in their appearance and behaviour have been regarded as a dysfunction in their capacities. For the woman without children, husband or domestic duties, there has been a social pity. If a woman scorned that pity, it turned to moral outrage and she was recommended for medical treatment, which invariably meant an adjustment was made to her reproductive system.[2]

In the nineteenth century, with the development of anaesthesia, treatment of many conditions by surgical intervention became possible. The woman who extended herself beyond customary social roles was, in some sense, ill and needing medical treatment. Baker-Benfield reports on uses of pelvic surgery, clitoridectomy, and the removal of ovaries as remedies, treatments and cures for disorders and disturbances in women's social roles and behaviour.[3] These surgical interventions were thought to 'elevate' women, making them more moral, 'tractable, orderly, industrious and cleanly'.[4] This kind of medical thinking has dogged the social status of woman for centuries, leading to a wide range of ghastly medical treatments and experiments that have been perpetrated upon her 'for her own good'.[5]

Until the twentieth century medical practitioners regarded female independence of mind as a form of hysteria or illness directly related to the womb. Then, they were 'justified' in providing gruesome treatments such as liquification (hot water baths of ten and twelve hours duration), surgery, and social isolation in therapeutic wards, as benevolent efforts to relieve women of the discomforts and distresses of being failed females.[6]

A parallel can be drawn to contemporary medical responses to female infertility. Not having a child can be seen as a failure to occupy the customary social role of woman. Just as nineteenth century women were directed to doctors to cure them of social marginality, so the twentieth century woman can seek from medicine a way out of her anomalous condition of childlessness. In both instances, medicine has embraced the role of helping women to fulfill social demands and expectations and, in doing so, has gained for itself an experimental field with a willing population of subjects, and lucrative returns.

It seemed obvious to the modern medical practitioner of the nineteenth century that female bodies were designed for human reproduction and that all their other activities, whether self-advancing (such as education) or social in nature (such as playing sports) should be governed by the demands of reproduction. In effect, this meant that formal education outside the home, or activities in the public domain, would 'starve' the woman of energies and resources necessary to produce healthy children. Sometimes women attempted to gain control over their own bodies (by joining health movements such as homeopathy which were popular in the United States of America, or by opposing the medical orthodoxy of male practitioners in some other way). But this was seen as putting in danger their biological destinies and violating their very natures.[7] After all, human reproduction was incontestably the lot of women and it was the principle through which all else was explained: a headache, sore throat, indigestion, and poor posture were all results of weaknesses in the reproductive system. Most often, they were seen as the result of a displacement of the womb.[8]

In the twentieth century, medicine is still attempting to restore the woman to her natural condition, that of *childbearer*. This is most clear in cases of infertility, irrespective of the origins of that condition. The sick woman was, and still is, the one who cannot give birth. In this sense, the belief that a woman's biology is her destiny has remained unchanged and continues to provide a justification for invasive medicine.

Of crucial importance to the relationship between women and medicine is the realisation that human medicine requires an experimental population to develop its techniques. The treatment of women for infertility is not only fulfilling the common belief that women should bear children but is providing medicine with a voluntary experimental population from whom data on various other, not necessarily related, frontiers such as biochemistry, genetic transfer, tissue construction and so on, can be gathered. The often unacknowledged contribution of women to the progress of medicine constitutes one of the principal problems attached to the new reproductive technologies.

EARLY MEDICAL PERSPECTIVES ON WOMEN

Early medical perspectives on women are divided between the academic learning of male physicians, which was remote from actual human physiology, and the popular knowledge of women's ailments that was handed on by word of mouth and 'hands on' experience, and in some instances recorded in written form. An eleventh century treatise, *The Diseases of Women*,[9] was extremely popular in its time; it contained information on female hygiene, appearance, and child-care as well as helpful hints on how to ensnare a man. Its author was Trotula of Salerno. The diminutive of Trotula was 'old trot', a colloquial term for prostitute, but also including any independent woman who was successfully self-supporting.[10] This early compendium also gave advice on abortion, contraception, childbirth and midwifery, having drawn together the practical experiences of inestimable numbers of women. That the 'old trot' or prostitute was also an expert she-physician should be no surprise:[11] the connection between the body trades of prostitution and medicine would have been and still remains essential for the economic survival and health of at least some women.

Women confined to the church were also an early source of information on women's health, and some nunneries were known to offer refuge to women in childbirth, thus providing what amounted to early lying-in hospitals. One medical personage from the church who was celebrated for her personal healing powers and her high political connections was St Hildegard of Bingen.[12]

The history of women as physicians is specific to places and times. In western Europe, before the feudal period, the practice of medicine was the natural duty of women; the secular universities in Spain, Italy and Germany provided women with formal licences to practise medicine. In contrast, women practising as physicians in France in the thirteenth and fourteenth centuries were arrested and frequently executed.[13] Until the fifteenth century, only five women in England appear in the records as formally being physicians. By 1423, male physicians had succeeded in establishing a decree to exclude all women from the 'practyse of fysyk', thus marking a significant increment in the dominance of medicine by men. Women continued to practise medicine and write treatises on women's ailments, although the time was fast approaching when such women would be hunted down and executed as witches.[14]

The gynaecological guides and treatises on health produced in medieval times were characterised by a concern for women. It was widely accepted that women only should examine and inquire into the maladies of other women. It was solely in women's own interests to do so; furthermore, a general distrust of men's intentions with regard to women's bodies was much in evidence. A passage from a fifteenth century gynaecological guide contains an expression of wariness of male interest in female matters, which has a modern resonance:

> And although women have various maladies and more terrible sicknesses than any man knows ... they are ashamed for fear of reproof in times to come and of exposure by discourteous men who love women only for physical pleasure and for evil gratification. And if women are sick, such men despise them and fail to realise how much sickness women have before they bring them into this world. And so, to assist women, I intend to write of how to help their secret maladies so that women may aid another in her illness and not divulge her secrets to such discourteous men.[15]

Until the fifteenth century, the practice of medicine in England was carried on by hundreds of unlicensed men and women, the majority of whom were trained in their craft by direct experience. Simultaneously it was equally possible to practise medicine with little experience or sense. The lack of licensing for medical practitioners meant that the ignorant, foolish and greedy could call themselves physicians and dispense whatever potions and practices took their fancy.

The profession of medicine in these early unregulated times could be a lucrative pursuit for the accomplished physician attracting patronage of the aristocracy, and for the clever quack or charlatan who established a reputation. The state of the medical arts meant that nonsense and successful remedies existed side by side. The theoretical field of medicine, dominated by male physicians, was anti-empirical, still guided by the Galenic balance of humours and celestial forces. The practical field of medicine was populated by various characters, mostly female, some discreditable, others expert, who were soon to be swept up into the historical transformation of Europe. The vast witch hunts of the sixteenth and seventeenth centuries coincided with the beginnings of modern science and technology. Witch hunting was, in part, a battle for control over knowledge and techniques, and women in great numbers were the victims of this revolution.

For hundreds of years the struggle for medical dominion continued throughout Europe. Until the sixteenth century, women were seen as the principal healers; after the nineteenth century, men had taken over this role but, for the centuries in between, this struggle was played out in witch hunts, legal decrees for exclusivity, and persecutions.[16] The social status of women was central: as long as women were thought to be much influenced by their reproductive capacities, their control of any kind of official or responsible work (such as that of physician) was untenable. Concurrent with women's struggle for control over their own bodies was—and remains—the fight to be recognised socially as more than a means for human reproduction.

Women have long suffered from the mystery men have made of them. For centuries women were held directly responsible for producing human monstrosities. In a sixteenth century commentary on the relationship between medicine and women, Ambroise Paré declared woman's reproductive capacity her most important characteristic, and that any deformity in an infant came from her negligence. Thus, 'women sullied by menstrual blood will conceive monsters', as would those with too narrow or small a womb, or the woman with 'indecent posture (who) sat too long with her legs crossed, or pressed against her womb'. There were also those women who brought suffering because of their own vivid imaginations of frightening experiences: 'a girl as furry as a bear (was born of a mother) having looked too intensely at the image of Saint John (the Baptist) dressed in skins, along with his (own) body hair and beard, which picture was attached to the foot of her bed while she was conceiving'.[17] This idea of maternal impressions—of women passing directly to the child any vivid or strange experiences—persisted, making women vulnerable to the regulation of others. The shape of a woman's body, the manner in which she conceived, her experiences during pregnancy and her ideas and behaviour, were considered important influences on the kind of child she would deliver.

These ideas on material impressions may sound quaint, but they have modern equivalents. Means of conception, lifestyle and manner of giving birth are each considered to be major influences upon the 'normalcy' of a child. In the event of a damaged infant, the previous experiences of the woman are invoked as probable causes. Did the woman conceive by ordinary means within a stable heterosexual relationship, or by unconventional methods such as artificial insemination by donor (AID), artificial insemination by husband (AIH), *in vitro* fertilisation (IVF), or self-insemination? Did she give birth in a hospital with specialist physicians, or at home, or with a midwife? Did she smoke? Take drugs?

WOMEN'S HEALTH

Throughout the history of medical knowledge of human reproduction, equal numbers of both lucid and lunatic episodes have occurred. For some time it was thought that the womb was part of the digestive tract and ultimately attached to the mouth and nose. As well, the womb was considered to have a life of its own and thus be capable of independent action. Accordingly, in the medieval period a common means of inducing birth became the practice of placing foul-smelling items like burnt hair and oil at the women's nose and sweet smelling aromatics at her vagina. This was meant to direct the movements of the uterus away from the nose and the foul smelling objects, toward the pleasant and the vagina, to enhance delivery of the infant. With a prolapsed uterus, the odours were reversed, and the uterus by its own movements would return to its rightful place! Foolish beliefs about women's bodies contributed to a general fearfulness that women harboured untold forces and mysteries within them. In turn, the ideas about women set women apart, justifying all manner of social, religious, and political restrictions.

From the eighteenth century on, beginning with industrialism and urbanisation, women's health deteriorated markedly. Women were physically burdened and weakened by a high number of pregnancies and childbirths. Their diets often left them anaemic and unresistant to disease, and the heavy physical work and poor living conditions in the urban lower classes led to high rates of rickets and tuberculosis. Engels noted that work conditions of factories and the necessity for women to work throughout their pregnancies led to misshaping of their pelvis and the higher rates of difficult births.[18] The health of women in the upper and middle classes was little better. The informal survey of women's health recorded by Catherine Beecher from her tours across the American continent in the nineteenth century reports 'a terrible decay of female health all over the land'.[19]

Statistics on morbidity and mortality were beginning to be collected systematically as a result of the increasing use made of large public hospitals. Between 1883 and 1894 at the Mount Sinai Hospital in New York City a portrait of women's health was revealed in all its dismal and painful detail. Of the 3 687 female patients admitted, 862 (23 per cent) suffered gynaecological consequences of childbirth, including cervical lacerations, rectal, bladder and uterine prolapses, and fistulas. In 1 844 cases (50 per cent) pelvic infections including endometritis, abscesses, infections of the tubes and ovaries, and peritonitis occurred.[20]

Childbearing was a source of discomfort and illness for women, often resulting in their death. Before the nineteenth century, women had on average seven or eight pregnancies in a lifetime, and about six live births.[21] About one quarter of these pregnancies presented difficulties, like positioning of the infant in the uterus, or with the length of labour. Difficult births and repeated pregnancies often meant that women suffered from a prolapse of the uterus, or tearing of the perineum, and lacerations to the cervix and vagina. Repairs to lacerations and tears were not surgically performed, so a prolapsed uterus, for example, remained a condition for life. Remedies for procidentia—a condition created by a prolapse and often associated with continuous urinary tract infections and other debilitations—appear in the first handbook of women's health, dating from the twelfth century. This gives plausibility to the proposition that prolapse of the uterus, bladder and rectum were extremely common conditions:

> Sometimes women have such difficulty in bearing a child that the skin between the two privy members (vagina and anus) breaks apart and is just a hole, and so the uterus falls out there and grows hard. To help women in this trouble, first boil butter and wine together for half an hour; and when the liquid is warm put it in the uterus.[22]

A general practice of traditional midwifery was to puncture the amniotic sac with a sharp fingernail or instrument. This technique was thought to hasten the birth, but it actually created septic conditions by introducing foreign materials into the woman's body, and it supported a continued intervention into birthing that was entirely unnecessary. With a long labour or complications, folkloric remedies were followed, such as violent shaking of the woman, hanging her upside down by the feet and jerking her about in order to 'loosen' the infant within her. 'Version' was also employed when the position of the infant was thought harmful. Version required the birth attendant to force a hand into the womb to adjust the fetus' position. Podalic version was the position most favoured by birth attendants for the long period 1500 to 1850; it positioned the feet to point outwards through the birth canal.[23] Version was attempted when the infant was jammed against the women's pelvic bone. However, if a human hand could not push past the infant to loosen it, destructive obstetrics were employed.

'Destructive obstetrics' meant ending the infant's life during birth. Embryotomy, cutting up of the fetus in utero in order to effect its removal, and craniotomy, the practice of perforating the infant's head, evacuating the brain and sliding into the skull a large hook by which to pull out the infant, were the principal techniques. Other techniques included amputation of limbs such as when an arm or leg had entered the birth canal and jammed the infant's body sideways.[24] If these gruesome techniques did not bring about death of mother as well as infant, it was likely that the mother developed an infection proving fatal after a period of suffering.

Post-delivery sepsis or puerperal fever or childbed fever has been common among women for centuries. Traditional theories ascribed the fever to the mother's milk: lactation caused the woman's temperature to rise. Thus, all women could expect to suffer after birth; indeed, it was part of the natural process. Scientific medicine provided no explanation of the chronic fevers, debilitation and instances of death in childbirth until the late nineteenth century, when germ theory was developed. Puerperal fever reached epidemic proportions with the advent of modern medical practices such as hospital delivery with physicians in attendance. However, the realisation that pueperal fever had less to do with the intrinsics of childbearing and more to do with the manners of the birth attendant was a long time in coming. Eventually it became undeniable that the infections suffered by mothers were conveyed by the examining hand of the birth attendant. Vaginal examinations to ascertain the position of the infant or amount of cervical dilation were the practices which brought disease and death to the mother. Oliver Wendell Holmes observed this pattern of contamination, indicating it was the modern physician, busy attending various patients, who was the chief carrier of infection:

Dr Campbell of Edinburgh states that in October 1821 he assisted at the post-mortem examination of a patient who died with puerperal fever. He carried the pelvic viscera in his pocket to the classroom. The same evening he attended a woman in labour without previously changing his clothes; this patient died. The next morning he delivered a woman with forceps; she died, also, and many others were seized with the disease within a few weeks, three shared the same fate in succession . . . The occurrence of three or more closely connected cases, in the practice of one individual, no others existing in the neighbourhood, and no other sufficient cause alleged for the coincidence, is prima facie evidence that (the doctor) is the vehicle of contagion.[25]

It is difficult to tell which was a greater danger to the mother: the traditional female midwife, who might fail to distinguish the uterus from the bladder and inadvertently rupture one or other in her vaginal explorings; or the male physician, carrying with him the bacteria which would result in puerperal fever. The female midwife confined herself to the woman in labour and usually stayed with her throughout, thereby keeping to a minimum the numbers of people she attended at any one time. In contrast, the physician attended many others with varying complaints and diseases. As a carrier of contagion he was more effective. Thus childbirth at home with a traditional midwife was probably safer for the woman than a hospital delivery with a professional physician in attendance.[26]

MIDWIFERY

During the nineteenth century women's jurisdiction over their health and childbearing practices finally and totally collapsed. The initial weakening of women's control of midwifery came with the male midwife, who supposedly began his career in response to a fashion. When Louise de la Vallière, mistress of Louis XIV, had the court physician attend her in childbirth in 1663, the male midwife or 'accoucheur' was also born.[27] Before the seventeenth century in England, midwifery was a folkcraft, practised mainly by women particularly in rural areas. In urban centres a male physician also occasionally attended childbirth, usually at the request of the female midwife.[28]

During the fifteenth and sixteenth centuries, the training and regulation of midwives was under the supervision of the church. The midwife was authorised to give baptisms to infants so that those those not surviving birth were, nonetheless, incorporated into the church. Supervision of midwives by the church was mainly to protect spiritual interests; so the quality of care given by these midwives varied greatly. More than 300 years years passed before the training of midwives was formalised, regulated and made uniform, when the Obstetrical Society of London began issuing diplomas to midwives in the twentieth century.[29]

For the millennium, from Galen's abstract humours to the beginnings of empirical medicine, obstetrics was overlooked by male physicians as a defiling activity. When the male midwives began to enjoy lucrative careers, obstetrics was quickly recognised as a means of enriching the physician's livelihood. [30] During the seventeenth century the terms 'man-midwife' and 'physician man-midwife' became current, and by the 1750s there were many financially successful male midwives. One such success was the Chamberlens, a family of male midwives reputed to be the inventors of obstetrical forceps. [31] By the nineteenth century, the early aloofness of the male physicians from female medicine was completely overturned and the physicians now claimed a virtual monopoly over obstetrics, gaining full supervisory power over female midwives who still attended childbirth. What was once a defiling activity was now the bread and butter of the physician's practice.

Rural areas were serviced by the traditional female midwife until the mid-nineteenth century. [32] The male midwife operated mainly in the city. Opinions differ over the origins and success of the male midwife. Some historians regard the invention of the forceps as the principal reason for emergence of the male birth attendant. [33] The forceps was used exclusively by the Chamberlens until the 1730s. The Chamberlens are reported to have 'attended at each difficult birth, arriving in a carriage and carrying between them a massive carved chest whose contents were revealed to no-one. Even the women they delivered were blindfolded . . . [The] kit consisted of three instruments: a pair of obstetric forceps, a vectis or lever to be used in grasping the back of the head of the fetus, and a fillet or cord used to help in drawing the fetus, once disengaged from an abnormal position, out through the birth canal'. [34]

The use of forceps gave physicians and male midwives their first important technique for controlling the childbirth field, when the proprietorial rights exercised by the Chamberlen family, which increased their 'market share' of the birthing process, extended to the professions generally. Forceps allowed physicians to force the woman's labour prematurely and shorten the time of delivery. As Donnison states:

> The forceps enabled its user to deliver live infants in cases where previously either child or mother must have been lost, and also to shorten tedious labour. It thus gave the doctor or surgeon an additional advantage over the midwife (to whom custom did not allow the use of instruments as an accepted part of her practice) and so further enhanced the position of men. [35]

Although forceps were not widely used by all male midwives or doctors[36] their impact on the birth process was substantial. The decline in the status of the female midwife had already begun as the professionalisation of medicine in general was gaining momentum. In childbirth, the professional strength of medicine was gained by promulgating the idea that parturition was dangerous and should be attended by specialists. As Donnison has described:

> Men-midwives... anxious to establish their own importance in the eyes of the public ... exaggerated the dangers of childbirth and frightened women into believing that extraordinary measures, and therefore male attendance, were more generally necessary than they actually were.[37]

Men midwives argued that birthing was a 'manual operation' requiring their extra strength and dexterity, and that in order to avoid complications at birth and increase the survival rate of the infant, would-be mothers should request a male birth attendant from the outset. With the success of this idea that childbirth could be dangerous, increasing employment of physicians and male-midwives at birth was becoming common. The would-be mother was seen to be acting more responsibly if she had the services of a physician because in the event of any complications, time was not wasted replacing the female birth attendant with a male physician.[38] This attitude is entirely consonant with current views on hospital rather than home births. Birth is still depicted as a potentially dangerous event, for which all should be fully prepared — and that means having a battery of high technology on hand. Even where hospitals have adopted the 'birthing centre' approach, conceding to mainly feminist demands that birthing need not be a sterile, clinical performance, these centres are legitimised on the basis that, being in the hospital precincts, the regular panoply of 'emergency' equipment can be utilised without delay should anything 'go wrong'.

By the time of Australia's settlement, midwifery was clearly a lower status occupation. In the early years of the penal colonies few professionals were available for the necessary services. Convict women acted as midwives or, in the vernacular, 'fingersmiths', out of necessity; and women on farms had little use for trained physicians located many miles away. Women helped one another or happily accepted the skills of a local aboriginal woman.[39] As urban centres developed, the Australian community was rigidly stratified into classes and the use of a physician or midwife at the birth was determined on a class and monetary basis. By the 1800s physicians' fees were four times as great as fees of female midwives.

Melbourne established a lying-in hospital in 1856, although most women continued to give birth in their own homes or in the private residences of female midwives who sometimes used part of their own homes for delivery. So relatively few puerperal fever epidemics occurred in the early years of Australian settlement. In 1875 practices in maternity hospitals were introduced specifically to prevent puerperal fever epidemics. Midwifery nurses were kept separate from all other nurses and restricted in their passage through hospitals. Nonetheless, some outbreaks of puerperal fever occurred. As doctors in these hospitals were permitted access to all sections, it was most likely that the physicians, not the midwives, were the carriers of infection causing puerperal fever. When the New South Wales Royal Commission of 1904 investigated the declining birth rate, concluding that the female midwife was largely to blame, the condemnation was part of a general hostility to the strengthening movement for women's emancipation and had relatively little to do with assessing the medical skills of the midwife.[40]

Midwives in Australia were unable to establish a formal professional body and regulate their own standards of services until the twentieth century. Midwifery was finally incorporated into a nursing degree in 1928 although the independent midwives were not pleased with being swallowed up by the nursing profession. With the independent midwife now constrained by the requirements of a formal nursing training, the physician had full control over the field of obstetrics.[41]

A traditional opportunity for women to be economically self-supporting was now closed, due to the deterioration in the position of the midwife and the new dominance of the male medical profession over obstetrics. It also meant that the would-be mother with any feelings of modesty about childbirth had no choice but to put herself in the hands of a man.[42] The conflict between male practitioners and midwives was of profound importance to women. It altered the status of women and mothers in ways that continue to have consequences.

The emergence of the male midwife heralded the rapid commercialisation of motherhood which remains in evidence in the late twentieth century. Generally the commercial aspects of obstetrics were widely recognised in most western countries by the late eighteenth century. As obstetrics became a lucrative career, the status of parturition changed from a normal event in life to one of economic opportunity for the new professions. Accordingly, the woman in labour became a candidate for exploitation for money, and even victim of physical harm in those instances where an expedient birth was procured.

From the earliest times until the seventeenth century, personal experience of childbirth was regarded as the proper qualification for a midwife. By definition this excluded men, and meant that only mothers would attend other women in childbirth. In this way, knowledge of childbirth was maintained amongst women. For men to enter into the birth experience they either had to wrest knowledge of childbirth from the closed circle of female culture, or alter and intervene in the birth experience by introducing new methods. The second course of action has proved successful. The earliest example of birth technology, the obstetric forceps, was the exclusive tool of the male-midwife and physician, and facilitated his entry into the birth event by granting him, for the first time, some control over birth.

The control of scientific instruments and techniques has been part of male culture throughout history. Through the increasing intrusiveness of technology into *all* aspects of human functioning women's part in reproduction has been fundamentally redefined. Now the birth experience, from conception to labour (particularly in cases of extensive medical intervention, like *in vitro* fertilisation) has been removed from female culture. The mysteries of conception and birth are now becoming mysteries to women as well as men.

CONTROL OF CHILDBIRTH

The male-dominated obstetrics found in modern society reflect the current stage of the centuries-old conflict between female midwives and male physicians. Since the late nineteenth century, this conflict has been largely resolved in favour of the male practitioner, who now controls the circumstances in which most women in the western world give birth.

In this period of male dominance, some significant benefits have been gained by women. After Semmelweiss' instructions on asepsis (how to kill germs) in 1847, and Lister's introduction of antiseptics twenty years later, the rates of infant and maternal mortality have dropped quickly. Between 1860-69 death by infection per 1000 deliveries was 31.1 per cent in hospitals and 5.7 per cent at home. Between 1890-99 the rate was 2.6 per cent in hospitals and 2.1 per cent at home.[43] However, in the wider community, better sanitation, hygiene, and fewer pregnancies per woman meant that the mother and infant were in better health.

Other benefits to women included relief from the pain of birth. Analgesics and anaesthetics, particularly the introduction of 'twilight sleep' in the early years of the twentieth century, provided women with reduced birth pain. This mixture of morphine also provided women in labour with the previously unheard of experience of feelings of euphoria. Needless to say, women came to demand of their doctors the administration of these relieving medications and, in this way, childbearing could be anticipated with less fear and dread than previously. Initially, physicians were reluctant to use the new anaesthetics but by the 1920s chloroform and other anaesthetics were widely accepted. Doctors also recognised in them an opportunity to gain further dominance by 'removing' the conscious and controlling woman from the birth event — in the name of 'helping' the mother. The irony is clear. The relief of the woman's labour pains was also the lever for increasing her dependence upon the ministering medical profession.[44] As Adrienne Rich has written:

> There are certain valid reasons for the prevention of exertion by the mother — such as heart disease, tuberculosis, or a previous caesarian, but women are now asking what psychic effect a state of semi-helplessness has on a healthy mother, awake during the birth yet unable to participate actively, her legs in stirrups, her wrists strapped down, her physical engagement with the birth process minimized by drugs and by her supine position. This 'freedom' from pain, like 'sexual liberation' places a woman physically at the disposal of men though still estranged from her body. While in no way altering her subjection, it can be advertised as a progressive development.[45]

The introduction of the caesarian section had much the same effect. Before 1800, caesarian sections were performed only in dire circumstances, when the mother was dead or nearly so. Often a priest giving the last rites performed the abdominal surgery in an effort to save the child. Before anaesthesia and antiseptics, caesarian section was a dangerous and most often fatal event for the woman. Even if the woman survived the surgery she was likely to haemorrhage and die later from blood loss or infection.

Some benefits for the mother came from a caesarian section. It replaced version, the need to use high forceps, and the mutilating techniques of pubiotomy (where the woman's pelvic bone was halved and separated in order to enlarge the pelvic area and birth canal) and symphysiotomy (cutting the two pubic bones for the same reasons). As the technique of the caesarian section improved, from the early incision high on the abdomen to the current lowflap or low-segment incision, so too did the surgical skill of the obstetrician.

These specialist services employed at the modern birth increase the woman's dependence upon the medical professionals and increase her own distance from the birth event. The irony of these developments in obstetrics is that they have reduced the pain and danger of birth for women but simultaneously have marginalised women's experience and shifted the value of reproduction away from the woman and onto the newborn child and the accomplishments of the medical team.[46] Furthermore, whilst modern technology may alleviate some of the pain of childbirth, it may lead to different pain arising out of the very use of the technology: such as 'wind' from caesarians. Technologies introduced to overcome pain are too often a response to earlier interventions, for example, placing the woman on her back to give birth, rather than in a more natural, upright position which is less convenient for the doctors in attendance.[47]

The history of pregnancy and childbirth is a long series of events and developments in which women have been ill-served by formal medicine. During childbirth, women have been the hapless recipients of cruel and gruesome practices such as craniotomy or hook extraction. At other times women have been the unsuspecting victims of their doctor, as when peurperal fever epidemics were spread by the contagion carried to women by the busy physician. Bates and Lapsley.[48] Broom,[49] and the Lennanes[50] provide evidence of interventions commony perpetrated upon women in modern childbirth. These include 'benign' customs such as shaving the pubic area to more consequential and directly harmful procedures such as epidural blocks and episiotomies. All told, these interventions make childbearing a highly circumscribed event that often functions to increase the dependence of women upon the medical professional. For example, in the early years of the twentieth century, pituitrin was given to women to stimulate the uterus. This medication had the effect of expelling the infant from the birth canal in much the same explosive way that some purgatives empty the bowel. Damage to the woman's soft tissues was common and trauma to the infant was high. Nonetheless the practice continued, because it provided control over birthing to those medical professionals who were administering the drugs, and direct financial benefits to pharmaceutical companies often using high level selling mechanisms to ensure high level sales.[51]

Modern medical interventions in childbearing are employed on the basis that they improve the process, but it is unclear who benefits most. With the chemical induction of birth, benefits to the mother and infant are difficult to assess whilst those to the medical professional (and drug corporations) are clear. McKeown[52] estimated that 60 per cent of births in Britain during the 1970s were chemically induced for no other reason than convenience to the hospital and medical personnel. Induction can, of course, be of benefit to the infant threatened with oxygen or nutritional starvation *in utero* but most often it is employed to gain control over the time and length of birth. Again, an assessment of the benefits of analgesics and anaesthetics gives rise to problems. For example, the epidural block anaesthetises the abdominal area and slows down the contractions, so further drugs are required to assist the woman's labour as well as the more frequent use of forceps.[53] The birth process has been regulated and artificially controlled by medication under the direction of the physician. As well, the labouring woman is often given an episiotomy. Even though tears to the perineum have been part of birth for centuries, the use now of the controlled tear or episiotomy is rationalised by the assertion that surgical cuts are easier to heal than natural tears. This is a virtually impossible assessment to establish scientifically. After the 1930s an episiotomy was used in cases of drug-induced birth when it seemed that the infant's head would act as a battering ram that widened the birth canal by force. By the 1940s, surgical intervention had become routine and by the 1970s the episiotomy was a standard practice in most major urban hospitals.[54]

The interventionalist technique of episiotomy has become increasingly controversial. Its necessity is often attributed to the dorsal or lithotomy position women are required to assume for childbirth. The lithotomy position of lying flat on the back for delivery is relatively new and its widespread adoption is attributable to fashion and the acquired preferences of the modern physician. Lithotomy is the operation for incising the bladder to remove stones. This surgery was first performed early in the eighteenth century and required the patient to lie flat on the back, knees bent backwards onto the chest and held wide apart. The position is currently favoured for childbirth and regular gynaecological examinations, often with stirrups added for comfort. Having the woman lie flat on her back for childbirth rather than on her side or any other position increases her sense of exposure and degree of passivity as well as preventing her adopting a position of greater natural leverage.

In the modern era, pregnancy and childbirth have become areas of active management by a medical team of highly trained specialists. Looking over the hidden history of the agonies and dangers of childbirth, it may be possible to welcome the advent of modern delivery techniques, noting with relief the low rates of infant and maternal mortality in the western world. At the same time, from reviewing the history of childbirth it is possible to see that the introduction of antiseptics and analgesics have been sufficient medical intervention to mitigate many of the dangers to women in natural childbirth. However medical intervention has not remained at this level of assistance. This supports the conclusion that medical intervention in childbirth serves more interests than simply those of the mother. Childbirth and birthing processes cannot be seen in isolation from the vested interests of medical professionals in economic profits; in technological, surgical and laboratory experimentation; and in career advancement.

Since the male midwife of the seventeenth century shrewdly recognised the capital gains to be made from obstetrics, the position of the pregnant woman has become increasingly that of a supplicant, someone in need of expert advice and support . . . at a price. Modern childbirth has successfully been redefined as a potentially dangerous event for both mother and child. We cannot expect birth to be trouble-free, so the would-be mother has a moral obligation to make medical technology available to her child. In this way, birth has become a 'crisis' event, necessitating sophisticated technology under the specialised direction of highly trained physicians and technicians. Developments in childbirth and birthing technologies are replicated in the new reproductive technologies. New developments serve the interests of medical professionals, as well as (even, sometimes, instead of) the interests of women and mothers. Birth resulting from natural conception has become the example, *par excellence*, of medical dominance. Developing in the context of this tradition, could birth resulting from artificial conception be any different?

Endnotes

1.   F. Edholm, O. Harris and K. Young, "Conceptualising Women" in *Critique of Anthropology*, 1977, vol. 3, nos. 9 and 10, p. 114. See also generally Erica Bates and Helen Lapsley, *The Health Machine: The Impact of Medical Technology*, 1985, Penguin Books Australia, Ringwood, Victoria; Edward Shorter, *A History of Women's Bodies*, 1982, Penguin Books, Harmondsworth, England;
Brighton Women and Science Group, *Alice Through the Microscope: The Power of Science over Women's Lives*, 1980, Virago, London.

2.   Barbara Ehrenreich and Deidre English, *Complaints and Disorders: The Sexual Politics of Sickness*, 1973, Feminist Press, NY;
      G. J. Barker-Benfield, *The Horrors of the Half-Known Life: Male Attitudes Toward Women and Sexuality in C19th America*, 1976, Harper and Row, NY.
3.   Barker-Benfield, 1976.
4.   Ehrenreich and English, 1973, p. 35.
5.   Barbara Ehrenreich and Deidre English, *For Her Own Good: 150 Years of the Experts Advice to Women*, 1978, Anchor Press/Doubleday, Garden City, NY.
6.   Michael Foucault, *The Birth of the Clinic*, 1973, Tavistock, London, p. ix. reports a gruesome case of a medical "cure" for female hysteria, which is reminiscent of Wilhelm Fliess' "treatment" of one of Sigmund Freud's patients by nasal surgery (reported by Jeffrey Masson, *Freud: The Assault on Truth — Freud's Suppression of the Seduction Theory*, 1984, Faber and Faber, NY):

      Towards the middle of the eighteenth century,
      Pomme treated and cured an hysteric by
      making her take baths ten or twelve hours a day,
      for ten whole months. At the end of this
      treatment for the desiccation of the nervous
      system and the heat that sustained it, Pomme
      saw 'membranous tissues like pieces of damp
      parchment . . . peel away with some slight
      discomfort, and these were passed daily with
      the urine; the right ureter also peeled away and
      came out whole in the same way'. The same
      thing occurred with the intestines, which at
      another stage 'peeled off their internal tunics,
      which we saw emerge from the rectum. The
      oesophagus, the arterial trachea, and the tongue
      also peeled in due course; and the patient had
      rejected different pieces either by vomiting or
      by expectoration'.

7.   C. Smith-Rosenberg, *Disorderly Conduct: Visions of Gender in Victorian America*, 1985, Alfred Knopf, NY.
8.   Ehrenreich and English, 1973, pp. 32-34.
9.   Trotula of Salerno, *The Diseases of Women* (trans. Elizabeth Mason-Hohl), 1940 edition, Ward Ritchie Press, Los Angeles.
10.   This phenomenon is described and analysed by Dale Spender, *Women of Ideas and What Men Have Done to Them*, 1980, Routledge Kegan Paul, London, particularly in relation to Aphra Behn and Mary Wolstonecraft; and also by
      Janice Raymond, *A Passion For Friends*, 1986, Beacon Press, Mass.
11.   K. C. Hurd-Mead, *A History of Women in Medicine*, 1938, Haddam Press, Conn.
12.   G. M. Engbring, "Saint Hildegard, Twentieth Century Physician", *Bulletin of the History of Medicine*, 1940, vol. 8, pp. 770–784.
13.   M. J. Hughes, *Women, Healers in Medieval Life and Literature*, 1943/1968, Books for Libraries, NY.
14.   R. H. Robbins, "Medical Manuscripts in Middle English", *Speculum*, 1970, vol. 45, pp. 393–415.
15.   B. Rowland, trans., *Medieval Women's Guide to Health: The First English Gynaecological Handbook*, 1981, Croom Helm, London, p. 59.

16. Hugh R. Trevor-Roper, *The European Witch Craze of the Sixteenth and Seventeenth Centuries*, 1969, Pelican, Harmondsworth.

17. Ambroise Paré, *On Monsters and Marvels*, Janis Pallister, trans., 1547/1982, University of Chicago Press, Chicago, pp. 4–5, 38.
    The theme was carried through into literature as for example in Victor Hugo, *The Hunchback of Notre Dame*, 1831, Signet, NY, p. 61 where pregnant women are urged not to look upon Quasimodo for fear of giving birth later to deformed infants.
    Kerren Reiger, *The Disenchantment of the Home*, 1983, Oxford University Press, Melbourne, reports on the idea of 'maternal impressions' existing into the twentieth century.

18. Frederic Engels, *The Condition of the Working Class in England 1844*, 1969, Panther, London, pp. 189–190.

19. Catherine Beecher, *Letters to the People on Health and Happiness*, 1855, Scribners. New York.

20. Shorter, 1982, pp. 304–310; also p. 278, Table 10.1.

21. M. Prior, editor, *Women in English Society 1500–1800*, 1985, Methuen, London.

22. Rowland, 1981, p. 103.

23. Podalic version was popularised by the sixteenth century barber-surgeon Ambroise Paré.

24. J. White, "4000 Years of Obstetrics", *American Journal of Surgery*, 1931, vol. 11, no. 3, pp. 564–572.

25. Oliver Wendell Holmes, "The Contagiousness of Puerperal Fever 1843" in: *Medical Essays 1842–1882*, 1891, Houghton-Mifflen, NY.

26. Ann Oakley, "Wisewoman and Medicine Man: Changes in the Management of Childbirth" in *The Rights and Wrongs of Women*, Juliet Mitchell and Ann Oakley, editors, 1976, Penguin, Harmondsworth, pp. 45–47.

27. Adrienne Rich, *Of Woman Born*, 1976, Norton, NY, p. 130.

28. J. Donnison, *Midwives and Medical Men: A History of Inter-Professional Rivalries and Women's Rights*, 1977, Heinemann, London, chapter 2.

29. W. Radcliffe, *Milestones in Midwifery*, 1967, Wright and Sons, Bristol.

30. Donnison, 1977.

31. Donnison, 1977, pp. 13–15.

32. T. Forbes, "The Regulation of English Midwives in the Eighteenth and Nineteenth Centuries", *Medical History*, 1971, vol. 15, 352-362.

33. Shorter, 1982.

34. Rich, 1976, p. 134.

35. Donnison, 1977, p. 59.

36. M. C. Versluysen, 'Midwives, Medical Men and Poor Women Labouring of Child', Lying-in Hospitals in Eighteenth Century London'. in *Women, Health and Reproduction*, Helen Roberts, editor, 1981, Routledge Kegan Paul, London, pp. 18–49.

37. Donnison, 1977, pp. 28–29.

38. Oakley, 1976.

39. Edith Pownall, *Australian Pioneer Women*, 1964, third edition, Rigby, Adelaide;
    Constance Ellis, "A Bombshell" in *Colonial Ladies*, Maggie Weidenhofer, compiler and editor, 1985, Currie O'Neill Ross Pty. Ltd, South Yarra, pp. 88–89.

40. Rosemary Pringle, "Octavius Beale and the Ideology of the Birth Rate: The Royal Commissions of 1904 and 1905", *Refractory Girl*, Winter, 1973, pp. 19–27.

41. F. M. Forster, *Progress in Obstetrics and Gynaecology in Australia* , 1967,
     Sands, Sydney.
42. Donnison, 1977, p. 61.
43. Shorter, 1982.
44. J. W. Leavitt, "Birthing and Anaesthesia: The Debate Over Twilight
     Sleep", *Signs* , Autumn, 1978, vol. 6, no. 1, pp. 147–164.
45. Rich, 1976.
46. Joanna Finkelstein and Penny Clough, "Foetal Politics and the Birth of an
     Industry", *Women's Studies International Forum* , 1983, vol. 6, no. 4,
     pp. 395–400.
47. Oakley, 1976;
     Ann Oakley, *The Captured Womb* , 1984, Basil Blackwell, London.
48. Bates and Lapsley, 1985.
49. Dorothy Broom, "In Sickness and In Health: Social Policy and the Control
     of Women" in *Women, Social Welfare and the State* , Cora Baldock and
     Bettina Cass, editors, 1983, George Allen and Unwin, Sydney,
     pp. 262–278.
50. J. and J. Lennane, *Hard Labour* , 1977, Gollancz, London.
51. Diana Wyndham, "My Doctor Gives Me Pills to Keep Him Out of My
     Misery", paper, presented to *Pan-Pacific Conference on Drugs and Alcohol,*
     1980, Canberra, ACT.
52. T. McKeown, *The Role of Medicine* , 1979, Blackwell, London.
53. Brighton Women and Science Group, 1980, p. 174.
54. J. Willmott, "Too Many Episiotomies" in *Midwives Chronicle* , February
     1980, p. 46.

2 Genetic & reproductive engineering – *All for the infertile?*

Ramona Koval & Jocelynne A. Scutt

In vitro fertilisation (IVF), artificial insemination by donor (AID), artificial insemination by husband (AIH), gamente intra fallopian transfer (GIFT) are proclaimed in the medical world, and in the 'popular' media as 'all for the infertile'. The message conveyed is that these programmes are designed to assist the infertile — those who have never had children, and cannot have children, without the aid of child-producing programmes run by a benevolent medical profession.

On 20 November 1985 the *Canberra Times* reported Dr. Patrick Steptoe, billed as 'the man who gave the world test-tube babies' as saying:

> '... genetic and embryonic research [has] helped married couples who [are] sterile ...'

Dr. Steptoe, the 'father' of test-tube baby Louise Brown, born in England in 1978, said that since his programme began in the 1960s, he 'had been surrounded by critics saying that his research was immoral, inhumane, and unnecessary', yet:

> 'At the Oldham clinic alone, over 500 couples have been saved from the curse of infertility since 1978, which is some form of justification ... We are the most successful [clinic] because we operate 24 hours a day ...'

On 23 January 1986, after this softening-up publicity, it was reported in the *Canberra Times* that an *in vitro* programme was to be opened at the John James Medical Centre at Deakin to serve infertile couples from Canberra and surrounding areas:

> 'Laboratories are now being fitted out. About 60 Canberra couples are already on the clinic's waiting list . . . The program will conform to the guidelines of the Australian Fertility Society and the National Health and Medical Research Council, and will treat about six infertile women a week using methods tried at Monash University by the pioneer team headed by Professor Carl Wood . . .
> It is expected that infertile Canberra couples presently treated at *in vitro* programmes in Melbourne and Sydney will transfer to the ACT, marginally reducing waiting lists in NSW and Victoria.
> It is expected that the Canberra waiting list will be up to one year compared with up to three years in other programs.
> Dr. Stafford-Bell [Canberra gynaecologist involved in setting up the clinic] said that the *in vitro* programme would benefit infertile couples in Canberra and southern NSW. Women from as far as Forbes were on the Canberra waiting list . . '

The sentiments echoed those surrounding the establishment of earlier clinics in Melbourne and Sydney. Similarly, in Canberra as elsewhere, groups made up mainly of women saw the venture as positive to the interests of the infertile. The *Canberra Times* reported further that the plan to establish the programme in Canberra 'has been applauded by Concern ACT, an infertility support group'.

Infertility, the need to 'help' infertile 'couples', and the boon to those biologically unable to produce children unaided, have been recurring themes in publicising the new reproductive technologies. Although women have every reason to disbelieve protestations of altruism by the medical profession, the infertile are themselves caught up in the publicity, despite their anxiety. 'Why not live with infertility?' a journalist asked in an article about the Canberra clinic. 'Why should we?' responded a member of Concern, protesting that she is already on the waiting list: 'The technology is here and we should be able to use it. We want kids, too.' Earlier, she pointed out: 'Going on an IVF programme is not necessarily going to bring you a child. But after you've tried everything else it's the last step. If it doesn't work then you bury that unborn child for the 50th time and get on with your life.'[1]

Yet the proponents of the new reproductive technologies spend little time pondering the reasons for infertility (at least from the perspective of prevention rather than 'cure' by artificial techniques). They do not question whether genetic and reproductive engineering are truly the 'answer' to infertility or why resources should be concentrated upon these programmes rather than on research into the 'why' of infertility and measures to prevent it, or to correct the infertility itself. It is assumed that infertility is a 'tragedy' for those experiencing it, needing a solution: the 'prize' of a baby.

THE BIOLOGY OF FERTILITY

A complex interplay between hormones, physical structures and emotional responses determines whether reproduction actually takes place. In women, eggs or ova are located in ovaries, one on the left, one on the right side of the body. After puberty, a single ovum each month is released (sometimes two or more, possibly resulting in twins or triplets), journeying down the fallopian tubes to the uterus. If sperm are present, one may unite with the egg to fertilize it. The fertilized egg then begins to divide, becoming an embryo, which implants itself in the wall of the uterus. If no sperm is present, the ovum remains in the uterus, then is washed out with the onset of menstruation. The cycle of egg release or ovulation and menstruation is carefully controlled by chemicals or hormones produced by the body, with cycles varying from 21 to 30 days. At birth, a girl's ovaries contain all the eggs she will ovulate as a woman, but in an immature state. Each woman has about one million potential eggs, but only 450 to 500 develop to be released. The remainder degenerate.

In males, sperm are produced by each testis, passing into a highly coiled storage duct, the epididymis, connecting with the urethra by the *vas deferens*. (Vasectomy is the cutting of the vas.) Several sets of glands contribute secretions and mucus which are ejaculated with the sperm, forming the seminal fluid or semen. Each ejaculation releases 150 to 200 million sperm, which must go through changes before being capable of fertilising an ovum. 'Ripening' occurs during storage in the epididymis and passage through the male ducts; 'capacitation' occurs only when sperm are inside the uterus. The production of sperm is controlled by follicle-stimulating hormone (FSH), similar to ovulation in a woman.

Both women and men can have primary infertility—where conception has never occurred; or secondary infertility—where one or more pregnancies has occurred in the past but no further pregnancies are possible. Currently in Australia approximately one in ten couples are infertile.

Male infertility

For a man to be fertile, he must be able to produce an adequate number of normal, live and 'motile' (the scientific expression meaning 'mobile') sperm, and an adequate amount of seminal fluid. He must be capable of ejaculating sperm into the woman's vagina (sometimes impotence can be a cause of infertility). Infertility occurs when any one of these factors is missing.

A semen test can determine whether sperm are present in sufficient numbers, whether they are motile and mature. Semen is collected simply, by ejaculation. If the sperm count and other factors suggest that the semen is of appropriate quality, then the man is probably not the major cause of the infertility. If the semen test suggests male infertility further tests will be made. A physical examination can reveal a varicose vein in one or both testicles, which reduces the number and quality of sperm, and affects fertility. Occasionally a biopsy may be taken: a small piece of tissue is removed from the testis to see whether sperm are being produced. A blood test can show whether the man is producing chemicals in his body (sperm antibodies) which attack the sperm, making them immobile. A blood test can also measure levels of testosterone, the hormone essential to fertility in males. Tests may prove that normal, healthy, motile sperm are being produced, but the sperm may have difficulty during their travels in the female reproductive system. Tests for this involve the female partner.

Female infertility

A woman may be infertile because she does not ovulate regularly: the necessary balance may be disrupted by non-production, or too little production, of necessary hormones. Although rare, some women may not have ovaries or a uterus. Some genetic disorders can result in undeveloped organs. Women using certain birth control methods may have no menstrual periods (amenorrhea) for a time, with resultant infertility.

If ovulation occurs, a mechanical blockage in one or both fallopian tubes can prevent the sperm from meeting the ovum. Scarring of the tubes from previous infection or the use of an intrauterine device (IUD) for contraception can cause this. Endometriosis is a painful condition where tissue resembling the lining of the uterus (endometrium) appears elsewhere in the abdomen, for example becoming attached to the ovaries , it can also cause scarring and blockage. When this tissue responds to hormonal changes causing menstruation, the tissue bleeds. Endometriosis is suggested by pain on intercourse, extremely painful periods or chronic pelvis pain.

Sometimes women produce antisperm antibodies which inactivate healthy sperm, although this affects less than five per cent of infertile couples. In some women, the antibody reaction is specific to her partner's sperm and in others the antibodies appear to be directed against sperm in general.

When cervical mucus is not the correct consistency, or is too acid or alkaline, it can act as a barrier to the sperm moving up into the uterus.

Other effects on fertility include extreme weight loss or extreme weight gain, excessive exercise (obsessive joggers lose their menstrual periods), and environmental and industrial toxins and infections.

One of the first test for female infertility is whether the women is ovulating and producing the necessary amounts of hormones. The simplest test, the Basal body temperature (BBT), follows the menstrual cycle by taking the woman's temperature each day and recording it on a chart. When progesterone is produced, her body temperature rises slightly. As more progesterone is produced during the second part of the cycle, the temperature is raised soon after ovulation, remaining high. Just before the beginning of a period, the level of progesterone and the body temperature both drop. If pregnancy occurs, the progesterone level and the temperature remain higher.

A basal temperature chart can show when ovulation is occurring so the couple can choose the best time to have intercourse (either to cause a pregnancy or to avoid one).

A blood test is a more precise way of testing for ovulation. A small amount of blood is taken and analysed to check the level of progesterone and other relevant hormones. This provides information of hormone production and whether the ovaries are responding correctly. Another ovulation test is endometrial biopsy, which involves the use of a small sample of the endometrium (lining of the uterus). The procedure is similar to a curette and because it is uncomfortable, many doctors perform it under general anaesthesia. The procedure usually has risks and umpleasant after effects and is most often performed when a woman is undergoing another test under anaesthetic such as a laparoscopy. Because the endometrium looks different before and after ovulation, ovulation may be detected by examining the tissues under a microscope. Endometrial aspiration is a slightly less painful procedure, whereby a very fine hollow tube is inserted into the uterus from the vagina and a sample of endometrium sucked out.

Testing reproductive organs

Reproductive organs may be tested for infertility. A physical examination checks the reproductive tract, breasts and general sexual development, detecting abnormalities such as lack of a uterus or change in size or shape of the reproductive organs. If no abnormalities show in the examination of the woman or the man, and the man has had a positive sperm examination, the post-coital test (Sims-Huhner test) is the next step. This test measures the ability of the sperm to survive in the woman's vagina after intercourse. It is carried out in the middle of the menstrual cycle, just prior to ovulation, because consistency of the cervical mucus changes at this time.

Many people dislike this test. The couple is required to abstain from intercourse for two to four days then make love a few hours before the test. A woman must not wash herself after intercourse. A small amount of mucus and sperm is then taken from the cervix, and placed on a slide under a microscope. If sperm and mucus are compatible the sperm should be swimming around freely. This post-coital test may have to be done several times before a final result can be known.

The process is an invasion of a couple's privacy. It may be difficult for them to 'perform on cue' to provide a sample of sperm in the vagina, and some women are embarrassed to go unwashed to a surgery, thinking perhaps 'everyone knows what you've been doing'.

Sometimes a woman's vagina may be too acidic for sperm to survive. Douching with bicarbonate of soda, or a change in diet, or taking oestrogen tablets may remedy this.

For blocked fallopian tubes, a tubal insufflation test (Rubens test) may be performed. A gas, carbon dioxide, is blown through the cervix into the uterus. If the tubes are not blocked, the gas will travel through them to the pelvic cavity (resulting in some pain in the shoulders). The gas is eventually absorbed into the body. If the tubes are blocked, however, gas will not travel through them and a pressure build-up will be observed. Some doctors believe this test process can clear minor blocks. However the test does not show whether one or both tubes are blocked, so another test is necessary to locate the blockage. This test involves an X-ray of the fallopian tubes, called a hysterosalpinography or HSG, after a fluid dye has been pumped through the uterus. The dye flows into the fallopian tubes and can show up a blockage. The HSG test is painful, perhaps the most painful of all infertility investigations, and oral medication for relaxation and/or pain killers may be given. A laparoscopy may be performed if there is a blockage or other abnormality of the reproductive organs. After general anaesthetic a tube is inserted through the abdomen, usually the navel. Carbon dioxide is then pumped into the cavity to push the abdominal wall out, separating the organs and enabling them to be clearly seen. The laparoscope is a long, thick, 'fibre optic' telescope with its own light source, enabling the doctor to see the organs and around corners. It is inserted through the hole (or sometimes a new incision), allowing the ovaries, the outside of the uterus and the fallopian tubes to be examined. A blue dye may be injected and, if the fallopian tubes are not blocked, it will pass along the tubes and into the pelvic cavity. A laparoscopy may require an overnight stay in hospital, and the process is painful as a result of incision and gas.

Fibroids ('piles') can bar fertility when occurring at the junction of the fallopian tubes and the uterus blocking the passage of an ovum to the uterus. There is a possibility that fibroids may also enlarge during pregnancy, affecting the blood supply of the fetus and causing a miscarriage. Risks are involved in their surgical removal: the muscle wall of the uterus becomes weak and any future pregnancy may require delivery by caesarean section.

Ovaries can develop small cysts which become enlarged, resulting in egg cells failing to develop and being unable to break away. They form cysts. Hormones or surgery can treat the cysts, but neither treatment is permanent.

Hysteroscopy is a relatively new method of reproductive canal investigation. A fibre optic telescope is passed up the vagina into the cervix and on to the uterus to inspect it from inside, without the need for a cut. Hysteroscopy can detect polyps, adhesions, fibroids, and other deformities of the uterus which may not be visible on ordinary X-rays unless they are present to a large degree. An anaesthetic may not be given. Although the investigation may be uncomfortable for a woman with a very narrow cervix, an anaesthetic is not necessarily given.

Outcomes of testing

It is usually couples who learn about their possibility of being infertile. Rarely does a single woman or single man become concerned about her or his possible inability to produce children. No doubt this arises from well established societal patterns still maintained today, where people in long-term relationships, or those contemplating long-term relationships, plan to have children, and single persons, or those engaging in transitory relationships, mostly do not. Having made the decision to begin a family the couple then look for reasons why the woman has not become pregnant.

Studies show that 25 per cent of women become pregnant within a month of 'unprotected intercourse' — that is, using no contraception.[2] Sixty-three per cent are pregnant within six months, 75 per cent within nine months and 80 to 90 per cent within a year. Only

16 per cent of couples who have intercourse less than once per week achieve pregnancy in less than six months, whereas 83 per cent of couples having intercourse four or more times per week achieve a pregnancy in that time. The figures indicate that for most women, the thoughts of possible infertility arise if a year of frequent, unprotected intercourse has not resulted in pregnancy. (Evidence shows that fertility decreases in women after thirty-five years, as they approach menopause. Maximum fertility occurs in women at about twenty-four years of age. (Men's fertility also appears to decline as they get older.)[3]

When pregnancy doesn't occur, frequently the initial belief is that the woman is infertile, or 'at fault'. Historically an almost automatic assumption on the part of women, couples and even the medical profession is that the woman is the infertile partner. Until recently tests were often carried out on the female partner before the question of the man's possible infertility even arose. Yet, as the recounting of tests for infertility clearly shows, tests for female infertility are far more onerous, painful and time consuming than are tests for male infertility.

There would be less stress, resentment and disharmony between a couple if the initial suspicions of infertility were followed routinely by testing the man first for infertility, on the basis that this is the least physically stressful, less onerous and less expensive test. Equally as important, medical services would be better utilised.

Ironically, testing for infertility may itself be a cause of infertility! It certainly does little to assuage the stress underlying infertility in some couples. Infertility places great emphasis on each individual, as well as on the relationship. In 10–15 per cent of couples who come to a medical practitioner for fertility testing, the condition cannot be diagnosed by any one of the previous explanations. Stress seems to play an important part. Much work has been done on the relationship between psychological stress and its physical results manifesting themselves in hormones and other chemical changes, which lead to infertility. Many of the chemicals which affect the ovulation are in turn affected by stress. Although studies have noted an increased number of psychological problems amongst infertile couples, few have provided evidence that this was the *cause* of infertility rather than the result of the infertility. Frustration and anxiety already experienced by infertile couples may create a vicious circle where the emotional and sexual relationship of the couple is stressed, further affecting their fertility.[4]

Once the infertility is pinpointed, the new reproductive technologies aim not at correcting that infertility, nor preventing similarly caused infertility occurring in the future, but at enabling the couple to have a child by artificial means. A couple may have been taken through a cycle of ups and downs, moving on from test to test, from possible explanation to possible explanation, a process going on for months or years — possibly up to six years. 'Manufacturing' conception for the couple does not solve the distress experienced from the initial learning of the infertility, nor the stress accumulated over months or years of raised expectations and dashed hopes as they go through all those tests.

REASONS FOR INFERTILITY

Before embracing reproductive technologies as the best or only way to deal with infertility, society as a whole, doctors involved in the programmes, and those participating in the programmes as patients, need to look at the causes of infertility. (Although it is often 'too late' for the women participants — they can be subjected to blame-the-victim attitudes which make it difficult for them to pursue the question of why they are infertile.)

All too frequently infertility is caused by technological 'advances', environmental conditions created in industrialisation, the use of pesticides, and weapons testing. It can be caused by the use of weapons during wartime where chemical warfare is used. The most recent example of this is the violence inflicted upon soldiers and civilians in Vietnam, and damage caused to Americans, Australian and New Zealand military, through contact with Agent Orange and similar chemical substances used in warfare against the Vietnamese.[5] Infertility can also arise from the use of similar chemicals in peacetime, for farming and crop dusting. Here, as in the case of industrial intoxicants and industrial methods which harm fertility, both men and women are at risk. And all too frequently the infertile couple, particularly the infertile woman, is seen as somehow imperfect. As Jennifer Darling of the Women in RMIT (Royal Melbourne Institute of Technology) group says:

> ... infertility causes emotional distress which the couple shares. However, with the exception of the male partner requiring vasectomy reversal, most of the procedures involved to bypass infertility are borne by the woman ...
>
> Infertility is pitied in a society which demands successful achievers. It is a problem because our male-dominated community declares it a problem. Women who cannot bear children, are allowed to feel less of a person [here in Melbourne, Australia] as in any patriarchal group.[6]

Infertility is often caused by pelvic inflammation, which can block fallopian tubes. Tubal defects in both males and females are a major cause of infertility. Tubal infections may develop from various causes. Some contraceptive methods lead to tubal defects. Surgery carried out by rough handling by doctors in high class private hospitals, moderately equipped hospitals, large public hospitals and bush hospitals leads to a high degree of infertility in women. Occupational and environmental hazards interfere with women and men's reproductive faculties. Smoking, alcohol and other drugs, and stress are noted as causes of infertility.

Infections

The fallopian tubes are particularly prone to infections that give rise to pelvic inflammatory disease (PID) or salpingitis. Infections can also arise after childbirth, abortion or pelvic surgery (such as appendectomy or cyst removal), and are more common in women using an intra-uterine device (IUD) for contraception. Sexually transmitted diseases (STD) or venereal diseases (VD) are often the cause of pelvic inflammatory disease. The more sexual partners a woman has, or the more partners her partner has, the higher the chances of acquiring a sexually transmitted disease.

Sexually transmitted diseases include gonorrhea, chlamydia, ureaplasma and syphilis. Their transmission is not new. Indeed during the nineteenth century many women were infected by sexually promiscuous husbands who concealed the disease, or simply demanded their conjugal rights despite it.[4] With most of these infections, damage to the reproductive organs can be minimised through prompt treatment. Unfortunately many people have become sterile through waiting too long before seeking treatment. Traditionally sexually transmitted diseases were regarded as an indicator of low social standing (less so today) with venereal diseases clinics often being seen as the haunt of prostitutes and sailors. 'Nice' people didn't get VD. But if they did, it was traumatic to seek the relatively simple help required to cure VD. The trauma was partly exacerbated by the punitive attitude that people experienced in the hands of some medical professionals.

Prevention of infections which lead to infertility requires availability of information (education) and treatment in a supportive atmosphere. Many women feel their concerns may be trivialised and dismissed by doctors, so they may be loath to seek medical care when they suspect infection. To slow the growth of infertility in the community, we need medical services, with reliable and accurate laboratory facilities and an open and supportive atmosphere.

Contraception

Several methods of contraception have been associated with sub-sequent infertility of women who try to become pregnant after their use.

Recent studies suggest that young, childless women planning to have children should not use intra-uterine devices (IUDs). Studies show that women using IUDs who have not yet had children double their risk of becoming infertile. Research in the United States of America shows about 88 000 women in that country are infertile as a result of IUD use. Some IUDs are safer than others. Studies found the Dalkon Shield, now removed from the consumer market, carried the highest risk of infertility, three to six times greater than women using no IUD. Copper-containing IUDs carry a risk of about twice that of not using an IUD.[8]

The birth control pill (the Pill) is believed to have a number of effects on women's bodies, though opinions differ as to the exact problem it causes. One of the most widely acknowledged effects is the slow return of periods and ovulation in women who have taken the pill for years subsequently giving up that method of contraception. Other studies indicate some women's fertility can be reduced for up to two and a half years after giving up the pill.[9] (This may not be true for the new formulation 'progesterone-only' pill.) Oral contraceptives may also aggravate growth of fibrous tissues in the ovaries, leading to infertility.

Other hormonal contraceptives such as the hormone injection Depo-Provera can cause temporary infertility and are also sus-pected of causing permanent infertility in some women, although as yet no scientific proof of this is available.

In general, barrier methods of contraception like the diaphragm or condom are far safer than other forms of contraception in terms of subsequent fertility. They do not disturb the delicate physiology and biochemistry of the body, and can provide some protection against sexually transmitted diseases. If used properly, they are at least as effective as the IUD.

However, problems can arise for women: the condom as a method of contraception is apparently not favoured by large numbers of men. Prostitutes report difficulties in demanding that clients use condoms, and this particular problem has become critical with the advent of auto-immune deficiency syndrome (AIDS).[10] Just as responsibility for pregnancy has traditionally been cast upon the woman, responsibility for contraceptive measures has not been seen as a male domain. Indeed, rarely has it been viewed as a joint responsibility.

In order to protect themselves from an unwanted pregnancy, women have logically accepted the need to adopt contraceptive measures. The Pill and inter-uterine device (IUD) methods were originally introduced experimentally on groups of low income women, or racial minorities particularly in Third World countries. When side effects occurred, they were ignored, or seen as hysteria on the part of the women concerned, or simply as inevitable. The medical profession has been reluctant to venture into the field of male contraception. Women cannot be blamed for being suspicious about this reluctance, particularly in view of the detrimental effects contraceptive measures have had upon women's health. The male-dominated scientific and medical profession appears to see a need for significant caution in the development of drugs or other devices aimed at lowering or inhibiting male fertility.

Abdominal surgery

Studies suggest a strong link may exist between poorly performed abdominal surgery and infertility. In a study of 108 infertile women attending Hammersmith Hospital, London, 79 had experienced previous abdominal surgery ranging from an appendix operation through abortions to treatment for ovarian cysts. One doctor from Hammersmith, Robert Winston, wrote:

> We found that nearly all [the women we treated] had marked adhesions or damage, often of extreme severity, which could be largely attributed to inappropriate tissue handling, avoidable post-operative infection, or removal of potentially visible organs. [Adhesions involve scar tissue where parts of the body adhere to each other where they should be separated.][11]

Evidence is available in Australia that some members of the medical profession exhibit overt or covert hostility towards women, which interferes with their ability to care for women as patients, whether in general consultations or in surgery. Many women report that their doctors have a patronising attitude and often refuse to explain to them fully the nature of any illness, or reasons for a particular treatment. Women beaten and abused at home consistently report that members of the medical profession whose assistance they seek dole out valium or librium, ignoring or skating over the reality of the physical abuse to which they have been subjected. Women involved in childbirth sometimes report rough treatment before and during labour. This rough treatment can lead to physical injury, which may result in adhesions and, ultimately, in infertility.[12]

Some studies have found that the increasing rate of caesarean sections performed over the past 15 years have increased the incidence of pelvic infections in these women after birth. This is made worse by the use of technologies to monitor fetal progress during labour before the operation. Pelvic infections may lead to pelvic inflammatory disease and subsequent infertility.[13]

These findings are disturbing. They indicate that special care of women generally is not taken by the medical profession, and particularly that special care is not taken when surgeons operate on women. It is ironic that the medical profession may be responsible in part for the infertility it professes to correct by introducing new methods of reproduction.

Occupational and environmental reproductive hazards

'Gonadotoxins'—chemicals having an adverse effect on ovaries and testes (the gonads)—can inflict damage on both men and women, resulting in infertility, 'spontaneous' abortions, and suspected birth deformities. Chemicals known to exert a toxic effect on the production of sperm (resulting in reduced, deformed or no sperm) include lead, chlorophene, dibromochloropropane and (shown by animal tests only) cadmium, mercury, ephichlorohydrin, ethylene dibromide, glycidyl ethers, and oxfendazone. Because the process of sperm production is continuous throughout the life of the human male, men are particularly vulnerable to gonadotoxins.

Some evidence suggests environmental pollutants such as insecticides and pesticides may become concentrated in the ovaries, and consequently become associated with infertility. In one study of German and Austrian women on an IVF programme the concentrations of these chemicals were from four to 16 times higher in their ovaries than in ovaries of other women. None of these women was able to conceive, even on an IVF programme.[14] Other possible occupational hazards to fertility include exposure to electromagnetic radiation in concentrated amounts, for example to radio frequency radiation from 'heat sealers' used widely in industry.

Investigations of the direct gonadotoxic effects of chemicals on women's fertility is unethical, since it would involve an otherwise unnecessary operation to extract the ova. It would be even more clearly unethical to deliberately expose the gonads to toxic chemicals for experimental purposes. Animal experiments are therefore the only 'ethical' way to research this aspect of the effects of chemicals on reproduction. Many would also object to the use of animals in this way.[15] (These difficulties have led to suggestions from industry and scientists that human embryos less than 14 days old should be used for these experiments.) Clearly it is vital that women and men working with chemicals and other materials of a possibly hazardous nature should know what exactly they are coming into contact with. Workplaces may provide only a brand name or name such as 'Formula X', making it almost impossible for workers and others to check possible side effects.

Drawn on by visions of greater profits, slick marketing and scientific 'advances', producers of chemicals and hazardous materials march on. They are apparently oblivious to the harm caused by their progress forward. They appear to see only the short term benefits—larger markets, more rapid production, leaving competitors behind. The long term costs—of which infertility is one—are ignored. The 'march of progress' idea which permeates science and technology, the practice of applauding any scientific discovery or invention as positive and good, whatever its ultimate (then unknown) results or side effects, ultimately leads to mopping up operations. When scientific 'advances' have caused infertility in women and men, it seems further scientific 'advances' are requested or initiated.

Other causes of infertility

Some evidence shows smoking and alcohol consumption reduces fertility by increasing the incidence of spontaneous abortion. A strong link is also shown between long-term and heavy use of cannabis (marijuana) and infertility. Research points to a lowered sperm count and an increase in the number of abnormal or damaged sperm in men, and perhaps irregular ovulation in women. Women who smoke cigarettes reach menopause earlier than women who do not smoke, which reduces the years of their fertility. Drugs which can affect the male reproductive system include some treatments for cancer, psoriasis, ulcerative colitis, and drugs taken for anxiety or depression, affecting the central nervous system.

Many infertile couples have secondary infertility due to previous sterilization of one (or both) of them. Careful counselling is vital when people contemplate sterilization, in order to minimize the number of people who subsequently regret their decision. As it is impossible to predict a change of mind it is advisable for people to seek 'reversible' sterilization techniques, which include the ring or clip methods.

Secondary infertility has also been observed in women relinquishing children of a former pregnancy. This may be due simply to stress, or to stress of a particular type in mothers who have given up their children for adoption due to pressures of a moralistic society. Fortunately, this form of infertility may be decreasing due to more tolerant attitudes; introduction of social security and community welfare provisions enabling single mothers to retain custoday and care of their child; and clinical abortions becoming more generally accepted. Excessive weight loss can lead to infertility which is reversed when a more healthy weight is gained.

TREATING INFERTILITY

Whatever the causes of infertility, the introduction of artificial insemination and fertilization programmes has been lauded as a real chance to overcome the 'problem'. Yet the dangers and stresses involved are rarely recognised. Even where the dangers are acknowledged, there is an emphasis upon 'couples', as if both women and men are equally involved in the dangers and stresses. The end result (a baby) is supposed to make parents forget any pain—emotional or physical—experienced during the pursuit of a child by artificial means. Yet there are many different dangers and stresses. Robyn Rowland says:

> Before IVF technology existed, infertile couples' needs were satisfied by adoption. An answer to another problem faced by a disapproving society. Single mothers were encouraged often under distress to relinquish their offspring to a 'better life' with a more acceptable status as children of married couples . . .
>
> Now that most unmarried mothers are choosing to raise their own children, the popular alternative to the childless married couple is IVF procedure.
>
> So women face yet another dilemma. The 'safe choices' [often referred to] include gassing-open blocked fallopian tubes, reversal of tubal ligation, hormonal stimulation of ova, ova collection by laparoscopy, and multiple embryo implantation.
>
> These are sometimes painful or at least uncomfortable operations requiring general or local anaesthesia, correct timing and access to funding, even though 75 per cent of the cost is reimbursed by government Medicare.[16]

A BABY — FOR WHOM? PATRIARCHAL UNDERPINNINGS

A social worker who has worked with infertile couples for nine or ten years says she was alerted to an attitude then prevalent that all infertile couples needed was to be given a baby—no matter how, be it by IVF, artificial insemination or adoption. She continues:

Many people go through intense grief when they are told they are infertile. Their self-image as a sexually mature, normal person may be shattered . . . . Their sadness and hurt fade with time, but are still there, and can resurface. Infertile people have to accept that they can care for and 'parent' another child or that they can be creative in other ways, and that takes time . . . . Adopting a child in the midst of negative feelings about oneself could possibly result in hidden resentment which can impinge on the relationship with the child, particularly in adolescence.[17]

The sudden awareness and continuing knowledge of infertility has been described as a 'life crisis' for the person involved. Commenting upon the experience of infertility as such a crisis, Naomi Pfeffer and Anne Woollett write:

One of the first signs of pregnancy is missing a period, and so it is your period on which a lot of anxiety is focused. Women talk about the cyclical nature of their feelings, about how they watch their bodies very carefully just before a period, looking for signs of pregnancy. If your period is late, your spirits rise, and you dare to hope that this time you have made it.

You go to the loo every five minutes to check whether there is any blood. You listen to every change and movement inside you. Then the blood comes and you are plunged into despair . . . Even when your period comes you think that perhaps it might be just a light show of blood, and not really a period at all. Your rush off to have a pregnancy test, just to make certain. And the days before your period is due become days when it can be difficult to face the outside world. Some women learn to protect themselves and avoid stressful situations. Each month brings another disappointment . . .

With each new disappointment your self-worth is chipped away. You begin to wonder what is wrong with you . . . You feel as if you have no control over your body and your life. You feel different, and isolated from the rest of the world.[18]

Loss of feelings of control are potentially destructive to personal identity, and may have far reaching effects. One women facing infertility said:

At first you try to think that it's not really happening. But this fear creeps up. This fear that the whole thing is so bad and the feeling so devastating that you don't know quite how devastating it's going to be. The depths of it are so great that somehow if you really open up, you might get out of control and you will never emerge again as a sane person.[19]

And another woman:

> You can't plan. Nothing holds any interest for you. It's almost an obsessive desire. I became obsessed with pregnancy. I felt like a flower operating on two petals instead of five. Because I didn't think about anything else, I didn't seem to be living my life. I was too tensed up all the time.[20]

Some women conjure up images of themselves as 'barren', their bodies a 'wasteland'. This battering of self-esteem and self-image may result in people experiencing feelings of blame for their infertility. As infertility may arise from sexually transmitted diseases, those who have engaged in sexual activity with multiple partners (however few, however many) may think of themselves as responsible, and as 'being punished' for what they may now pejoratively label promiscuity or sexual indiscretion. As some studies concentrate upon the possible negative effects of abortion on women's fertility (as a cause), women finding themselves thus classified as infertile may experience guilt for an operation which was necessary at the time. If the man is infertile, he may regret his 'free living ways' and feel guilt at not being able to father a child with his partner. He may resent not being able to produce a child as proof of his manhood. Jeff Smith, who publicly acknowledged his infertility, stated that it was 'easier for him to accept than most men, because his wife, Bronwyn, is infertile, too'. He continues:

> We are a male dominated society. Especially in Australia we have the image of the bronzed great lover and great father. There is a tremendous amount of peer pressure in society to act out that role. And therefore for someone to stand up in that society and say 'well I am infertile . . . '
> When you think about it, it is just as devastating for a woman as it is for a man—men just agree not to talk about it . . . [21]

Each may be drawn to ask: How much of a man am I if I cannot produce virile sperm? How much of a woman am I if I can never be a (biological) mother?

Learning of infertility can cause feelings of grief, like those feelings experienced after the death of a close, loved relation or friend. Experiencing grief means going through various emotional stages including disbelief, guilt, anger, rage, distress, deep sorrow and ultimately resolution—if the means to resolve these feelings is at hand. Once faced with infertility, reactions can range from, 'I can't be infertile' or 'it's not me' (with the implication, sometimes, that it's the other partner's fault), to 'why me?' or 'why us?' Relationships may suffer, as Pfeffer and Woollett point out:

> The experience of infertility can damage your self-esteem. It can make you feel very vulnerable and in need of love and support. But because infertility is such a taboo topic, this support may be difficult to ask for. Other people feel awkward and do not know how to respond or to deal with you, whilst you come to feel more and more abnormal and isolated from the rest of the world. . . . Infertility reveals itself in the attempt to create a relationship, that of mother and child. Not succeeding can affect all your other relationships to a lesser or greater extent . . . The dilemma is that by devaluing or by sacrificing existing relationships in the quest for motherhood, you may become more isolated . . [Y]our family and your friends may be finding it difficult to cope with their own reactions to your infertility. They may feel distress or embarrassment and exclude you from their circle. It can be difficult to break this conspiracy of silence and you may resent having to take on the responsibility to do so at the time when you feel as though you have enough on your plate. Really, there is nothing anyone can say or do which will solve the problem for you . . . [22]

Feelings of anger and jealousy may be directed at friends and relations who have children, pregnant women and even apparently happy family groups passed casually on the street or noticed in parks or cafés.

Entering an *in vitro* or other pregnancy promoting programme will not guarantee that persons who are infertile will receive counselling to enable them to come to terms with their infertility. Rather, the contrary is true. Many counselling programmes are delivered by those associated with IVF programmes who may therefore have a 'conflict of interest'. The chances for independent counselling are slight.

The emphasis is on performing—producing a pregnancy to please the doctors and staff running the programme—but most particularly the doctors; going though the testing, the operations for extracting ova or producing sperm which is put under a microscope, or mixed with other sperm and artificially inserted into the uterus of the fertile partner, and so on. Even where provisions exist for counselling, as required by legislation in Victoria and some other jurisdictions, the purpose of this counselling is to ensure that participants in infertility (or artificial reproduction) programmes accept their involvement in these programmes and participate voluntarily. [23]

Counselling is not necessarily directed toward confronting and dealing with the grief or other emotional feelings aroused by the discovery that oneself or one's sexual partner or husband is infertile, to achieve a calm resolution.

Some persons finding themselves infertile can feel loss of control, which augers ill for artificial reproduction programmes as a solution. Although these programmes are frequently praised as providing couples with greater choice—the choice to have a child, even though they are infertile—in fact those 'choices' are provided in a well regulated atmosphere. Women on IVF programmes frequently talk of their lack of control and feeling of powerlessness, their dependency on the doctors and staff involved in the programmes.[24] Women participants fear that if they reveal any anger or hurt about their treatment on the programme, then they may be classified as unstable or emotional and not worthy of being at the top of the list, or even *on* the list. They fear they may be refused treatment through artificial reproduction programmes unless they confirm to the stereotype of 'a good wife and mother'. They fear they may be removed from the list, or demoted to the bottom, until they fall back into line. Their lives become empty of purpose when they are not undergoing treatment, or launched into a new cycle of hopes, fears, and expectations about a possible pregnancy.

Even the promotion of artificial reproduction programmes capable of fulfilling the need for a child is misleading. Although spectacular 'successes' are bruited about, the truth is a low success rate for live birth in IVF programmes. In *The Health Machine* Erica Bates and Helen Lapsley quote figures from the Queen Victoria Hospital programme in Melbourne, where 'the world's most successful team' of *in vitro* fertilisation and embryo transfer technocrats produced only 20 successful pregnancies from the 401 ova inseminated with donor sperm between 1980 and 1983. Yet, Bates and Lapsley state:

> By March 1982, two years after the programme started, there were over 1200 couples on the waiting list in Victoria, of whom 300 were being treated at the time. On past performance only ten to fifteen of these 300 would eventually be able to produce a child.[25]

A study titled *In Vitro Fertilisation in Pregnancies — Australia and New Zealand 1979–1984*, produced by the National Perinatal Statistics Unit (NPSU) and presented at the Fourth World Conference on *in vitro* fertilisation held in Melbourne late in 1985, considered 909 pregnancies which resulted in 496 live births (including multiple births) in eleven Australian IVF units and one in New Zealand. All pregnancies in Australia and New Zealand attributed to IVF programmes between 1979 and late 1984 were included in the study and compiled from a national register developed by the NPSU. The study indicated a low success rate for live births in the IVF programmes—55 per cent or 496 from 909 fertilisations.

A Royal Women's Hospital counsellor on infertility, Kay Oke, said that disappointment for couples on the programme 'can be bitter':

> Figures mean nothing to anyone. By the time I see people they have usually been told they have only got a 15 per cent chance, but I still have to sit with them and explain that of the six people who go through the program only one gets pregnant.
> Only 60 per cent of the pregnancies will continue to full term. It is misleading to say that we have had 1000 pregnancies from IVF. These are pregnancies, not babies.[26]

Dr. Paul Lancaster, Director of the NPSU in the School of Public Health and Tropical Medicine, University of Sydney, points out that due to monitoring techniques, rates of pregnancies occurring in *in vitro* fertilisation programmes have a tendency to be higher than the rates which would be expected in the general community:

> ... monitoring in IVF units ensures that pregnancies lasting for only a few days are reported, boosting the number of pregnancies initially reported compared with live births.
> Women in the IVF programme are closely checked for early hormonal changes so that within days we know if they are pregnant. Sometimes they abort spontaneously soon after, but that pregnancy would be recorded.
> In the normal population such information just wouldn't be available, and many women wouldn't know if they'd been pregnant briefly. Furthermore, it's been estimated that even in the general population there is a pregnancy failure rate of about 25 per cent. Seen in that light, the IVF figures aren't so dramatic.[27]

Are all the pregnancies attributed to the programme correctly labelled as technological successes? Experience shows that a seemingly infertile couple, after adopting a child, may commence a pregnancy within a short time of the adoption. It is equally likely that 'successes' from *in vitro* fertilisation programmes could have been 'ordinary', biological successes without medical intervention if only the couple had stopped worrying about their supposed infertility.

The problem is that drama tends to surround IVF and similar programmes, which appear to have deliberately sought out publicity at all levels of the media. This has resulted in 'successes' from the programmes being depicted as stupendous, and doctors being portrayed as 'gods' who not only deliver babies, but actually design their conception. The promotion of pregnancy and birth 'successes' by those running the programmes must surely be closely linked with the number of couples clamouring to get on to waiting lists, and being prepared to stay on those lists for years.[28]

Even the depiction of 'success' is questionable. Is the solution to infertility enabling the infertile couple to produce a child, the womb to give up its barrenness and the testes to regain their manhood? This 'solution' assumes that women can be fulfilled only by producing a child, and that men need to father their biological child, or at least a child which they can regard as biologically their own. (The original procedure in IVF programmes was to mix the husband's infertile sperm with fertile sperm. This is explicable only on the basis that practitioners considered the man would feel happier if he could persuade himself that maybe it was his sperm which fertilised his wife's ovum, rather than the foreign sperm with which his was mixed.) This attitude disregards the fact that many people who have never borne a child and never fathered a child live fulfilled lives. But men and women can care deeply and sincerely for children whom they have not biologically produced. Instead of assisting the infertile to accept their infertility and branch out into other areas of life and living (as they would be bound to, even had they produced their own children), this emphasis on a successful pregnancy perpetuates the cycle of depression, despair, hope. It promotes the idea that if only the couple tries 'hard enough', 'just once more', then the 'miracle' will come to pass and the child of their dreams — or nightmares — will be conceived and come to term.

For one of the Australian programmes it is reported:

> At Epworth, where about 20 women undergo IVF treatment every week and the waiting list is two years long, every woman has her own story of sorrow and hope. The women know they are called obsessive in their drive to have a baby but resent tags put on them by social workers.
>
> One woman, who discovered seven years ago she was infertile, claims she is not hung up on IVF, though she does not put any limit on the number of times she will attempt the procedure. 'I'll come to terms with it, one way or another,' she says.
>
> Some come back every six months or, maybe, once a year. One says: 'You learn to live with it. You adjust to the idea. This is your lot.

Another person may have their leg cut off. It's never going to grow back. So you learn to live with it. Right?'

Another, who has been a regular patient at Epworth since 1980, is beginning to accept that even IVF may not work for her. She has taken up greyhound breeding. 'In the past 12 months, a lot of my life has revolved around my greyhounds', she says. 'I've put a lot more into them. Maybe that's going to be an outlet for me.'[29]

For those on the programmes, life revolves around the programme, the hospital, the possibility of pregnancy and the possibilty of failure. Yet studies show that if these women were not placed on IVF programmes, their chances of becoming pregnant may well be higher. In Belgium a study of 17 women who became pregnant after unsuccessful IVF treatment noted that the stress of feeling that a woman *has* to be pregnant may interfere with her ability to become pregnant. Many of these women who had decided to accept their infertility became pregnant in the first few months after an IVF failure. The authors say:

> Spontaneous pregnancy after unsuccessful IVF appears in a typical setting: if a woman no longer *has* to be pregnant, she can become pregnant. Adequate treatment with IVF for infertile couples should take into account not only the stress of the IVF itself, but also the psycho-dynamic changes produced by the treatment.[30]

The stress involved in being on an IVF programme may well be counter-productive.

Conversely, studies of pregnancies brought about when patients were involved in attending an IVF or similar programme show that not all pregnancies were brought about through the techniques: rather, conception and pregnancy came about naturally. Perhaps the woman who took up greyhound breeding could have had a child or children and greyhounds as well, six years earlier, had she not spent the years since 1980 trekking backwards and forwards to Epworth Hospital. The woman who after seven years of trying declares she is not 'hung up' on IVF may have come to terms with her infertility seven years ago, had the programme not been available to lead her on, and today her life might be full.

Certainly for those who become pregnant through IVF programmes, the joy of pregnancy is a personal reward. However, every pregnancy, every woman involved in the programme, every report upon the 'miraculous' doings at the various hospitals and clinics, is a palpable reward to the doctors involved. The medicos appear to benefit most profoundly from the existence of infertility, the longing of women on the programme to produce a child, the desire of partners to father their biological child, an heir. When newspaper reports declare 'It's all for the infertile', readers should be wary of taking the words at face value. Far better to support an approach which accepts infertility as too often being caused by technological and industrial 'progress'. We should be seeking to reverse that trend by working toward eliminating infertility and changing the nature of a world which socialises men and women into believing their fulfilment lies only in producing their own biological children.

Endnotes

1. *Canberra Times* 23 January 1986.
2. Maternal age may affect the receptivity of a woman's body to implantation of the embryo in the uterus. In relation to IVF and this issue, see Roger G. Gosden, "Maternal Age: A Factor Affecting the Prospects and Outcome of Pregnancy", *Annals of the New York Academy of Sciences*, May 1985, vol. 442, pp. 45–57.
3. See generally M.G.R. Hull, C.M.A. Glazener, N.J. Kelly, D.I. Conway, P.A. Foster, R.A. Hinton, C. Coulson, P.A. Lambert, E.M. Watt and K.M. Desai, "Population Study of Causes, Treatment, and Outcome of Infertility", *British Medical Journal*, December 1985, vol. 291, no. 6510, pp. 1693–1697; Carl Wood, "In Vitro Fertilisation—The Procedure and Future Development" *New Doctor*, September 1985, no. 33, pp. 20-22.
4. See Naomi Pfeffer and Anne Woollett, *The Experience of Infertility*, 1983, Virago, London; C. Kasby, "Causes and Treatment of Infertility in Women", *Healthright*, May 1983, vol. 2, no. 3, p. 8.
5. See generally Jock McCulloch, *The Politics of Agent Orange*, 1984 MIT, Ma. (distributed in Australia by Heinemann).
6. Letters to the Editor, *The Age* 1985.
7. See for example the English case of *R.* v. *Clarence* (1888) vol. 22 *Queens Bench Division* p. 23
8. See J. Rakusen and N. Davidson, *Out of Our Hands: What Technology Does to Pregnancy,* 1982, Pan Books, London;

Jad Adams, "Who Stood to Gain on the Dalkon Shield? *New Scientist* 26 September 1985, pp. 6–7.

9. See generally Andrea Boroff Eagan, "The New Pill — Should You Take It?"*Ms Magazine,* October 1985, pp. 35–36, 38, 124;
Ellen Grant, *The Bitter Pill,*1985, Elm Tree Books, USA.

10. Submission from the Prostitutes Collective, Victoria, to the Commission of Inquiry into Prostitution in Victoria, 1984, Melbourne, Australia.

11. Robert Winston runs the *in vitro* fertilisation clinic at Hammersmith Hospital, London. Together with Dr. Anne McLaren and Professor Martin Bobrow (working in genetic research) he set up an organisation called Progress, to promote knowledge about "pre-embryo" research, in November 1985.
See Virginia Ironside, "How to Breed Healthy Babies", *Guardian* (London), 18 November 1985, p. 10;
Robert Winston, "The Quads: Nothing to Apologise For", *The Observer,* May 1984.

12. On medical treatment of women during pregnancy and labour, see generally Anne Oakley, *The Captured Womb,*1984, Basil Blackwell, London. Gynaecological or obstetrical procedures which may result in infertility where carried out without due care include cervical conization, dilation and curettage, endometrial biopsy, myomectomy, tubal insufflation, oophorectomy, caesarean section, hysterosalpingography, uterine suspension, hysteroscopy and hydroperturbation.

13 See William R. Keye, "Strategy for Avoiding Iatrogenic Infertility, *Contemporary Ob/Gyn,* 1982, vol. 19, pp. 185–195.

14. V. Baukloh et al, *Jrn. In Vitro Fertilization and Embryo Transfer*, 1984, Vol 1, No. 2.
also S. Pollock, "Refusing to Take Women Seriously: 'Side Effects' and the Politics of Contraception" in *Test Tube Women. What Future for Motherhood?* Rita Arditti, Renate Duelli Klein and Shelley Minden, editors, 1984, Pandora Press, London, pp. 138–152;
Phillida Bunkle, "Calling the Shots? The International Politics of Depo-Provera" in Arditti, Duelli Klein and Minden 1984, pp. 165–187.

15. Organisations such as Animal Liberation, formed in the 1970s, have taken a far stronger stand on animal experimentation than traditional organisations such as the RSPCA. Animal Liberation protests against experimentation and against certain agricultural or animal husbandry practices. For further information on the links between the new reproductive technologies, farming and human experimentation, see Marion Brown, Kay Fielden and Jocelynne A. Scutt, "New Frontiers—Or Old Frontiers, Recycled? New Reproductive Technologies as Primary Industry", in this volume.

16. Robyn Rowland, "A Child at Any Price?" *Women's Studies International Forum,* 1985, vol. 8, no: b, pp 539–546.

17. In Pfeffer and Woollett, 1983.

18. Pfeffer and Woollett,1983.

19. In Pfeffer and Woollett, 1983.

20. In Pfeffer and Woollett, 1983.

21. Accent Age, *The Age* 1986.

22. Pfeffer and Woollett, 1988;
see also Barbara Burton, *The Need for Reproductive Control Self-Determination for Infertile Women,* n.d., Infertility Federation of Australasia (copy held by present authors).

23. *Infertility Procedures Act* 1984 (Victoria);

see also "Psychiatry's Role in In Vitro Fertilisation", Ob/Gyn News, 15-31 May 1985, Vol 20, No. 10, p.8a.

24. See Christine Crowe, "Bearing the Consequences—Women Experiencing IVF", this volume and Anna Murdoch, "Off the Treadmill—Leaving an IVF Programme Behind", this volume.

25. Erica Bates and Helen Lapsley, *The Health Machine*, 1985, Penguin Books Australia Ltd, Ringwood, Victoria.

26. In Bates and Lapsley, 1985.

27. In Bates and Lapsley, 1985.

28. On "success" in *in vitro* programmes, see Helga Satzinger and Farida Akhtar, "Sterile Solutions", *Connections*, December 1985, pp. 10-11;
    and see further this volume, particularly Gena Corea, "Women, Class and Reproductive and Genetic Engineering — The Effect of New Reproductive Technologies on All Women", and Renate D. Klein, "Genetic and Reproductive Engineering — The Global View".

29. see Christine Crowe, "The Reproductive Fix", *Australian Left Review*, Autumn, 1985, pp. 4–9.

30. Paper from conference, held by Ramona Koval.

3 Bearing the consequences – *Women experiencing IVF*

Christine Crowe

The actual experiences of women on the IVF programme are remote from any description of the technical aspects involved in IVF procedures. Indeed, for many medical scientists the emphasis on 'technical' virtuosity seems to be the dominant value by which to consider IVF. The 'subjects' of IVF, the infertile women themselves, take a poor second place in discussions of the procedure. Medical terminology, with its apparently 'neutral' tone, depicts the events of IVF—the taking of ova, fertilization of ova outside the (woman's) uterus, and the (possible) replacement of fertilized ova - as happening to specific parts of a woman's body. The disparity between technical and other values became apparent when I spoke to women who have participated in an IVF programme.

The IVF programme offers some women with fertility problems the hope of motherhood. Their desire for motherhood may silence any of their overt criticism of the programme. All women I contacted were willing to share their views with me; there was a general feeling of readiness on the part of the women to present *their* side of IVF. Not all the women speaking with me were overtly critical, but all expressed their doubts, fears and anxieties about participation.

In Western society, where 'ownership' of children is determined either by a biological relationship or a relationship of exclusive nurturance sanctioned by the state, alternative forms of parenting are virtually non-existent. Women with fertility problems may view IVF as their 'last chance' for motherhood. Many are prepared to take this 'last chance', living in the hope that they may be one of the lucky few to conceive, have a full-term pregnancy, and give birth.

IVF may be seen by many women with fertility problems as the last in a long line of medical procedures. Usually a woman does not begin IVF without first having undergone extensive tests to determine the exact nature of her fertility problem. Women participating in IVF programmes say they have already become accustomed to having their lives scheduled around doctor's appointments, visits to clinics, and frequently invasive examinations necessitating rigid adherence to medical procedures. Some women feel that they 'owe it to themselves' to attempt this last possible avenue before making further long-term decisions about their life. Once undergoing an IVF procedure many women find it difficult to discontinue. One woman described IVF as a 'whirlpool' where hope is offered 'just around the corner'. The fact that IVF is possible, and its persistent lure of 'next time', makes it even harder for a woman to consider life without a child born of herself.

Women revealed their anxieties, hopes and fears to me about IVF. They talked not so much of IVF in positive terms, but of their strong desire for motherhood and lack of alternatives.

HOPE AGAINST HOPE

For many of these women, each stage of the procedure is fraught with possible disappointment:

> It involves a lot . . . both physically and mentally. You know that when you go for that attempt it is virtually your only chance, your only hope to fall pregnant. So much is built up mentally already because you really want it to work.
>
> From the fifth day [of the cycle] you've got to take a triple dose of Clomid [a superovulation drug]. On the ninth day you go into hospital. Every day, in the morning, you've got to be there early . . . sometimes you're given injections to boost your ovaries. They do blood tests every day. You hope that your blood's going to rise nicely, so that you *will* be given the chance.
>
> Then, if all goes well in that department, they'll give you a scan. You're hoping that they'll find good eggs. Then if all goes well you go into hospital everytime anytime, depending on your cycle, from the twelfth to the seventeenth day. You go to the hospital at midnight for the needle then you have to go back the following morning for blood tests, and you take your urine sample with you. All going well, you get into hospital that day. Meanwhile, you come home and wait till 2 o'clock. If you don't get a phone call, nothing's going wrong, so you go into hospital.
>
> Then you're hoping that the next day they're going to get eggs

. . . that they don't miss your eggs. Then they get eggs and you've got to hope that they're fertilised . . . Then you get them put back.

Then you come home and wait for a fortnight and hope against hope that it's worked.

THE DOUBLE BIND

Accompanying these hopes was the knowledge that few woman were 'successful'. Many were caught between realising that the chances of pregnancy were small, and thinking that if they did *not* participate in the procedure with the highest hopes and expectations they would, through their 'negative' thoughts, be responsible for any 'failure'. Women expressed ambivalences about participating:

You go in there saying to yourself that it's not going to happen but deep inside you're saying — yes, it is going to happen. I was just so disappointed afterwards. . . I was really down, down, down, *again*.

It really does have a big effect on you mentally. You lose hope, and when the time came for my turn . . . you build yourself up again, pysche yourself up. You're telling yourself: 'No, it's *not* going to work', but you're wishing and praying that it *will* work.

I know it's not going to work again, but we'll try anyway. You try to protect yourself. That self-protection is very strong. . . All you're trying to do is to cushion that emotional blow at the end.

IVF is the focus of women's lives not only during participation on the programme, but at all times. A maximum of three attempts per year is currently the recommended limit to participation. All the women said that as soon as they considered participating in the programme, this thought pervaded their lives. Many were anxious, after an unsuccessful attempt, to participate again as soon as possible:

You have yourself psyched up *all* the time. As soon as you start thinking to yourself, we'll give it another go, maybe next month . . . we'll ring up and see if we'll get accepted . . . for about two or three weeks, you're waiting for your period to come, to make that phone call, and then you're waiting all day for the phone to ring, for them to ring up and say 'yes' or 'no'. If it's 'yes', you're still psyched up, and if it's 'no', you think—'oh, now I've got another month to go!'

AFTER EMBRYO TRANSFER

Every woman I interviewed said that the two weeks after embryo transfer was a period of intense anxiety. Waiting for a period 'not to come' is the focus of attention:

> The worst time is definitely that two weeks between when you get out of hospital and your period. There's nothing that can describe what you go through, the mental torture you put yourself through.

If menstruation began after the transfer, women experienced frustration and a sense of failure. Understandably, the days on which menstruation was due highlighted an overall obsession with the body:

> When you get your period . . . you can't believe it. The two days you are due is shocking. You feel every twinge in your body. You're completely obsessed with your body.

Women felt a disparity between the intensive care received during the IVF procedure and their seeming abandonment after the embryo transfer:

> When we're not actually being treated, there's just no one looking into what's going on inside our heads. While you're being treated, it's terribly intensive—you're being monitored 24 hours a day, you might be having three blood tests a day to see what your hormones are doing. If you're in hospital, you'd be visited once or twice a day by a specialist gynaecologist. After you've had the transfer . . . you have no more contact. There's no follow up . . . there's no one to talk to. You're going from intensive care to being quite isolated and cut-off. When you're not pregnant, to go back on the programme is up to you . . . If you don't ring up the hospital, no one ever rings you and says: 'what's happening and how are you feeling?' or: 'Are you coping?' or: 'Do you want to see a counsellor?'

To deal with stress involved in being on the IVF programme some women seek help through psychiatric consultations:

> The emotional part of it was getting far too hard, way out of control. I was using antidepressants, and it got to the stage where I thought that I just couldn't keep taking tablets all the time . . . I ended up seeing a psychiatrist, whom I still see. He's helped me with all the problems—it's another outlet.
> I can understand suicide. I sought professional help . . . talking it over with a psychiatrist. I felt I needed help . . . Because I just couldn't understand all the resentment and all the guilt, and all the other feelings I had. I still continue seeing him . . . simply through fear. It's like a lifeline.

DOCTORS AND COUNSELLING

Many doctors who acknowledge that women on IVF programmes undergo stress often advocate more counselling. Advocating counselling to deal with anxieties raised by participation in an IVF programme does not acknowledge the relationship of power between the IVF team and the women who participate.

Women's comments showed an acute awareness of these power relations. They felt an implicit pressure to demonstrate to the doctors a 'rational' attitude to their attempt at pregnancy through IVF and its subsequent 'failure'. They considered doctors were more likely to recommend further IVF 'treatments' if they 'accepted' a failure and declined to 'make a fuss':

> Patients feel they're under a lot of pressure *not* to 'crack up', and they have to be 'suitable', and if you show *any* signs of emotional distress, you'd be 'out'.
>
> It becomes very difficult sometimes to ask questions because you've got to figure out some way of phrasing them so that they're questions 'for the sake of intellectual knowledge' rather than because you're worried to death about the answer.

Some women I interviewed felt that if they had a frank discussion with a member of the IVF team, their access to the IVF procedure would be jeopardised. Where counsellors were available at the hospital, several women stated they feared their 'negative' attitude, expressed during these counselling sessions, would also jeopardise their access to the procedure:

> You *couldn't* really say what you wanted to say because you could feel the repercussions coming from it . . . it might affect your position in the queue.

The feeling of having to conform to some vague standard is evident from the first interview:

> When we first went to see the doctor [at the IVF clinic] I was saying to my husband: 'Now, whatever you do, keep your mouth shut and be good, because this is the last chance we get'.

Many of the women expected no more than a rather perfunctory role from the doctors:

> They're technical, they're success oriented, they want to get pregnancies — that's their job . . . to do IVF and to put embryos back,

and to keep doing it day after day after day, with lots of women coming through on a conveyor belt.

I don't see how they can *avoid* just seeing women as objects because after all that's what they are to them . . . just uteruses and tubes. Also, they have no training in the psychological or emotional aspects. They'd be *terrified* to get into that!

There was a stage in the programme where some women felt like guinea pigs, although they generally perceived that the IVF programme was primarily concerned with overcoming fertility problems of particular kinds. They also wanted more information about the effects of the use of the drugs they were obliged to take and the use to which their eggs were put:

I'm concerned about long-term effects of taking those fertility tablets. We've got a synthetically produced high hormone level. You get bombarded with these tablets, triple the normal dose every three months. I'm wondering about the long-term effects. I asked the doctors about that and they said: 'We don't know'. Lots of women keep it to themselves and don't say anything.

As a patient, we aren't aware why the researchers are doing something. We *are* guinea pigs. We have to have trust in them and [have] faith in their reasons for doing it. We want a child and they say they can give us a child. We don't know what's going on behind the scenes because nobody tells us. There's a definite barrier. I would imagine all patients would not *dare* to interfere with them . . . to ask questions, to doubt. They could be varying the strength of medications they give us . . . They'll come and say: 'I'm sorry, your eggs didn't fertilise' . . . and you'll just take it as that. You don't know why [they have not fertilised]. You don't know whether it's because they tried to see whether it [the egg] will go twelve hours before they're fertilised, and it didn't work. You just cry your tears and go home . . . You are kept in the dark and you don't dare ask too many questions.

DAILY LIFE

Apart from anxieties related to the programme itself, women stated that participation interfered in their lives, particularly where opportunities for seeking or for continuing paid work outside the home were concerned. It was a 'double bind'. Being on the IVF programme more than once a year interfered with their paid work:

After my first go, they [the employers] told me that I either go on the programme and give up my job, or keep my job and give the programme away. I've heard of a few girls who've had that happen. They *know* their job is on the line by having to go into hospital every day.

To be available for the procedure, and knowing of the likelihood of losing their job once on the programme, many women resign from paid employment. At the same time, many said they would prefer to remain in paid employment outside the home because they would not be so anxious about the results of the embryo transfer if they had other interests such as their job:

> If you are lucky enough to have embryos put back, and you've got that two weeks before your next period, your job, as long as it's not a physically taxing job, is a mind-saver.

It is difficult anyway for some women to establish both a personal and a social identity apart from 'possible' mother. Options apart from paid employment outside the home are similarly restricted:

> I want to go to Uni, . . . I put my name down this year to start, but I thought, how can I do that around being accepted on the programme. Especially when I don't know when I'm going to have a go. You will only know that month, and you have to drop everything that month. I've put that off, and put it off, and put that off . . .

THE MOMENTUM OF IVF

The desire for a child, accompanied by the limiting of options for personal and social identity makes it very difficult for some women to discontinue IVF. Those who had set a time limit to how long they would participate in the programme found it extremely difficult to adhere to their initial resolve; none kept to their original limit:

> I've been chasing a baby ever since I was 22. You've got to draw the line somewhere. Thirty-five was going to be 'it' . . . but I still feel that physically and mentally I could still have a child.
> For the last twelve months I've been trying to kid myself into saying that I don't care if I quit anyhow. I'd like to be in a position so that I feel freer and not subject to any manipulation, and it's not so important to me . . . but *really*, for all that twelve months it's been a struggle inside myself, and I've *never* really reached that stage where I could say I could quit.

A factor contributing to women's participation in the programme was that they felt compelled to attempt all avenues possibly resulting in motherhood, before they could accept a life without children. Many women felt they had a 'duty' to themselves to participate in the programme:

> When you know you've got a chance out there and you're not making the most of it . . . It's hard to make a decision when to call it quits because you don't want, in years to come, to think—if *only* we'd tried *one* more time!

Media reports, invariably about the 'successful' mothers, highlight to those women who have not 'succeeded', the fact that public attention is focused on the positive results of the procedure only. As Robyn Rowland has said:

> The impact of 'failing' to become pregnant on IVF programmes for the eighty-six out of every hundred women who try, has yet to be considered in a caring way and is at present totally ignored by the medical profession and the community.[1]

Since media reports have concentrated on 'successes', the overall understanding of the community is that these 'successes' are representative of results obtained from the procedure. Women who decided to attempt pregnancy through the programme 'only' once more, and those deciding to discontinue altogether, stated that their friends were 'shocked' when the decision was disclosed to them:

> People would say—'Oh, but *surely* you're going to keep going?' They couldn't understand it . . . that you'd consider dropping out.

WOMEN'S VIEWS OF IVF

All women viewed IVF as a 'treatment' to help women with specific fertility problems. However several women expressed fears of reproductive technology becoming 'out of control':

> Maybe it's the *beginning* of a lot of other things. . . That scares you.
> IVF, I think, is not to cure infertility. IVF may have been originally to cure infertility, but it's just opened up so much *more*.

Some women attributed the development of medical science in the direction of reproductive technology to the 'scientific personality' and the pursuit of knowledge for the sake of knowledge alone:

> Science is forever ongoing . . . they're always experimenting . . . I guess anything can happen . . . They probably started this simply because it hasn't been done before. It's that absolute *lust* for knowledge that scientists have. It's the most important personality factor that a scientist can have.

Other women suggested that medical science has taken this direction because the scientists themselves are (overwhelmingly) male:

> They find technology interesting. Reproduction is one of the most fascinating areas, and this fires them on.
>
> Well, they always think they're superior, don't they? Men do . . . you've only got to see the way they act in a group.
>
> I think it might be an ego trip for them to produce a baby outside of a woman.

Participation in an IVF programme requires women's faith in the doctors and the programme. Women voiced their doubts about IVF with intense ambivalence. They could not deny their experiences and subsequent criticisms; yet the desire for motherhood in the context of seeing IVF as their 'last chance' tended to override the import of these doubts and criticisms. The constant lure of motherhood 'maybe next time' perpetuates this situation.

For many women the decision not to participate in the IVF programme is virtually synonymous with the decision to consider their lives without children. Women at present live in a society where the ideology of motherhood means motherhood is perceived as one of the most important sources of women's identity. The focus on motherhood as a 'natural' situation for women places the woman with fertility problems under much personal and social scrutiny. The development of IVF, together with an apparent lack of viable alternative options for motherhood, are preconditions for women's participation in IVF programmes.

The women who spoke with me emphasised motherhood as a social relationship rather than a biological relationship. Medical science depends upon women's co-operation for research into reproductive technology. Motherhood as a commercialised product relies upon the dominant view of motherhood as biologically based. It is particularly relevant today to question whose interests are being served by this rigid definition.

Endnote

1.   Robyn Rowland, *Social Implications of Reproductive Technology*, Paper delivered at St Vincent's Hospital Bioethics Centre Annual Conference, 1984, at p. 4.

4 Off the treadmill –
*Leaving an IVF
programme behind*

Anna Murdoch

For the past four years the press has shown photographs of radiant women holding babies conceived by *in vitro* fertilisation. What has not been shown are the faces of the 85 per cent of women for whom the treatment does not work. Isobel Bainbridge, who started the IVF Friends with another woman in Melbourne in 1981, gave up the treatment five years ago and is now studying psychology so she can counsel people who finish infertility treatment. She is critical of most of the publicity about IVF:

> When you are on the program you are set up to be a parent . . . You are very supported by the team. It is like a little world away from the real world. You are encouraged to be the person you think you want to be, that is a parent, and not what you are, which is infertile. IVF pressures the community into thinking that anyone can now get pregnant. There is an emphasis that if anyone wants to be happy they must go and have this baby transplanted into them. 'Medicine will make me happy.'

Medicine does not make the majority of these women happy. Embryos, which have been fertilised outside their bodies in a way that is beyond their control, for some reason fail to implant and die. They must wait two weeks before finding out whether or not they

---

*   This is an abbreviated version of a feature originally appearing in *The Age*, Accent Page, 10 April 1985, under the title, "When IVF is a Lost Labor".

are pregnant. Many have knitted clothes and set up a room for a baby, or have started planning its future. When the pregnancy test is negative they see themselves as failed nurturers.

Some women try this treatment up to six times. Isobel Bainbridge had seven IVF treatments before giving up. She had tried for 17 years to become pregnant. She is now 42:

> I got to the stage where I wanted to make the decision about my own life. If I was not going to have children I wanted to say that to myself. I did not want doctors telling me how my life should be.

The majority of women are forced to give up the IVF program, often because of the expense. Each treatment costs $1200 (in mid-1985 figures), not counting health insurance rebates. Some women have to give up their jobs because employers will not give them the time to go on the program. And for many, the emotional and physical effects are traumatic. Isobel Bainbridge says:

> It is a very brutal way of coming to terms with your infertility. I think there could have been kinder ways.

The final acceptance that nothing can help you produce a baby is extremely harrowing. For Isobel Bainbridge, it was 'a long, dark tunnel' of desperate depression:

> Sometimes I feel depressed still, but I know how to handle it. I do not think to myself 'maybe if I get pregnant things will get better'. It has taken me five years to get to this. When I was on IVF I saw that no one was prepared to give up wanting children. Even if they know they cannot, they did not think 'I will give up this want for my own peace of mind'.

She feels IVF has increased the already powerful belief in the community that a family is the way to a good life:

> There are other things you can use these mothering instincts for. Now I feel I am in charge of my own life. I can be whoever I like. I am off the treadmill. It was scary at first. It has become very exciting. Infertility is part of my life. I am making it part of my work. Hopefully, I can help others because of my experiences.

There is also criticism from women still on the programme. Dr. Barbara Burton, the founder of IVF Friends and the IVF Patients Self-Support Group in New South Wales, is a patient as well as a medical researcher. She interviewed 12 women from 27 to 42 in the Sydney and Newcastle areas who had one or more IVF treatments. IVF had given them hope. But the majority felt not enough information had been given about the treatment [but they felt they couldn't ask]. Dr. Burton says:

> One very assertive, self-confident woman, an out-and-out feminist, told me she was unable to ask questions while she was going through treatment. When anyone told her about the treatment it was as if it was leaked information. She was made to feel grateful for what she had been told so far and did not want to push things.

For most women the major problem with IVF is the low success rate compared with the media's representation of it as a modern miracle. One said:

> I entered the programme with a rosy glow of expectation. It was a rude awakening to meet other women who were going through for their fourth or fifth attempt.

Friends and family often assume that after treatment the woman is pregnant and will stay that way.

The women all said they needed to know why it had not worked. One said:

> You don't get any feedback. It would be nice to be given a reason, a follow-up phone call from the medical co-ordinator. You want to be told it is not your fault you bombed out. You just go home and feel a failure.

Another said:

> I would really have liked to have gone back and talked to [my gynae-cologists] after it didn't work, but as [an IVF scientist] says: 'You're history, we are on to the next one, we haven't time for you now, we want to get on with it'.

Barbara Burton says one way the teams cope with their own failure is to avoid follow-up contact with the patients.

The IVF programme had put enormous strains on the women's marriages and their sexuality. Most had considered divorce so their husbands could have children with someone else. Almost all the women felt less inclined to make love. One said:

> When you are really wanting children, you revert back to the old-fashioned thing of 'why bother?' when you know it does not work.

Another said:

> My husband thinks I have lost interest in him. It is not that. It is just
> that that whole area is so painful I want to deny it exists. The other
> night while we were making love I thought 'this isn't something
> special between the two of us, it is something which involves all these
> other people'.

All [women] said they needed counselling when infertility was diagnosed, information when they joined the IVF waiting list, and support during the treatment and after. 'At the moment most of these
women are returning home not pregnant,' Barbara Burton says.
'There are no calls. People are really desperate at this stage and no
one does anything about it.'

The demand for IVF treatment is increasing. About 10,000
women are on waiting lists around Australia. There are many
reasons why women cannot conceive and have a baby. Often, Barbara Burton says, young women have tubal ligations after having
children, then remarry and want another child. Many women's
tubes are scarred after operations. For about 30 per cent of the
patients the reason for their infertility is unknown.

When Barbara Burton was 20 a gynaecologist was paid a lot of
money to carry out an unnecessary operation on her. 'The best treatment I could have had was nothing, for which he would have been
paid nothing. I am angry about gynaecologists who think they know
about women, talk to them like little girls and don't consult them
about surgery.'

5 Surrogate motherhood – *Refusing to relinquish a child*

Terese McFadden

I have no answers as to whether a surrogate programme is 'the answer' for some infertile couples, but I am aware of some of the real problems that it causes and will cause. There are no mid-line decisions to be made on this issue. Pregnancy is not an intellectual experience which women can control and therefore stand back from to become an incubator for other couples.

BACKGROUND

Unfortunately the women who have been able to give up their babies at the end of the surrogate procedure have been most in the public eye. I am pleased to be able to show the other side of the story. I made my decision to become a surrogate mother by adding up the pros and cons. The list wasn't long. I felt I was ideal. I had already had six children, enjoyed pregnancy and birth, found them easy and felt good about helping a childless couple. I asked family members beforehand how they felt. My husband wasn't really happy about it, but said it had to be my decision. My children thought it was good to be able to help other people in that way. Because I had decided to become a surrogate mother without a couple approaching me first, some time passed before I found an article in a Sydney local paper. The article was written because three months previously a couple had put an ad in their paper for a surrogate mother.

---

*   To protect the identities of those involved, substitute names and addresses are contained in this article.

The article referred to a couple with pseudonyms of Peter and Ann who were childless. They told me they had just returned from America where they had seen an organisation called 'Surrogate Parenting Association' which could, they said, supply a couple with their own 'biological' child. Peter felt good about being able to produce a biological child of his own; in fact, so much so that he said in the article that he was willing to divorce his wife to marry a fertile lady if his wife Ann didn't agree to a surrogate providing him with a child. Ann said she had had two miscarriages and even though she was a doctor herself, felt she had been left in the dark as to why they had occurred. As she had to be on fertility drugs to conceive in the first place, she said she didn't want to go through the experience again.

Ann had seemingly resigned herself to being childless and as she had a stimulating and rewarding career, felt OK about the situation. She was willing for her husband to go ahead with the programme as she didn't want him to leave her. They described themselves as professionals with a good income. They both loved children, and Peter said that he got on extremely well with his nieces and nephews.

THE AGREEMENT

Ann and Peter asked for a surrogate mother who was attractive, intelligent and who had at least one child to prove her fertility. I replied to the article by ringing the journalist, who then rang Peter, who rang me. Apparently I was the third to apply. The two others had already been 'interviewed'. I gave Peter details of my background and he sounded very pleased with them. That night his wife rang and she was also happy with me. Ann said she didn't want to see or meet me but would I please send a picture, would I agree to some form of contract between us, and would I have nothing further to do with the baby after the birth? I agreed to all these conditions. However I told them there could be no legally binding contract, but that if they wished they could write an agreement which, though not legally binding, would at least give me an idea of what they wanted.

This is the agreement they sent!

I, Terese McFadden, of 21 Dunbar Street, Tralee, NSW, hereby undertake to:

1.   Be artificially inseminated with the sperm of Peter Brown (who is not my husband) until either pregnancy occurs or until the agreement is terminated in the event that pregnancy does not occur in a reasonable period of time, as

determined by the physician or between Peter Brown and myself.

2.   Abstain from intercourse for two weeks prior to insemination and two weeks after insemination.

3.   Not to attempt to make any form of contact with the child born subsequent to the surrogate procedure, with Peter Brown or his wife.

4.   Not to attempt to form a parent/child relationship with the said child.

5.   Avoid all alcoholic beverages, tobacco products and drugs (whether legal or illegal) unless prescribed by my physician.

6.   Assume all risks of pregnancy.

7.   Submit to paternity tests.

8.   Execute all documents necessary.
   a)   to have the child's birth certificate accurately reflect the identification of Peter Brown as its natural father.
   b)   to give legal custody of the child to its natural father (Peter Brown).

9.   Agree to termination of the pregnancy if the unborn child is found to be abnormal, or if my physician determines that my future good health is in serious danger.

Dated at Tralee on 7/4/83.

. . . .

Terese McFadden

I didn't feel good about the agreement and told them so. Yet knowing it wasn't legally binding, I signed the form. I realise now and did during the pregnancy that some of the restrictions were impossible. For example: Item number 4 says I should 'not attempt to form a parent/child relationship' with the child. Those having had a child will realize the parent/child relationship begins long before birth.

PREGNANCY AND BIRTH
I did the first insemination myself and became pregnant. This preg-

nancy ended at 11 weeks with a miscarriage and a great change of heart by myself and Ann. Ann became distant, hurt and hurtful. Peter just wanted to keep trying. My husband John wanted us to go ahead with another pregnancy as he now felt sorry for the couple. I was very hurt at the loss of the pregnancy and now felt more worried about my ability to give the baby up.

John and I decided to go ahead a second time and again pregnancy occurred with the first insemination. But I felt that this time things were quite different. Ann wouldn't ring and didn't want any contact with me.

At about 20 weeks pregnancy I had a scan done and realized that of course I already had a relationship with the baby. I had been coping before by denying the baby was mine, by telling myself and the couple that I was carrying their child. The night after the scan I rang Peter, first to let him know the results were good and secondly that I wasn't able to deny the baby any longer, that although the baby was biologically his, it was also mine. He didn't seem too threatened, but in retrospect, I feel it wasn't only the end of my ability to cope with a surrogate programme, it was also the end of their ability to cope with me.

Ann had especially denied my existence, by not wanting to see me and not wanting to speak to me. Now I was asking that she see me as the mother of the child she was hoping to raise. Arguments began over the phone between Ann and myself. She denied she had previously said she would let me have pictures and progress reports of the baby. (I was really becoming a big threat to her.) I really wanted to meet her and talk to her in person.

I had seen a television show with two surrogate mothers. One was nearly due with a first time surrogate baby (she had three daughters of her own). She had had lots of contact with the couple; in fact her whole family had. She said that she felt very comfortable handing over her baby to them. The other women had a child (again in a surrogate programme) and had contact with the adopting couple. They had become such good friends that this mother had given back the $10 000. The baby girl was named after her and she was the baby's godmother. She was just about to have another baby for the same couple. I thought I could cope a lot better if I could have the same contact. Ann couldn't handle my change of heart and consequently hit back as hard as she could. She said she wasn't going to stop working; that she was going to employ a nanny to care for the child. She wouldn't send pictures, or information about the child, and she didn't know if she could even love the baby.

This I guess was the beginning of the end.

By the time my pregnancy had reached near term, I had no way of coping with what I was about to do. I felt so confused about the couple to whom I was handing over my baby. I began to consider alternatives such as another or normal adoption. What I had realized at this point was that I really wanted to keep my baby myself, but John said he could handle anything but my keeping the baby.

Tim was born two weeks earlier than expected. Everything that could go wrong did. I couldn't contact Ann and Peter to let them know the baby had arrived. Peter was first contacted by my doctor, who chose to take the job on himself. Peter was very hostile about this. He felt I hadn't been going to let Ann and himself know, even though, at this stage, the baby was going to them. I had tried all day to ring them, but apparently I had the wrong number.

John and I eventually spoke to Peter, and John suggested he come up to see his child. Peter and I had agreed beforehand to talk to each other while I was in the hospital. He now said that he wasn't happy doing this and would see the baby at the handover. He told us the baby's name and he rang each day to find out how the baby was.

John stayed with me day and night looking after the baby and caring for me as I cried most of the time, didn't sleep, and felt suicidal. On day five I decided I couldn't hand over my baby. I told John that night and although he wasn't delighted with my decision, he was going to support me in it. My family was told and we had huge problems with our eldest child who was then 14 years old.

The press began to harass us, because after telling Peter of my decision to keep the baby, he told them my name, the hospital I was in and our address. We kept trying to duck for cover but when we didn't give them a story or pictures, they wrote their own story and took pictures through windows. We had no comeback.

I received letters from friends, strangers and acquaintances all of them on one side of the fence or the other, giving advice, support or airing their hostility. I lost quite a few friends.

AFTERMATH

Tim is now one year old. Peter and Ann are both still very hurt by my keeping him.

Tim is loved by us all. His favourite person is his father John who loves him dearly. His brothers and sisters all know about the circumstances of his birth and Tim will know himself when he begins to talk and understand. I have lots of regrets over choosing to become a surrogate mother, but one of them isn't my son, Tim.

In retrospect, John and I feel we may have stopped the organization called 'Surrogate Parenting Association' from trying to set up shop here, as it tried to in England. It was eighteen weeks before Tim's birth, that the two mothers from the organization were interviewed. Just after Tim's birth the lawyer attached to the Surrogate Parenting Association came out to Australia. He was interviewed on the *Mike Walsh Show* as well as other programmes and said he would fight for Peter's cause in any way he could. He said I had kidnapped my baby, because the baby had never been mine, but had belonged to Peter and Ann. He said the organization in America has legal back-up, as the laws are different there.

It all seemed very coincidental that the surrogate mothers and the organization's lawyer were out here 'advertising' only eighteen weeks apart.

Six days after Tim's birth the *Artificial Conception Act* came into operation in New South Wales. Because of my married status and the fact that my baby was conceived by artificial insemination, the Act made my baby legally John's as well as mine. (The Act came into being to protect couples involved in the AID (Artificial Insemination by Donor) programme, but it was timely for us as it also meant that I was legally bound to have John written on the birth certificate as Tim's father.)

REFLECTIONS

I feel I have learnt a lot about myself through this experience. I now want just what is best for my baby. I have hurt Peter and Ann, my family and myself. I only hope that with time and honesty we will all recover.

I also feel very differently about how our society copes with a couple who are unable to have children. They are subjected to test after test in a hospital. Then if all else fails, they are categorized as having one form of infertility problem or another. Their only avenue left then is either to accept the situation (which very few couples choose), go on an AID programme (if they can afford it, and if that is the answer to *their* particular intertility problem), adopt a baby (which will put them on a 10 year waiting list), or look for a surrogate mother to give up her child for them. With all of these methods, bar the acceptance of their inability to have children, the emotional and physical problems still exist. Those problems have just been temporarily covered up. These couples must have extra pressures attached to the normal parenting ones, because at no time has anyone helped them cope with their feelings of inadequacy at not being able to produce a child which is completely biologically theirs. At a future date, they then have to cope with telling their child the reasons for their unusual conception or their adoption.

Maybe we should be shifting the emphasis away from parenting as necessary to fulfil us as human beings.

6 New frontiers or old recycled?
New reproductive technologies as primary industry
Marion Brown, Kay Fielden & Jocelynne A. Scutt

In vitro fertilisation and other new reproductive technologies involve the intervention of medicine and sciences in the process of human conception. Simply put, eggs may be removed from a woman's body, mixed with sperm in a petri-dish, and fertilised *in vitro* (in glass); the resulting embryo is transferred back into the woman's uterus, or into another woman's uterus. Alternatively sperm can be artificially introduced into a woman's uterus to fertilise the ovum *in vivo*. Other techniques include the 'flushing' of a fertilised ovum from the uterus of one woman, to be placed into the womb of another; of hopes for 'genetic repair' with the replacement of defective genes in an ovum or embryo with 'good' genes.[1] To understand why Australia is generally acknowledged as a world leader in the field of new reproductive technologies, developments can be seen against a backdrop of social, political and economic history.

The predominance of primary industry in Australia is a key factor: at school, children learn about the role played in Australia's survival as a wheat growing nation, with the breeding of 'rust resistant wheat'. Children also learn of the significance of sheep breeding to the economy: Australia 'rode to prominence on the sheep's back' runs the tale. So the breeding of 'better' plants and 'better' animals for marketing purposes is an old story in a relatively newly established, European-Australian economy.

New reproductive technologies now used for human reproduction were first developed in the context of animal husbandry, to
enable the production of high quality genetic stock at a rate beyond
that which nature could provide. The nation was, at least in the early
days of European settlement and well into the twentieth century,
heavily dependent upon primary industry. Modern scientific
breeding practices developed in the farming industry. Initially,
farmers and technicians involved in 'better breeding' used artificial
insemination to ensure that the 'best' stock multiplied: bulls of good
genetic stock were sold as breeders; their sperm fetched high sums
on the market. Later, eggs (or ova) of high quality breeding stock
(mainly ewes and cows) were 'retrieved' and fertilised outside the
animal's body, then transferred into average stock. Alternatively,
ova could be fertilised *in vivo* (inside the ewe or cow's body) and
flushed out, to be inserted into the bodies of animals with less significant pedigrees. These stock bore and nurtured the pedigree
lambs and calves. Breeding herds expanded at a rate much greater
than that dictated by the natural fertility cycle of the animal, as several sheep could simultaneously gestate embryos derived from the
prime breeder ewe, or multiple cows could gestate embryos from
the prime breeder cow. The gene-stock animal could be used exclusively as a gamete donor, avoiding any possible breeding impairment
which may occur during gestation and birth.

Somehow the complex implications of such direct interference
in reproduction did not concern the public while it was comfortably
located in the context of primary industry. In Australia the impact
of commercial breeding and production techniques on the animals
being farmed and consumed is only now beginning to be acknowledged. But during the mid-1970s the technological manipulation
and multiplication of reproduction was an entrenched commercial
practice in the field of animal husbandry. Transferring this technology from sheep and cattle to women and men was relatively
unproblematic.

THE MYTH OF MOTHERHOOD

The economics of a dependency on primary industry is sufficient
explanation for general acceptance of breeding technology where
plants and animals are concerned. Yet the introduction of the same
technology into human sphere, where no clear economic impetus
is apparent — at least in terms of the breeding of human infants
(the economic impetus behind the development of high tech sunrise industries is another issue) — without fuss requires
explanation.

Why did artificial insemination and *in vitro* fertilisation techniques meet so little resistance in the community? We must understand the historical context of motherhood for white Australian women. Significantly, black women in Australia have rarely, if ever, been involved as recipients of artificial insemination or *in vitro* fertilisation. Their concern is maintaining the health and life of their children in the face of an infant mortality rate that approximates those of the Third World. From the first days of Anglo-Australian settlement until the post war migration of the mid-1940s, Australia's European community suffered from a chronic shortage of women. This was combined with relatively high wages paid to white men, the low levels of unemployment, and the social pressure to populate the country to enhance the size of the domestic market and the paid workforce. Above all there was a need to demonstrate the superiority of the imposed European culture, social structure and genetic pool. The result was that the focus of women's existence necessarily became marriage and childrearing. Indeed, marriage and family were widely promoted and accepted as the only 'career' for women.

Australia's original settlement as a penal colony is significant. More men than women arrived from the British Isles, causing considerable concern to the colonial authorities. Katrina Alford reports in *Production or Reproduction? An Economic History of Women in Australia 1788–1850* that the problem of a preponderance of males was expressed as early as 1786:

> . . . .when a proposal to procure women from the South Seas Islands was mooted, Lord Sydney argued that a numerical imbalance between the sexes was in itself a cause of 'gross irregularities and disorders'. This view subsequently became the conventional wisdom among policy makers and commentators on early colonial life.[2]

Marriage and the production of children to create families became the ideal. This led to many women convicts being transported for far less serious offences than the men who were transported. When the assisted immigration of free settlers was supported by the British government, the overwhelming theme was that 'sufficient numbers' of women of a marriagable age should swell the ranks. In 1831 a system of assisted female immigration was introduced for New South Wales and Van Diemen's Land, the basis being, in the authorities' eyes, that this would assist to create a stable populace.

There is little doubt that the aim was to provide marriage fodder. For while young women were encouraged to emigrate, few paid jobs were available for them. Women did not come to Australia necessarily to marry, whatever historians traditionally say about their travels.[3] Yet they were offered little choice. The ratings of the various colonies against one another shows the overwhelming desire that marriage-and-family should everywhere rank first. The importance of marriage and childbearing for women is clear, in that the colony of South Australia continually rated far better than any of the other colonies. Not only was South Australia not a penal colony, but:

> ... the more even sex balance in South Australia ... was claimed as the basis of the colony's much vaunted moral superiority, a claim which echoed throughout the spate of literature on South Australia in the 1830s and 1840s ... The grandiose claim [was made] that 'the general character of the South Australian Community for religion, morality, intelligence, enterprise, sobriety, and industry, is highly respectable ... 'The conclusion?
> 'There also seemed a freshness and gentility about the females of South Australia; and a person coming from the eastern colonies would not fail to be struck with the superior ruddiness, simplicity, and purity of the South Australian damsels'.[4]

A marriage and family attitude persists today. In 1983 a study by English and King showed that apart from some 'relatively small groups in society, such as those with university qualifications':

> ... there is still a high level of support for the attitude that it is proper to marry and to have children. In other words, the majority of people irrespective of age, sex, religion or place of birth are in low or medium support categories on the attitude that one can have a useful life without marriage and a complete life without children. This is reflected in the behaviour of Australians in general.[5]

This attitude is not exclusive to Australia. As Jessie Bernard has pointed out for the United States in *The Future of Marriage:*

> ... women come in a wide variety of shapes, sizes, colours, talents, temperaments and degrees of 'motherliness' ... They differ in standards and styles ... Some are rich, some are poor, most are in between ... Some are educated, some are not ... But, despite their differences, practically all women become mothers ... We expect every woman not only to want babies but also to love motherhood. If she does not, we make her feel deviant.[6]

But the degree of its fixation has origins in a country's history.

Two hundred years after the European settlement of Australia not so much has changed. Women have gained a significant and crucial control over their fertility. This now enables more married women to re-enter or remain in the paid workforce, with greater consistency. Yet women still face a dramatically sex-segregated labour market. In the main they are relegated to the low paid, often unskilled, service industries. Women are more likely to be working in part-time paid employment to cater for their child-care responsibilities. Marriage and motherhood remains very much a part of women's self concept, if not a sole or primary career choice.

In the mid-1970s other social factors impinged on the historically amplified drive for motherhood. In 1975 the Whitlam Labor Government introduced a social security benefit payable to any woman, married or single, having the care of dependent children and lacking financial support. The Supporting Parent's Benefit provided young, single women with a viable and often palatable alternative to surrendering their ex-nuptial, or father-deserted, children for fostering or adoption. As well, progressive court decisions in the 1970s led to more liberal access to abortion. The combination caused an acute shortage in the availability of babies for adoption. Suddenly—dramatically, it must have seemed—the (usually) middle class couples seeking children to adopt and raise as their own could no longer find children to meet their needs.

Simultaneously some of the ramifications of the so called 'sexual revolution' of the 1960s and 1970s were seriously endangering or impeding women's reproductive health. Throughout the 1970s and 1980s women across the world began to feel the pain and suffer the damage caused by dangerous contraception. 'Side effects' shrugged off or ignored by a cavalier medical profession at last began to be acknowledged as real. The complications associated with the use of several intra-uterine devices (IUDs), notably the Dalkon Shield, had disastrous consequences for the fertility of many users and even for their lives. Sadly, many infections and disorders of the female reproductive system show no symptoms until the infection or disease is well established, and often until it has extended to the fallopian tubes and ovaries. By the time pelvic infections are detected, the damage may be so severe as to require surgery to remove contaminated organs, or scarring from the infections makes reproductive organs impotent.

The contraceptive Pill and onset of the 'sexual revolution' meant many women could engage in sexual activity without the constraints of traditional marriage relationships and the consequences of pregnancy. Currently, 'modern sex' declared existing, less glamorous, mechanical methods of contraception such as the diaphragm and condom to be unfashionable. In abandoning their less modish contraception (condoms, diaphragms and abstinence) in preference for high tech hormones and IUDs, women unwittingly abandoned the most effective devices for preventing the passage of sexually transmitted disease. Our 'sexual liberation' was won at an enormous cost to our physical integrity and reproductive health. Today, women are still counting the cost.

So by the mid-1970s the scene was set for research to conquer the 'heart-rending affliction' of infertility which beset approximately 10 to 15 per cent of heterosexual couples. So doctors and scientific researchers devised means of manufacturing motherhood for those 'afflicted' with infertility. It should come as no surprise that this response to infertility (often caused by a lack of preventive medicine, or poor standard of traditional medicine intervention) looked to new technology, rather than addressing the diseases and technology producing impaired fertility in the first place. After all, a reliance on high technology and drug therapy has characterised western medicine for the best part of the twentieth century, and has its origins in earlier times.[7]

Medical research has traditionally concentrated on symptoms rather than underlying causes. The problem may be more easily approached from that end, but it is difficult to resist the cynicism that suggests preventative medicine and health care would eventually take the money out of the 'health care' business. Scientific research is ideologically attractive, based on the assumption that *man* can dominate, control and manipulate *his* environment. No doubt genuine excitment is experienced by researchers as they painstakingly push back the frontiers of knowledge, and in this case change the unique and miraculous process of human conception into an external and technical procedure conducted outside, and independent of, any human body. In looking back to the way in which childbirth was wrested out of the hands of women as midwives, and medicalised and institutionalised, to become firmly located in the control of men (as male doctors), some of the current fear that the new reproductive technologies are a way of completing the same process of male control and medicalisation one step earlier—at conception itself—can be understood. Before assessing the virtues and vices of *in vitro* fertilisation and other new methods of artificial reproduction, the application of this technology in its original sphere—through primary industry involving animals, and commercial developments in plant and animal breeding—should be examined.

HIGH TECH IN PLANT AND ANIMAL BREEDING

Genetic engineering now has an accepted place in plant reproduction. It is portrayed as a blessing, particularly where benefits can be demonstrated for Third World countries. The November-December 1985 issue of *New Scientist*, in 'Genewatch' reports that biotechnology is being developed to design non-herbicide weed control strategies. The idea is to:

> ... facilitate better crop rotation systems, aid in the domestication of new crops, or enhance the use of allelopathic genes in crops ...
>
> [A]grichemical manufacturers and new biotechnology companies are enlisting the powers of bioengineering to enhance and broaden the use of herbicides in agriculture: that is, they are planning to give crops that may be damaged or killed by herbicides the genes that will make them resistant to the chemical's damaging side effects.

In other words, the aim of genetic engineering in this field is to enable toxic chemicals to be used to kill off weeds: chemicals which would in the normal course kill the crops as well. By making the crops gene-resistant to the herbicides the crop will be preserved in weedless fields. Yet the 'Genewatch' article goes on to point out that this development comes at a time when the USA Enviromental Protection Authority has 'listed several popular herbicides for groundwater monitoring and special toxicology reviews'. The latter have indicated that laboratory animal studies 'have shown some of these chemicals to be possible carcinogens':

> At least 15 herbicides—many of which were once billed as rapid breakdown and non-persistent products—have recently been detected in surface and groundwater across the country.

Thus we are confronted with a seemingly nonsensical use of biotechnology: crops will be preserved from the carcinogens of herbicides by being made gene-resistant to them; weeds will be killed by the herbicides; but the population which the crops are apparently preserved to feed will run the risk of being adversely affected by the carcinogen qualities of the herbicides! No doubt the high tech 'solution' would be to ensure that the people who eat the crops are themselves made 'gene-resistant' to the carcinogens by genetic engineering alongside the crops.

New Scientist (November-December 1985) laments the failure of commercial interests to take up the issue of the application of new technology to food production:

> Food production is a natural target for the new technology because agricultural conditions in many developing countries are so poor. People have been unable to raise enough food near populated areas,

where it is most needed. Attempts to distribute food on large scale fail because of inadequate transportation systems. Thus, the use of biotechnology for the development of food resources in local environments would be a great step forward. Presently however, there is little or no commercial investment in this problem.

This issue notes special problems in the application of biotechnology to improve conventional crops:

> For example, it would be helpful to improve rice strains using genetic engineering, but we know very little about the biochemistry and physiology of the world's largest food crop. It will take many years of basic research on rice before molecular biologists know how to intervene to increase productivity.

The high tech mindset does not however question why food production in certain countries or certain areas is inadequate; questions which may well have a political and economic base rather than one attributable to the quality of land or the quality of rice or other crop. Why is the quality of land impaired? Often this is not the fault of nature, but rather the results of man's interference with the soil by the use of pesticides, the denuding of the land for the purpose of short-term gains in high production of crops, leading in turn to the deprivation of the soil and its inability to grow further crops. In Third World countries in particular, land became dependent upon chemical pesticides and fertiliser. This provided markets for First World corporations manufacturing these items. But their constant use depleted the soil, leading to greater famine. The solution on offer now appears to be to introduce more technology — this time, genetic engineering of crops such as rice — to 'overcome' problems introduced by technology in the first place. Reminiscent of high tech 'solutions' to human reproduction and infertility?

Commercial interests will surely become involved in genetic engineering and other technologies in the area of plant development when it is perceived there are ready markets, willing to pay. Whether payment comes direct from Third World countries or indirectly through First World 'aid' programmes is not the point: if the money is there and available for these projects, the projects will be developed. Thus *Science News* (1985, vol. 29), reports on a 'controversy' over an attempt by a biotechnology company, Advanced Genetic Sciences, Inc., to spray genetically engineered bacteria onto a patch of strawberry plants. The proposed field test was intended to protect plants from frost damage, and 'would be the first deliberate release of genetically engineered microbes [bacteria] into the environment'. *Science News* continues:

> The company obtained permission for the experiment from the California Department of Food and Agriculture, following the approval late last year by the federal Environment Protection Agency ... But once a specific site — in Monterey County, near Catroville — was proposed, local opposition arose. The exact site has not been publicly disclosed. In addition to the local opposition, Jeremy Rifkin of the Washington, DC-based Foundation on Economic Trends again asked the federal court for a preliminary injunction to delay the field test.[8]

Advanced Genetic Sciences, Inc., apparently has plans to spray the bacteria onto a test plot in a suburban, tract-house area. Jeremy Rifkin argues because the plot is close to homes this makes the problem of human pathogenicity (whether the bacertia can cause diseases in people) crucial. A statement by Advanced Genetic Sciences (AGS) in Oakland reveals that some strains of the bacterial species to be released 'have been associated with the diseases in patients who have impaired systems'. But:

> 'We have done toxicological studies that indicate that this strain [the one to be released] would cause no harm to man,' counters Douglas Sarojak of AGS. 'Although some strains may be low-grade pathogens to patients with advanced stages of cancer and other severe immunodeficiencies, people are in constant contact with the species,' he says. 'A typical carrot carries ten million or more bacteria of this species,' he adds.

Advanced Genetic Sciences, Inc. defends its proposed test site because it is 'rural, maybe semirural . . . it meets all the criteria set by the regulators'. Demonstrators picketed Advanced Genetic Sciences, Inc., and the company is set to 'defend its plans at [a] . . . public meeting' set up by the Board of Supervisors of Monterey County.

Companies are already involved in the game of technological interference in plant production, and in genetic engineering of the plants themselves, whether they be strawberries programmed genetically to resist frost-bite, or rice plants programmed genetically to produce bigger and better grains. There has been agitation in Australia against the patenting of various seeds produced through breeding mechanisms. Petitions have been tabled in federal parliament to demand that the federal government reject any plans for legislation to grant breeders rights over seeds developed in this way. The petitions state that the federal government should:

1. Uphold the principle that the seeds and cuttings of plants are a public resource and a common heritage to all and that accordingly seeds should be freely available to all, freely multipliable, able to be sold, exchanged, exported and imported by anyone who wishes. This is seen as a matter of national food security.

2. Recognise that plant breeding is a highly co-operative venture often involving private enterprise at the very last stages after basic seed collection, storage, and research has been publicly funded.

3. In view of the aforementioned paragraphs, recognise that any system giving 'property' or ownership rights over seeds to individuals, organizations or enterprises is inappropriate and unjust.

4. Recognise that legislation establishing plant patenting schemes overseas has had serious adverse effects, namely:

(a) a slowing down of scientific information exchange and exchanges in basic plant breeding materials, that is, germ;

(b) subordination and/or curtailment of public breeding programmes;

(c) farmer unrest at seed prices;

(d) monopoly control of seed production and sales has passed into the hands of giant petrochemical and drug corporations who also market crop chemicals;

(e) increased uniformity of crop varieties leading to a vulnerability in pest and disease attack.

5. Reject any proposal to legislate for any system such as the drafted Plant Variety Rights Act, which gives exclusive ownership rights over seeds to individuals, organisations or enterprises.[9]

Hopefully, this agitation will develop public concern about the development of genetically bred plants of the type discussed in 'Genewatch' and *Science News*.

Yet the implications and commercialisation of plant technology, worrying as they are, are only a mirror image of what is occurring in the world of animal production. Commercialisation in the world of animal breeding is rampant. Thus in *New Scientist* on 10 April 1986 it was reported that the Brave New World came a step closer 'when an auction of embryos was held in Sydney, with video links throughout Australia and New Zealand. Eighty-nine embryos were sold for $AUS 304,750.' Reporting on the sale, the *Institute of Medical Ethics Bulletin* of April 1986 says, somewhat laconically: 'The embryos, however, were not human but of Hereford cattle.'

In the *Business Review Weekly* of 20 June 1986 John Waugh reports more extensively of developments in Australia on the animal breeding scene:

> Luccombe Maralyn Starlie generates about $750,000 a year doing what comes naturally, but not in a natural way. Eight-year-old LUCK, as he is known on the books of Elders Breeding Services' establishment at Tongala, in one of Victoria's lush dairying regions, is Australia's top artificial insemination (AI) donor bull. Each year he produces about 75,000 doses of semen, at $10 a service, which is used to improve dairy herds in Australia and overseas.
>
> And he still has many 'work' years ahead of him. Semen from his Canadian father—he worked until he died at 14, three years ago—is still being sold on the world market for $400 a dose.

LUCK, John Waugh goes on to report, is 'part of a revolution that has been slowly transforming Australia dairy herds for about 20 years.' This revolution is now 'gathering pace through embryo and gene-technology research and development that could eventually generate millions of dollars for Australian agribusiness'.

In addition to the dairy industry, these developments are taking place in the beef industry, the meat and wool aspects of the sheep industry, and in pig and goat industries. The aim is to upgrade herds and flocks 'and improve their efficiency'. John Waugh adds, reminiscent of rust-resistant wheat, pesticide resistant crops, and frost resistant strawberries: 'It could even lead to disease-resistant animals.'

Again, these developments are praised—as placing Australia in the forefront of genetic research. Australia was late in adopting genetic evaluation methods of animals, but this has meant that the system now being used is 'rated among the best, if not the best in the world'. Government resources have been employed to develop and promote this research, predicted to generate, in the future, 'millions of dollars' for those involved in the agriculture business—at least, those involved at the 'top end', in large farming enterprises. Whether the smaller farmers will have access to, or resources to utilise, these genetic advances is not mentioned. The Victorian Department of Agriculture has done some research and the Victorian government computing service determines genetic evaluations. The Australian Meat and Livestock Research Development Corporation, financing 'about $13 million' worth of projects in 1986, is 'one of the organisations heavily involved in the funding' of various projects related to this technology. CSIRO Australia (Commonwealth Scientific and Industrial Research Organisation) has an animal production division involved in gene transfer into embryos. New England University (NSW) is doing genetic research on beef cattle, concentrating on Angus, Limousin and Simmental breeds; and the Reproductive Biology Unit at Adelaide University has well publicised its work into production of a 'super mouse' and plans 'jumbo-sized' pigs through transgenic engineering, projects which will be relevant to the agriculture industry.

In the United States and West Germany, as in other countries, experimentation in genetic engineering for the production of 'bigger and better' animals for ultimately commercial purposes is well advanced. On 13 March 1986 *New Scientist* reported on experiments similar to the 'super mice' from Adelaide University in South Australia. *New Scientist* comments:

> Richard Palmiter of the University of Washington and Ralph Brinster of the University of Pennsylvania were one of the first groups to microinject genes into the pronucleus of the fertilised eggs of mice. They thus successfully introduced several copies of a foreign gene into each cell. They called the resulting infants 'transgenic' mice. Palmiter and Brinster injected a fusion gene, consisting of a promoter from a mouse bound to a rat or human gene for growth hormone. These genes produced the protein hormone at levels three times higher in the blood and the mice grew twice as large.

But it is *quantity* that is most enhanced by this gene transfer. *New Scientist* says that gene transfer does '*not* produce mice that are perfectly normal, just bigger'. Because some tissues are disproportionately affected—the promoter working better in some tissues than in others—'growth is asymmetrical'. The mice in the experiment grew a liver four times larger than normal, whilst their brain was approximately normal size. The mice had a tendency to be infertile. Another procedure, using human growth hormone releasing factor in the fusion gene, causes less disruption to the animals' biology; these mice more often tend to be fertile. The article concludes:

> Tinkering with the genes of embryos has side effects, however ... The microinjected or virally transported genes integrate randomly in the chromosomes and sometimes disrupt normal genes in the process. Palmiter estimates that 10 to 20 per cent of transgenic mice have mutations.

There has been little agitation in Australia about the implications of genetic and reproductive engineering in the animal world. Rather, the reaction appears to be applause for the forward-looking, entrepreneurial efforts of agribusiness. The production manager of Elders Breeding Services complains about the difficulties facing private business, in competition with publicly funded operations. Lamenting that 'we have a long way to go' and that 'only half the cows in Australia are artificially inseminated'. John Waugh in *Australian Business* quotes him as saying:

> This [rate of insemination] is an appalling comment on the methods used [in Australia] when compared with the rate of artificial breeding used by developed milking countries. Farmers have not been under pressure to use AI [artificial insemination] until recently. The failure has been partially ours. We have not adequately educated farmers in the need for AI. They still look on it as a short-term expense rather than a long-term benefit in increased yields and the construction of superior herds.

Waugh reports that several commercial ventures in Australia have failed over the past 15 years, and 'three main non-government centres, Victorian Artificial Breeders at Bacchus Marsh, Elders Breeding Services at Tongala, and the Riverina Artificial Breeders at Wodonga, are competing directly against the state government-funded projects. 'That's one of our bitches', says the Elders Breeding Services production manager:

> We've got to compete against agencies which are subsidized, which makes it very difficult to make money. On an individual bull basis it would appear very lucrative, but only one out of every five bulls you have comes up to the mark; and you have to hold them all for four years before they are proven . . . or sent to slaughter.

In 'Race for the Biotech Billions' *Australian Business* shows evidence that the system is 'paying off handsomely' for some. One family has 'done well' in Victoria's south-west, using artificial breeding exclusively. Now, their herd is 'among the top two per cent of Australian breeding values rated herds in Australia':

> 'Our target is to have a herd average of 5000 litres [of milk] per cow, with a test of 4.5 per cent yielding 225 kg of fat,' [the farmer] says.

AID (Artificial Insemination by Donor) is not a gentle process in animals—at least in terms of the recipient of the sperm, the ewe or cow. In *The Mother Machine* Gena Corea outlines the procedure in the United States, where cows are super-ovulated, then artificially inseminated, to produce multiple embryos. Embryo transfer is even less gentle. Corea reports on the cavalier way in which animals are treated during the operation.

> The cow was now bound in the squeeze chute, a metal contraption used to restrain cattle. A tag labeled #300 had been stapled in her ear . . . A hypodermic needle containing an epidural anesthesia was stuck in the cow's back.
>
> 'The cow can't move,' [the farmer] explained to a neighbour who had come to watch the transfer. 'The chute's got all kinds of adjustments. She just can't move a muscle in it.'. . .
>
> Twisting slowly [the veterinarian] inserted a foley catheter into the left horn of the cow's uterus. A flushing solution contained in a bottle hanging high from a rafter in the barn would flow through the catheter and into the uterus by gravity. A graduated cylinder on the barn floor would catch the solution and eggs as they flowed out of the cow. . .
>
> They flush each horn seven times. . .
>
> As they flushed, they joked about the microscope supercows that might be flowing into the cylinder. Watching the flowing water, Bob [the vet's partner] quipped: 'That's a million-dollar bull just went by.'[10]

There has been little if any sustained outcry against these procedures on grounds of cruelty to animals. Legislation relating to cruelty to animals in Australia is specifically drafted to eliminate any possibility that procedures as these might be classified as 'cruelty'.

HIGH TECH IN BREEDING HUMANS

At least new reproductive technologies and genetic engineering are not portrayed as of benefit to the plants and animals utilised for the procedures. Rather the theme is that these developments advantage humanity in the supply of plant and animal life for the survival of humans through the production of food and other necessities of (human) life. Yet where women are concerned, the new reproductive technologies and genetic engineering are portrayed as for *their* benefit, and (less vociferously) for the benefit of their husbands. The community at large has relatively little knowledge or understanding of what is actually involved in the new reproductive technologies procedures. More particularly, there has been a conspicious lack of information about the experiences of women undergoing the procedures.

A 'treatment cycle' on an *in vitro* (IVF) programme originally involved the artificial stimulation of a woman's hormones to induce 'super ovulation' whereby in the course of one menstrual cycle the woman's ovary would produce three to eleven ova instead of the usual one ovum. She would then undergo a laparoscopy under general anaesthetic, a procedure whereby a fibre-optic tube is inserted through the abdominal wall and with a further two abdominal incisions, eggs are retrieved at the edge of the ovary. Once eggs have been obtained they are mixed with sperm and fertilised in a petri-dish. The resulting embryos are then 'replaced' in the woman's uterus (at the four cell stage), or may be frozen to be used at a later time, or for a subsequent procedure.

Most clinics now advise the implantation of three or four embryos at each attempt, as this is supposed to increase the chance of obtaining a continuing pregnancy. The entire treatment cycle lasts about three weeks. In some programmes, women will be dismissed as unsuccessful after five or six treatment cycles have failed to produce a sustained pregnancy. In other programmes, there are no limits, so the number of attempts women undergo will be determined by their emotional and financial resources and the limits of their physical endurance. In each treatment cycle a woman exists in the midst of hope and despair:

- did 'they' get any eggs?
  if 'yes', continue hoping
  if 'no', despair and consider if you can go through it all again next time
- did the eggs fertilize?
  if 'yes', continue hoping
  if 'no' despair, etc.
- did the embryo implant?
  if 'yes', continue hoping it will hold, worrying perhaps that more than one embryo has successfully implanted
  if 'no', despair and try to cope with the loss of a viable embryo—potential baby—can you face that loss again?

The emotional trauma is no doubt exacerbated by the extreme physical intrusion that is part of IVF technology. At first the woman is required to chart her temperature daily and will have to submit to blood tests. She will also receive hormone medication to induce super-ovulation. (No longitudinal studies appear to have been conducted to determine what side-effects such treatment may have on the woman and any offspring she may produce.) As the critical time of ovulation approaches, there will be further tests including an ultrasound scan. When ovulation is imminent, the woman is admitted to hospital.

In hospital, the monitoring is increased significantly. Urine samples are collected every three hours, except for the six hour interval from midnight to 6.00 am, to allow some sleep. Blood tests are carried about daily until it is time for the 'egg pick-up'. At this stage the woman is prepared for a general anaesthetic and undergoes the laparoscopy, involving three surgical incisions in her abdomen. To facilitate the laparoscopy, the woman's abdominal cavity is pumped with carbon dioxide to provide the space and vision necessary to conduct the procedure. An unfortunate side effect of this is that her internal organs are pushed up against her diaphragm and chest cavity, leaving the woman with relatively severe post-operative shoulder pains as well as the pain produced by surgical incision.

If eggs are retrieved, the woman's husband or donor is called in to provide semen for fertilisation. If fertilisation occurs, the woman remains in hospital, continuing to chart her temperature daily until the fertilised egg is implanted in her uterus. Where the clinic has facilities to freeze embryos the woman may be able to take some time to recover from the abdominal surgery and hormone therapy before she 'receives' her embryos. Embryo implantation is achieved by transferring the embryo in fluid into a catheter (tube) which is then inserted into the woman's vagina, through her cervix so that the embryo will be released into the uterus. This procedure does not require any further anaesthetic. However, women are offered tranquilisers on some programmes, to reduce anxiety and combat any possibility that anxiety might produce a hormonal reaction that in turn increases the risk of embryo expulsion. Usually the woman is discharged a day or so after implantation but has still to undergo a further blood test, one week later, to see if she is maintaining the pregnancy.

Clearly this technology is both physically and emotionally intrusive for the women subjected to it. Understandably, women involved in IVF programmes exhibit a very high emotional commitment to 'the programme' and their hoped-for outcome of bearing a child. But even in the most sophisticated of technological regimes the success rate in terms of live births is alarmingly low. Pregnancy rates for many programmes in Australia are quoted as 20–25 per cent, but this is not an accurate gauge of eventual outcome.

Women in IVF programmes experience a higher than average rate of spontaneous abortion. This is now explained as a reaction to the hormones used to superovulate women on the programme. There is some speculation that researchers have underestimated or overlooked the sophistication of the female reproductive process. They have not fully understood the complex hormonal responses triggered by the fertilisation of an egg in the fallopian tube. These hormonal responses are important in preparing the uterus to be receptive to an implanting embryo.

It is possible that a woman who has been striving to conceive, possibly for years, who is implanted with a variable human embryo may find that her body will not sustain that embryo. Certainly, some women have spontaneous abortions after conceiving in a more traditional manner, but where such an abortion occurs within the duration of her regular menstrual cycle, the woman may not realise she had conceived.

It is sometimes difficult to understand why women persist with this technology when it seems to extract such a heavy emotional and physical toll. Obviously the IVF teams are sensitive to 'consumer resistance' and new techniques are being introduced which, they hope, will make the technology less hostile to women's bodies and therefore less stressful to the women on the programmes, and less hostile to 'ethical purists'.

'Advances' involve a technique of ultrasound pick up which is now on trial and being adopted as a preferred procedure. A needle is inserted either through the vaginal wall or the bladder into the centre of the ovary for egg 'retrieval'. The procedure can be performed under local anaesthetic and does not require the abdominal cavity to be filled with gas, thus avoiding the very uncomfortable post operative shoulder pains. Some proponents also claim it is possible to collect more eggs using this technique, as the needle can penetrate much further into the ovary than is possible with the laparoscopy procedure. However, this is offset by the increased chance of retrieving immature eggs when ovaries are accessible beyond their immediate exteriors.

As the technology is modified so that it is less physically invasive, its range of applications is expanding. IVF is now adopted as a legitimate form of therapeutic management for ideopathic (that is, physically inexplicable) infertility problems. Some commentators suggest that such a condition may relate to a woman's prior, unpleasant sexual history, such as an unresolved trauma associated with the termination of a pregnancy or the involuntary relinquishing of a child for adoption. This hypothesis seems to indicate that at least a portion of the infertility currently plaguing women could be avoided if women had access to safe, cheap, reliable contraception and sound sex education. Women should have adequate protection from sexually transmitted diseases from the earliest days of their sexual activity, and protection from unwanted sexual encounters.

Male factors such as ligspermis (low presence of sperm in semen) and reduced sperm motility are now also considered appropriate conditions for IVF. Semen can be spun down and a very small concentration can be mixed with the ovum to achieve fertilisation when this is conducted outside the woman's body. In such circumstances, women would have to proceed through all the monitoring and surgical intervention of a treatment cycle, despite their reproductive system being completely functional.

The procedure of Gamete Intra Fallopian Transfer (GIFT) is now being tested in several IVF clinics in Australia and this method may overcome objections from the Roman Catholic church.[11] Theoretically, GIFT allows fertilisation to occur 'naturally', in the fallopian tube. Eggs are removed with an ultrasound needle and immediately mixed with semen in the syringe. The mixed solution is then injected into the woman's fallopian tube. This procedure is appropriate only for women with intact fallopian tubes, as blockages or adhesions could result in an ectopic pregnancy (a pregnancy outside the uterus, which would be unlikely to give a live birth). Apart from patient pain, the cost is retarding possible expansion of IVF programmes and other reproductive technologies and genetic engineering.

In mid-1980 clinics charged around $AUS 3,000 per attempt. (In the United States the charge per treatment is estimated at between $US 4,000 and $US 5,000. In Britain the estimate roughly corresponds at approximately £2,000.) In Australia all but $600 or $700 of this is refundable if the woman has maximum-cover private health insurance. Some programmes also allocate a number of places for public patients who are charged the equivalent of the Medicare cover for procedures only, the hospital making up the shortfall in funds. One significant element in the cost structure is the necessity for a general anaesthetic and theatre costs associated with a laparoscopy. With the introduction of ultrasound egg pick up, this part of the procedure can be completed in the out-patients facilities under a local anaesthetic, considerably reducing costs.

Data collated by the National Perinatal Statistics Unit located in Australia does not, unfortunately, include the total number of women treated in IVF clinics across Australia and New Zealand. This means that the only statistical analysis available is limited to the 20–25 per cent of women recorded as becoming pregnant whilst undergoing IVF. An analysis of this data from 1979–1984 shows that these women had a 24.9 per cent rate of preclinical abortion and a five per cent incidence of ectopic pregnancy. So a significant number of women with embryos implanted in them by an IVF procedure, and notified to the National Perinatal Statistics Unit, did not carry the fetus full term. For the women sustaining a pregnancy beyond 20 weeks gestation, they encountered an overall perinatal mortality rate (loss of fetus) of 47 per 1,000 total births (4.7 per cent). This is approximately four times higher than the national rate for 1983.[12]

IVF is popularly promoted as a benevolent exercise to help infertile couples, just as genetic engineering possibilities are portrayed as a potential exercise of benevolent import, to 'save' babies from hereditary diseases. Disease, all would agree, may lead to a quality of life well below that which most people would want to share, or have their children share, or even tolerate. But what sort of benevolence is it that encourages infertile couples to endure profound emotional and physical trauma in the face of such poor success rates? How honest is it to hold out hope to such people knowing that most of them 'will try anything' to achieve a pregnancy? IVF client couples have attempted to relieve some of the anxieties associated with undergoing the procedure through the establishment of patient support groups. But with names such as 'IF' and 'WISH' and 'HOPE' and cartoons of bouncing babies and hatching chickens decorating the pages of their *Combined Newsletter*, it seems even these groups are reluctant to admit the reality that perhaps 85 or 90 of every hundred women on the programme will leave it without a baby in her arms.

HUMAN REPRODUCTIVE TECHNOLOGIES AS 'MONEY SPINNERS'

Some may protest that there is little or no relationship between plant and animal reproduction and technologies, and new reproductive technologies in the human sphere. Yet the parallels are too significant to be ignored. At regular intervals newspapers publish stories from leaders in the new reproductive technologies field in various states protesting that, because of lack of financial or government support, or the 'intrusiveness of government regulation', they will be forced to pack up and move to another state, or even overseas.[13] Protests are vigorous that the sale of the technology abroad is 'the only way to go', and that objections to this sale simply reveal the troglodite or luddite mentality of those opposed to the sale, or daring to question it. Similar stories appear in the press where these technologies inhabit the plant and animal world.

On 19 May 1986 Bill Birnbauer reported in *The Age*, under a large headline 'Gene Advance Goes Overseas', followed by a smaller statement, 'while the federal Treasurer bemoans Australia's lack of high technology industries, another domestic scientific advance has been licensed to the Americans', a tale of woe. Birnbauer continues:

> Another Melbourne world first in biotechnology research has been licensed to a US corporation because no Australian company was willing to back the work. The plant cell biology research centre at Melbourne University succeeded recently in cloning a gene which regulates fertilisation in plants . . . An early commercial application of the breakthrough might be in production of cheaper, more vigorous tomatoes . . . The world's tomato growers want hybrid varieties [produced by this method] because they are more resistant to disease, provide higher yields, are hardier and produce uniform tomatoes at the same time each season.

The commercial potential of such developments is expressed well by those involved in the marketing of IVF. The voices seem to echo the comments and actions of those involved in marketing IVF abroad, through the Queen Victoria-Epworth Hospital-Monash University triad.[14] Like the Monash University venture, it also seems that academic openness about research results is being forgotten in the rush for commercial gain. After approaching companies in Australia which expressed little interest, Birnbauer reports:

> In the end, the plant biology centre signed a licensing contract with the US-based, biotechnology research company Agrigenetics. Under the agreement, Agrigenetics provided about $2 million for the research and guaranteed a percentage of total sales and royalties. The Melbourne University group [involved] *agreed to delay publishing its findings for a maximum of six months so that patents could be issued.* It also retained the Australian rights to the technique. (Emphasis added.)

A professor involved in the venture is reported as saying that the alternative to licensing the 'breakthrough' was 'just to publish it: then anyone could have taken it up for nothing':

> We thought at the time we might as well get some funding and learn about the commercialisation process at the same time. You are really in a cleft stick: someone has identified this group as being world leaders in this technology and they have also identified there is some money to be made from this technology . . . Our responsibility as university researchers is in the acquisition and dissemination of knowledge. We can't wait to publish while we set up a company in Australia, nor do scientists have the necessary experience or business knowledge . . .

Fortunately for the professor and her colleagues, American expertise in utilising knowledge for its full commercial potential has been made available readily. The agreement with Agrigenetics 'helped solve this problem'. The professor continues:

[Agrigenetics]has one of the abilities I think we lack in Australia, that is the vision to look far down the track. I would be the first to say commercial development of this is a long way off. But major corporations recognise and are positioning themselves early in areas of fundamental science and they are gambling that some of them will lead to commercial products.

These corporations also will take the responsibility for finding the commercial products in that very good science. I think that's something we don't really see in Australia. We see people who are willing to invest when you've got a product that is a sure-fire winner without taking a gamble.

Placing information in the public domain is apparently against the principles which should be applied in this business:

The question of what is the application of the science is left in the hands of the scientist [generally, in Australia] who often has very little experience in the business world. If the scientist doesn't recognise there is something in it, *very often it's published and put in the public domain where anyone can pick it up.* We've not developed those skills as well as others have. Other nations have entrepreneurs who are both science literate and business literate and have developed the skills of early recognition of potential . . . (Emphasis added.)

Just as in the world of IVF technology questions must be asked about the community's attitude toward the commercialisation of projects which were devised through the use of public funds so too in the world of plant biotechnology, what is the public's right of access to information developed thus? Just as in the world of IVF technology, questions arise as to the appropriateness of 'keep it to the chest until it's patented/copyrighted/registered' rather than allowed without hindrance into the public domain 'where anyone can pick it up'.[15]

There is a 'sunrise industry' potential seen in research, development and sale of plant biotechnology and animal reproductive technology and genetic engineering. IVF and other reproductive technologies appear to be a genuine sunrise industry. Clinics offering IVF and GIFT technology are an expanding area in a national health care system that is otherwise limping from cuts, rationalisations and staff shortages. Yet this technology is by no means cheap. More accurately, it should be called experimentation and research, given the very high level of uncertainty for the outcome of any treatment cycle. But the medico-entrepreneurs are at work in Australia. Campaigns are run through the media as feature stories, promoting the line that Australia 'leads the world with its IVF programmes' and has 'many firsts achieved by our doctors and scientists' (the women whose bodies are vital to the enterprise are conveniently forgotten in attributing achievement). They have 'sparked international interest'. Yet, it is simultaneously reported:

> While clinics and hospitals in United States are doing excellent work, even the biggest clinic there is only about a third of the size of our smallest one, the Wesley Hospital in Brisbane, which handles about 1200 patients a year.
>
> There is a waiting list of well over 2000 women for the Queen Victoria IVF programme . . .
>
> The 25 scientists in this IVF program have a budget of $50,000 — which would be incredibly low to American scientists.[16]

The IVF procedure, and stories relayed about the programme by the doctors and scientists involved, typifies the approach. Women are the subjects of the technology, objects to be studied, experimented on, and profited from.

In 'Why Do We Need All This?' Maria Mies, a German sociologist, proffers the explanation that genetic engineering and new reproductive technologies are essential to the ongoing growth of capitalism.[17] The techniques are the new industry 'chosen' to replace the old worn out industrial technology. Hence the link of scientists with big business which will eventually lead to mass distribution of the products by multinationals with the aid of governments. Mies states:

> It is an historical fact that technological innovations within exploitative relationships of domination lead only to an intensification of the exploitation of the groups oppressed. This applies in particular for the new reproductive technologies, the technology of the industrial production of human beings.

For Mies, the stage has already been set with the selling and promotion to the more affluent the notion of the 'right' to have a child of 'one's own'.

Interviews with women participating in IVF programmes reveal that this notion was manifested in the partner, and (contrary to some other reports) was not commonly held by the women, who were subjected to the 'treatment' and 'assembly line'.[18] In contrast, women in poorer nations are being sterilized or encouraged to abort female fetuses. In Bangladesh 'family planning' programmes women are coerced into having tubal ligations in makeshift operating theatres with minimal use of antiseptic and anaesthesia, for the promise of one month's salary and a new sari.[19] Some of these sterilization 'factories' are funded by USA aid agencies which pay for the sterilisation procedure only, and not for post-operative care. Often the 'aid' is tied to food programmes, so it is little wonder that women 'present' themselves for 'treatment'. Drug companies set up an office in Third World countries and market experimental hormone concentration injections (for women) with little regard for side-effects and other hazards.[20] These are the same drug companies which are actively engaged in IVF and other reproductive programmes promoting the 'right' to have biological children for those living in more affluent countries.

These technologies are not only used to produce *more* babies. They can be used—and are being used in some countries—to produce *less* of certain types of babies. In India the technique of amniocentesis is used to screen fetuses and systematically abort female fetuses.[21] This development is not isolated to India. David Weatherall, Professor of Medicine at Oxford University and described as head of one of the world's top genetic research units, said in the *Sydney Morning Herald*, 21 June 1986, that his group 'had been approached by three overseas doctors who wanted to learn how to determine the sex of the fetus within the first ten weeks of pregnancy':

> One doctor had made it clear that he was interested only in detecting the Y-chromosome (which determines maleness). Professor Weatherall would not name the countries from which the three doctors had come, but said they were from overcrowded regions where male babies were preferred ... Many cultures — particularly in overpopulated nations — favour male babies ...

These developments are occurring in India amidst a background of increasing protest by Indian women against patriarchal abuses of suttee, dowry murder, rape and sexual abuses of women, and the mortgaging of wives by husbands to raise money.

It might be suggested that with less women, there will be less protest—at least from women. In China similar methods are used in the name of population control—and again only female fetuses are aborted. In the United States and other western countries surveys have been conducted indicating a preference for male offspring, especially for the first born, whilst in Japan medical scientists have developed a technique, as yet unmarketed, for inseminating women with preselected sex sperm to ensure male progeny.[22] Sex determination has a role to play in primary industry or the agricultural business, too — although in that industry, the selection is of female embryos as being more valuable for reproductive purposes, and male embryos being the more superfluous.

Primary industry developed the idea of surrogate motherhood, using 'less desirable' animals as incubators for embryos created initially by pedigree cows and ewes and their 'mates' (usually a semen-filled syringe). Now in the human reproductive industry surrogates are becoming commercially viable. Women from less affluent countries, or women in the lower socio-economic levels in their own countries, are being used by private practice entrepreneurs in the surrogate mother industry. In 'Reducing Women to Matter'[23] Rita Arditti reports that in 1986 there were 16 surrogate businesses in the United States using as surrogates women from Third World countries. The surrogate earnt approximately $US 10,000 for her services, with pre-natal classes, pregnancy and postpartum support therapy if required. Advertisements for surrogates are placed in newspapers on a global scale, and some firms keep directories of women supposedly 'willing to serve'. Some of these clinics conduct research on unsuspecting surrogates in hope of offering more saleable products, depriving women of any autonomy in the process.

Although cloning has been publicly derided as 'not being possible', or a procedure which will not be adopted on ethical grounds, Robyn Rowland states that cloning can be used to replicate either sex. The technique bypasses sexual reproduction 'by using one of a number of available methods: nuclear transplantation, chemically induced self-replication, development from single blastomeres, or egg fusion'.[24] Using any of those techniques a new individual can be created who is genetically identical 'to the parent of the original cell nucleus'. So far, frogs, mice, fruit flies and some other animals have been cloned and the technology is commonplace in plant breeding and development. The only impediments to the use of cloning of humans are the current 'moral' dilemmas, lack of social approval, and financial restrictions. However these problems could be overcome in a world where public opinion can be manipulated through media representations of the 'successes' of IVF as positive and good, without clear and correct information about the procedures and their real outcome, and with governments currently anxious to promote industrial and technological growth for economic reasons.

In the meantime, scientists in the United States have developed artificial mechanical wombs and are experimenting with 'spontaneously' aborted fetuses.[25] Arguments put forward to rationalise this 'advance' include improvements in fetology (fetal medicine, focusing on the fetus-as-patient); fetuses could be pre-immunised ensuring healthier babies; the environment of an artificial womb could be 'controlled' and would therefore be much 'safer' than a female uterus; geneticists would have improved access to the fetus for recombinant therapy, gene-repair or for other purposes; 'better' children would be produced; sex-determination would be easier; and male parentage could be determined with certainty.

FINANCIAL COSTS OF HUMAN REPRODUCTIVE TECHNOLOGIES

Plant and animal reproductive technologies are promoted as commercially important and this appears to be publicly acceptable, where the issue is addressed.[26] It is more difficult to promote human reproductive technologies in terms of crass commercialism, although something of this flavour has crept into the debate, at least in Australia, with the Monash University sale of technology through IVF Australia. The costs in non-monetary terms less often hit the headlines: the voices of women mistreated by the procedure are rarely heard, but in these times of economic restraint it is significant that the financial cost of IVF and other reproductive procedures, not only to individual participants but to the public health budget, has received scant attention. Most clinics quote the cost of $AUS 3,000 per attempt, but the actual cost for the public health budget will be much greater than that. The sum of $AUS 3,000 excludes building maintenance costs, staff wages, power bills, administrative costs, labour oncosts and other overheads.

Detailed cost estimates are difficult to come by. In 1984 a New South Wales Department of Health policy analyst estimated the cost to the public hospital budget of the Royal North Shore IVF clinic in New South Wales, Australia, as $AUS 110,000 to $AUS 170,000 for that year. In 1986 there were four public hospitals running IVF clinics in New South Wales, as well as other private clinics where most of the procedures are rebateable under Medicare.

IVF is not simply a matter of infertile couples having a (remote) chance to procreate. In the context of our current health care economy money that is directed to high technology, low success research is money that will *not* be spent in researching the causes of infertility. Preventative health care strategies must be developed so that women are not made infertile in the first instance. Consider the possibilities of a spermicide cream that prevents the spread of sexually transmitted diseases—but that is hardly high status Sunday-paper-profile material, attracting precious research and development funds and funds for commercial exploitation.

An aspect of the cost of this technology to the community which is even more easily overlooked is the relatively high incidence of pre-term pregnancies (babies born before 37 weeks), running in Australia at 27.4 per cent, which often indicates a need for further high tech, high cost intervention and medical management. It may appear cruel to argue that infertile women on programmes (and their potential babies) should not have unlimited access to the very limited resources of Australia's public health system. But the differentials in treatment and access are remarkable between various groups of women and their babies. Research repeatedly shows that few black Australian women and their children have access to even bare minimum health care (let alone clean running water), whilst inhabiting a continent where money is diverted into high tech reproductive programmes and the necessary high tech resources that are created to care for the products of these programmes.

It is of concern that, without counting the costs—financial and otherwise—IVF and similar reproductive technologies have been and are being promoted as the acceptable face of genetic research and manipulation. Who can be 'against' motherhood? IVF is only one aspect of a range of reproductive technologies based on the premise that science can create, control and 'perfect' life forms. In the name of motherhood (the 'curing' of infertility) genetic researchers have, through IVF and embryo freezing technology, been presented with refrigerators housing the basic raw material upon which their research is dependent. Fears of cloning and gene 'therapy', as well as embryo selection, are hastily dismissed as exaggerated. Yet ten years down the track, the community is only just realising the current state of play of IVF. The reproductive technology industry is already entrenched in our public and private health system, and commercially marketed abroad.

If current trends are any indication, IVF and similar reproductive technologies such as GIFT will become more common throughout the public and private health sector. If for no other reason than a lack of attention to the environmental and social factors that will continue to produce alarming rates of infertility in otherwise healthy women, this promotion will continue and expand. Major decisions on health care for Australians have had little to do with commonsense. But we *should* demand a more rational and long term 'cost effective' approach, in devoting research and medical dollars to redressing the known causes of infertility, such as dangerous contraceptive devices and pelvic inflammatory disease, rather than into high tech clinics seeking to 'cure' by high tech the damage done initially by high tech itself. Why do we continue to fund existing and new IVF clinics when there is not a universal bulk-billed, screening test for chlamydia—a frequent cause of infertility and other problems for women—available to women on the same basis as 'pap' smears?

In time, just as in the agricultural world—where these procedures are less expensive than they were originally, and are now routine—with more sophisticated procedures IVF treatment may cost less. Less dollars may be spent, and there may be a reduction in physical pain (although this cannot be depended upon, as women's experience in the field of high tech contraception shows too well). The technology and indeed the technicians will 'improve' over time. A gradual increase in overall 'success' rates of programmes may be expected. Objections to the level of violence towards women inherent in this technology may thereby subside. The technology will be modified and become more 'user friendly'. The 'user friendly' approach will be more easily promoted because of technological advances. But this optimistic forecast does not answer legitimate objections to IVF and other reproductive technologies.

FEMINISM AS GLOBAL COMMITMENT

There may be occasional acknowledgements by those in the new reproductive technology industry, of the origins of human-based new-found reproductive methods in the animal world. *Nature* on 18 July 1985 reported in the 'Texture of diversity in Australian Science' that Carl Wood of the Queen Victoria–Epworth Hospital programme 'says that his work is a natural extension of veterinary developments in Australia'. Yet others seek to distance themselves as far as possible from the self-same developments in the agriculture business. It is well known in the feminist community in Australia which concerns itself about these developments, that one of the 'leading lights' in a 'leading' IVF programme in Melbourne, Victoria, is a veterinary surgeon by training. Yet when this fact was published, in conjunction with a story about 'advances' in reproductive technologies, in *The Age*, a major daily newspaper, objection was apparently taken by the vet. Thus on 4 June 1986 the following article appeared in *The Age*:

Dr. Alan Trounson and report on IVF in 'The Age' An article headed 'IVF—reproductive A-bomb' published in 'The Age' on 12 May, referred to Dr. Alan Trounson's presence in Brazil giving a practical course on IVF during which time one of 12 infertile women involved in the course died.

Dr Trounson wishes it to be known that while he trained as a Ph.D. in animal reproduction, and not as a medical doctor, he has spent nine years working in the Monash Department of Obstetrics and Gynaecology as the scientific director of the Monash IVF team. He is recognised as a world expert in this field.

Dr. Trounson also wishes it to be known that while he, along with other scientists from Monash, was involved in teaching laboratory procedures in the practical course in Brazil, he was not involved in any clinical procedure to do with patients. He took no part in administering the anaesthetic which caused the woman's death prior to the performance of an intended laparoscopy.

'The Age' did not intend to give any impression that Dr. Trounson was not competent to run such a workshop or that he was in any way responsible for the woman's death.

This aside, why should certain sectors of our community be so keen to spend much time, effort and public funds in making relatively few middle class (and occasionally working class) white women pregnant, when the same sorts of resources are directed at forcibly sterilizing and/or aborting women in China and the Third World? The relationship of human reproductive technological development to similar developments in animal husbandry and plant breeding cannot be ignored. The human race has accepted domination over nature as an important feature of human 'progress'. It is not so far from the domination of plants and animals to move to the domination of particular groups of human beings.

Gena Corea observes in *The Mother Machine* that before the discovery of paternity 'in the time of the Goddess, one way women were thought to conceive children was through having eaten animals':

So humans felt a kinship to animals as ancestors, as totem. They saw animals as blood relatives with whom they shared the soul of the Great Goddess. True, they hunted and ate animals, but their relationship with them was roughly equal. Weapons were primitive; hunting an equal contest. Later, . . . we established a vertical master/slave relationship with animals. We took animals in. We fed them. We befriended them. We killed them. We ate them. In the course of this betrayal, the slaughter of beings we had first befriended, we killed some sensitivity in ourselves.[27]

In *Women's Creation* Elizabeth Fisher writes of how this betrayal and growth of an ethic justifying domination 'numbed' human sensitivity:

> When [humans] began manipulating the reproduction of animals, they were even more personally involved in practices which led to cruelty, guilt and subsequent numbness. The keeping of animals would seem to have set a model for the enslavement of humans, in particular the large scale exploitation of women captives for breeding and labour.[28]

Women cannot allow other women to be exploited through new reproductive technologies, just as we cannot allow women to be exploited through harmful contraceptive and sterilization programmes. Certainly the majority of feminists realise that even if women were in power, social conditions and relations between men and women would not alter a great deal, if being 'in power' were a condition occurring within the world as it presently operates, along hierarchical lines, and tolerating—even promoting—class and race dominance. However an option remaining open for women is to continue to speak out to challenge these exploitative and dominating technologies. It is foolish to accept technologies that do little for female integrity and health. Governments should be actively discouraged from aiding and abetting reproductive and genetic engineering techniques on humans, and lobbied to direct much needed funds elsewhere. Stringent controls should be placed on drug companies, biotechnology and genetic engineering industries to ensure that we do not lose more control over our own bodies and our lives. These strategies cannot be a whole answer, but a concerted effort must be made. Genetic engineering and its reproductive companions are patriarchal developments fast becoming successful tools designed and used to control the sexuality and reproduction of all women.

Endnotes

1. *Nature*, 15 August 1985, vol. 316, p. 567, "NIH/FDA Dispute Likely to Delay Research" reported that the first gene therapy proposals are for treating either Lesch-Nyhan syndrome or adenosine deaminase deficiency, both rare inherited diseases, by infecting the patients' bone marrow cells with a retrovirus carrying the missing gene. The cells would then be replaced into the patient. *Nature*, 19 September 1985, vol. 317, pp. 205-206, "Targeting in Mammalian Cells" and pp. 230-234, "Insertion of DNA Sequences in the Human Chromosomal B-globin locus by homologous recombination" reported that the incorporation of foreign DNA has always occurred randomly. It has not been possible to target a gene to its proper place on the chromosome. But a new study has shown that it *is* possible to create a plasmid with a specific gene and get it to insert itself where that gene normally is found on the chromosome. This is a first step towards experiments aimed at gene therapy and gene replacement in humans. The human B-globin gene was chosen, because of future possibilities of curing such diseases as thalassemia and sickle cell anaemia, which are caused by mutation or lack of this gene.

2. Katrina Alford, *Production or Reproduction? An Economic History of Women in Australia 1788-1850*, 1984, Oxford University Press, Melbourne, p. 14.

3. See for example Charlotte J. MacDonald, "Ellen Silk and Her Sisters: Female Emigration to the New World" in *Men's Power, Women's Resistance — The Sexual Dynamics of History*, 1983, London Feminist History Group, Pluto Press, London, p. 66.

4. Katrina Alford, 1984, p. 4.

5. Raymond English and John King, *Families in Australia*, 1983, Family Research Unit, University of New South Wales, Kensington, p. 52.

6. Jessie Bernard, *The Future of Marriage*, 1972, Yale University Press, New Haven, Connecticut.

7. See further, Joanne Finkelstein. "Women, Pregnancy and Child Birth—Plus ça change encore la méme chose", this volume.

8. *Science News*, 1985, vol. 29, p. 56. The immediately following quotations come from the same source.

9. Senate Weekly Hansard, 5 December 1985, no. 19, p. 2975.

10. Gena Corea, *The Mother Machine*, 1985, Harper and Rowe, New York, pp. 62-63.

11. See Ruth Mason, "BabyGIFT", *Health*, June 1985, p. 16;
    Philip McIntosh, "New Test Tube Method a Spur to Twin Births, Says Doctor", *The Age*, 20 November 1985, p. 15:

12. Philip McIntosh, "In Vitro Technique Needs Perfecting, Says Scientist" *The Age*, 20 November 1985, p. 15 reports: "The high miscarriage rate with *in vitro* fertilisation pregnancies suggested that there was 'something not quite right' with the technique, the scientist responsible for the world's first IVF birth said yesterday." The article describes other problems experienced by those on the programmes and the embryos/fetuses/children resulting from the experiments.

13. See for example *National Times on Sunday* 17 August 1985; also Ramona Koval, "The Commercialisation of Reproductive Technology", this volume.

14. See further on the Queen Victoria-Epworth Hospital-Monash University venture in Ramona Koval, "The Commercialisation of Reproductive Technology", this volume.

15. On 16 July 1985 in *The Age* Philip McIntosh reported on the sale of IVF overseas by Queen Victoria-Epworth Hospital-Monash University stating.

amongst other matters: "The sale of Melbourne's leading *in vitro* fertilisation technology to the United States could be a model of how Australian ideas can be marketed overseas, the managing director of IVF Australia, Mr. Robert Moses, said yesterday . . . The irony that two of the entrepreneurs behind the private company, including Mr. Moses, were Americans,* was not lost on him . . . One of the criticisms of the new venture has been that the secrecy required by commercial considerations has compromised free disclosure of information by its publicly accountable partner, Monash University. Mr. Moses acknowledged the tension between the competing demands but said 'commercial negotiations simply cannot be conducted in the newspapers'. He said he could not name hospitals that would provide the IVF services in the US because negotiations were continuing . He did not want to talk about projected profits from the company. With estimates of as many as 10 million infertile people in the US alone, the potential return to investors, and in royalties to Monash, runs into millions of dollars. . . . "("IVF Company Head Vows to Keep Australian Control".)

* Mr. Moses has, apparently, since adopted Australian citizenship.

16. Fiona Whitlock, "Australia's IVF teams lead the World", *Weekend Australian Magazine*, 17-18 August 1985, p. 6.

17. Maria Mies, "Why Do We Need All This?", *Women's Studies International Forum*, 1986, vol. 8, no. 6, pp. 553-560.

18. Christine Crowe, "The Reproductive Fix", *Australian Left Review*, Autumn, 1985, pp. 4-9;
Christine Crowe, "Women Want It — IVF and Women's Motivation for Participation", *Women's Studies International Forum*, Autumn, 1985, vol. 8, no. 6, pp. 545-552.

19. Report by Farida Akhtar, Director of the Policy Research for Development Alternatives, UBINIG, Bangladesh, to *Women's Emergency Conference on the New Reproductive Technologies*, Lund, Sweden, July 1985;
"Bangladesh is Coerced into Sterilisation", *New Scientist*, 19 September 1985, pp. 20-21;
Betsy Hartmann and Hilary Standing, *Food, Saris and Sterilization*, 1985, Bangladeshi International Action Group (BIAG), PO Box 94, London, N5 IUN, Britain.

20. Farida Akhtar, "Sterile Solutions", *Connexions*, December 1985, p. 11.

21. Maria Mies, 1986, p. 558;
see also International Centre for Diarrhoeal Disease Research, Bangladesh,*Report*, 1985 (a UBINIG Investigative Report), roneoed, held by the present author.

22. Robyn Rowland, "A Child at Any Price?", *Women's Studies International Forum*, 1985, vol. 8, no. 6, pp. 539-546, at p. 541.

23. Rita Arditti, "Reducing Women to Matter", *Women's Studies International Forum*, 1985, vol. 8, no. 6, pp. 577-582.

24. Rowland, 1985, p. 541.

25. Rowland, 1985, p. 542.

26. See for example Birnbauer, 1986;
John Waugh, "Race for the Biotech Billions — Genetic-selection breeding offers unlimited opportunity for Australian agribusiness if it can hold off the tough competition overseas", *Business Review Weekly*, 20 June 1986, pp. 46-51;
"Embryo Auction", *Institute of Medical Ethics Bulletin*, April 1986, p. 12.

27. Corea, 1985.

28. Quoted Corea, 1985.

7 The commercialisation of reproductive technology

Ramona Koval

For most human cultures, through time, reproduction has been a secretive and shadowy affair. Pregnancy was hidden until it was plain even to the most unobservant onlooker. (Even then, many women, as far as they were able, kept themselves out of sight as well as they could.) Birthrites were conducted mostly by women, and birth carried with it many complex and magical rituals.

Reproductive technologies have removed the secrecy from the conception and birth processes. Society is now privy to the sight of ova, sperm and embryos; we can tell a woman she is pregnant only days after conception and even long before she misses a period. Conception, pregnancy and birth are now very public events. For the patient on an IVF program the interventions by doctors are enormous — her health and sexuality are open to the intrusive interests of professionals, family and friends.

However the public nature of the woman's experience is in no way matched by the formal structures of the reproductive technologists. This area of science and medicine, which is now entering the marketplace, has a secretive nature far more akin to that of traditional reproduction. While it is mandatory that *we* reveal all — that our innermost secrets be exposed — doctors, scientists and business interests are under no such obligation.

IVF-Australia was the first Australian commercial venture into marketing reproductive technology. It was an attempt to cash in on the high stocks of Australian IVF programs, more successful here than anywhere else. It was arguably a disastrous public relations exercise for Monash University, and a timely reminder of the dangers of unfettered technological optimism driving an economic salvation to the problems of research funding.

THE CASE OF IVF-AUSTRALIA

For some years now, the focus of human reproductive technology in Australia has been the Monash University Department of Obstetrics and Gynaecology, led by Professor Carl Wood at the Epworth-Queen Victoria Hospital. Carl Wood and the associated doctors, nurses and scientists have long been regarded as one of the most successful IVF groups in Australia, and in the world. Media comment has referred to Carl Wood as 'the Godfather' of IVF, and to the group at Monash University as 'the team'. IVF support groups, composed of IVF patients (both aspirants and, occasionally, successful parents) speak in glowing terms of 'our team', as did early media reports on 'world firsts' and 'record breakers'. In a country where sports heroes are revered and where feelings of national inadequacy remain, the idea of 'our team' making headway on an internationally significant issue in science and technology brings together so many areas of Australian pride.

But the rewards of hero-worship are apparently not enough. The case of the establishing of 'IVF-Australia' provides an example of the pressures of marketing and money on the traditionally free communication in science. The 'conception' of IVF-Australia (IVF-A) was shrouded in secrecy and the 'birth' of the IVF-A clinic was achieved in shame.

The 'IVF team' is a group of scientists, obstetricians and gynaecologists, employed in the Monash University's Department of Obstetrics and Gynaecology. At the time the department had off-campus centres in the Queen Victoria Hospital, Prince Henry's Hospital (now combined in the Monash Medical Centre) and at the Epworth Private Hospital, all in Melbourne. As a university department, it was controlled in the same way as other departments on campus, and was answerable to the council of the university. The council set up various committees which reported to it — including academic boards and the finance committee. The council is appointed by the Victorian Government, and members of the university staff, two students, a Trades Hall representative and even a representative of the general community (who in 1984 was a senior executive of Broken Hill Proprietary Ltd) sit on it.

The IVF-A case began relatively quietly. In retrospect it seems that the proponents of the venture thought they would be able to pass it through on a rubber stamp. The minutes of the November 1984 meeting of the Monash University Council Finance Committee discussed a proposal for the 'Manufacture and Marketing of a University Invention':

8.1 *Commercialisation of the IVF Process*

The Committee received and discussed in depth a comprehensive proposal under which the University would transfer IVF technology to a Company in which it would hold the major but non-controlling equity interest. This equity interest would be shared between the University and key staff members of the University having the know-how.

The other parties would be a small specialised management team with whom the proposal originated and outside investors not yet identified.

The proposal envisages a substantial cash flow from the Company to the University for Research and Development in the Department of Obstetrics and Gynaecology before arriving at distributable profit.

The proposal also envisages that the company would establish and operate IVF Clinics in the USA to provide basic IVF services, i.e. IVF husband/wife/sperm/eggs. It also envisages that at a later date, enhanced services would be provided including additional fertility/ infertility services, possible extension to non-husband/wife combinations and to frozen embryos.

The Finance Committee considered that as a first step Council should consider the ethical questions raised by such a proposal and determine whether in principle it was agreeable to such a proposal. If Council is agreeable in principle, the Finance Committee will further develop the financial, legal and commercial aspects with a view to submitting a detailed proposal to the Council in December. Sufficient work has been done in this regard to justify a belief that a suitable proposal can be developed which would have the support of all parties.[1]

Clearly it was thought that any 'ethical issues' could easily be tidied up by the council at their next meeting, and after that the proposal would be ready to go ahead. But at the council meeting queries were raised by some members, and the discussion was adjourned until a later meeting. At this stage there began a public debate on the issue of commercialisation of reproductive technology. The 'secrecy' of the council room was shattered in the public interest and the media interest began. Letters to the editor and feature articles in *The Age*, a Melbourne newspaper, asked questions about what exactly was being sold and who were the parties to the sale?

But at the March 1985 meeting of the Monash Council the Vice-Chancellor, Professor Ray Martin, was authorised to enter into a licensing agreement on behalf of the university. It was reported that an earlier proposal for members of the university's infertility clinic, including Carl Wood, to have an equity interest in the company had been replaced by a proposal for royalties to be paid to medical team members.[2] The minutes of the March 1985 Monash University Council report:

> ... the Vice-Chancellor stressed the need for details of the abovementioned debate and the resolution arising from it to be kept in strict confidence pending the outcome of continuing negotiations with the proposed management team. Professor Martin [the Vice-Chancellor] said that any further 'leaks' at this stage could prejudice the negotiation of a successful agreement on the University's behalf.[3]

The confidentiality of this proposal was, indeed, so important to the proposers that even in mid-1986, a full year later, the proposal and subsequent agreement had not been made available to the members of the Monash University Council, and certainly not to the rest of the community. It did not appear that this pattern of secrecy would alter. Public disquiet continued. Even an advertisement placed by 46 academics, unionists, public servants, doctors, scientists, lawyers and business people questioning the public accountability of a publicly funded institution failed to inspire any action by either the University Council or the Victorian government to clarify the issues.[4]

It was not until July 1985 that the company, IVF-Australia, was announced. It was to be headed by Robert Moses, a former IVF patient in the Monash IVF programme, and a former business development manager for the multinational chemical company ICI. Negotiations were to take place to set up IVF clinics in Japan, Singapore and the USA. A statement issued by the accounting company Price Waterhouse told of the proposed financial structure, saying that 'at present IVF medical service is virtually unavailable to most Americans'.[5]

In the United States press release from IVF-Australia dated 30 October 1985 it was announced that IVF-Australia (USA) Ltd and United Hospital had signed an agreement to establish an IVF programme to begin in February 1986 at the Port Chester, New York Hospital. As far as can be ascertained, no announcements were made in Australia. This IVF 'baby' was not proudly announced in the community birth notices. And the shine on the 'team' was fast losing its glow. While previously IVF technology had been justified by stressing the altruistic motives of the reproductive technologists trying to bring children into the empty arms of infertile people, now more mundane motives of money had been exposed. Ray Martin, Vice-Chancellor of Monash University, had said that the beneficiaries of the sale of IVF technology should be the Monash Research Fund, the Department of Obstetrics and Gynaecology, and members of the IVF team. He said: 'One way to hold our group together would be to offer some form of profit sharing or equity in the Company.' In the same report Carl Wood said that some of the top scientists and doctors in the IVF 'team' had been offered two to three times what they earned in Melbourne. This shift in the public debate was the beginning of IVF technology for sale.

There was another effect of the public concern. The 'team' had previously experienced a honeymoon with the media, but this public challenge was not so much appreciated. It seemed as if the 'team' had decided not to talk any more. Carl Wood and Robert Moses of IVF-Australia even withdrew from a television debate on the IVF-A company, which had been promised for many months.[6]

ISSUES RAISED BY THE IVF-AUSTRALIA CASE

Issues raised by this particular case include:

- the academic freedom to publish research material
- the conflicts of interest inherent in a situation where academics hold shares in commercially exploitable procedures
- the disruption of the social relations of life in the laboratory (of concern to the whole community, both inside and outside universities)
- denial of the rights of the public to review and comment on questions of science and technology, and the public accountability of scientists and university administrators

When the council gave the Vice-Chancellor the authority to sign a licensing arrangement to sell the university's IVF technology overseas, he effectively had *carte blanche* to deal with unidentified business interests, to sell undisclosed technology, and without members of the university council ever having seen the proposal! Repeated requests by a member of the council for wider discussion were met with silence.

Professor Martin was given five guidelines to observe in his negotiations. One was that IVF treatments would be limited to those treatments and procedures that have been approved by the laws of

Victoria. But since Victorian law cannot be properly enforced out-side its borders in Australia, much less in New York, Singapore or Japan, public concern was raised about the potential abuses of the deal. Presumably other companies could be set up after individuals working with IVF-Australia had learned the technical 'secrets' and moved on. No such limiting agreements would be binding on sub-sequent companies. Even if contracts with individuals originally serving with IVF-Australia incorporated clauses providing for them not to set up in competition in the jurisdiction for a term of years, this could not prevent new companies from entering the field without being subject to limitations or controls outside Victoria.

Another guideline was that the IVF team would be free to publish results of their research, subject to 'customary limitations such as those applied to enable property rights to be secured.'[7] Securing such rights can take from 12 months to several years. Again, if the university was concerned to bring IVF technology to understandably anxious infertile couples, then surely this lag-period was counter to their oft-stated claims of concern for the infertile?

More alarming is the prospect of the shroud of secrecy over research which might be claimed to be commercially sensitive, but may in fact be *ethically* sensitive instead. There is also the concern that this practice will restrict the free flow of information that is part of the academic scientific traditions. In effect, the ability of mem-bers of the community to enter into debate on these issues is severely curtailed, with research and marketing progressing under wraps until announcements are made after the event. It is extremely difficult to discuss or challenge research decisions under these circumstances.

The Monash Council suggested that the ethical issues inherent in the commercialisation of IVF technology could be dealt with by a council-appointed ethics committee. It is extremely undesirable that an in-house committee, established by an institution which stands to gain from a commercial venture, is given the power to decide over this extremely important area. Indeed the Asche Com-mittee report to the Family Law Council in 1985, *Creating Chil-dren*, said:

> The various Reports recognised that the range and complexity of the issues of an ethical character which have been or are likely to be thrown up by changes in medical technology, and the public policy implications of these issues, are such that it would be insufficient to entrust their resolution to the ethics committees of particular organ-isations or institutions.[8]

Lessons may be learned from overseas experience with commercial schemes in academia. In 1980, a Harvard University faculty dismissed a proposal from their university administration to share in the equity of Genetics Institute, a company being set up by one of its professors of molecular biology, Mark Ptashne. Under the proposal, Harvard would receive a ten per cent share of the equity in Genetics Institute, which Ptashne was establishing with privately raised venture capital. In return, the company would be given exclusive rights to any patents emerging from Ptashne's research at the university.

Critics claimed this proposal could create undesirable secrecy in the laboratories. Some students in other universities had already been sworn to secrecy about their work, even though it was done in publicly funded institutions. Other problems were those of undue influence over academic appointments, and the undermining of public credibility in the university. After some consideration, the Harvard University president Derek Bok announced: 'All in all, the financial advantages to the university appear more speculative than we have supposed heretofore, while the dangers to Academic Science seem real and severe.'[9]

Elsewhere the commercialisation of research has brought other problems. Professors have offered post-doctoral students jobs in companies in which they were acting as consultant, while denying them help in finding academic positions. This can result in the growing 'brain drain' caused by academics leaving university laboratories to pursue private research; they benefit from higher salaries, better equipment and more technical support. This trend leaves the universities with decreased ability to train a new generation of research workers. The public investment in their education is shamefully squandered.

There is also the fear that students' ideas have been transmitted without their knowledge to outside companies for whom their supervisor works. The labour of post-doctoral fellows, students and technicians is already exploited and appropriated by the senior scientific staff in many institutions; it is standard practice for some senior staff to add their names to papers written by their juniors. This can hardly make for easy social relations in a laboratory, where scientists are pitted against each other — withholding information and new ideas for fear of either, for some, protecting or, for the others, being exploited by, a patent.

Professor Adrienne Clarke of Melbourne University has extensive experience setting up commercial ventures in the field of plant biotechnology. She says:

Because of the commercial implications, the traditional patterns of scientific reporting are being eroded. Both publication and public lectures constitute public disclosures and as such jeopardise future patents. Most research contracts specify a period during which the corporation may hold up publication while it firstly investigates the patent potential of new information and secondly places a patent where appropriate. However these restrictions certainly restrict public communication of information. It is not so noticeable in the publications, as normally there may be a delay of up to two years between the work being done and its appearance in the Journals. However it is very noticeable at the international scientific meetings where key lecturers must withhold information or skirt important scientific issues to protect their patent position. The most effective means of communication in the fast moving fields is always word-of-mouth. This means now becomes more important, as conversations between colleagues do not constitute invention disclosures. However, although it is possible to establish which broad areas are being actively researched by particular groups, the proprietary nature of the information prevents any discussion of the detail. The question of confidentiality in the process of manuscript and grant reviews has now raised doubts about the future of this traditional process. To protect themselves, many authors do not include DNA or protein sequence data in these documents. The information is then inserted in manuscripts after review.[10]

The question arises of credit for discovery. The Boyer-Cohen patent, granted for a method of manipulating genes which underpins a wide range of work in biotechnology, in turn draws on the work of many groups of researchers in molecular biology. Yet other groups who want to use the method have to seek permission from Stanford University, who hold the patent. Legal battles have been fought between universities and private companies — each claiming rights over patentable products at different stages of their development. Donald Kennedy, president of Stanford University, has said:

> Scientists who once shared prepublication information freely and exchanged cell-lines without hesitation, are now much more reluctant to do so . . . The fragile network of informal communication that characterises every especially active field is liable to rupture.[11]

There is a distinct and alarming danger that technical advances in universities will be directed towards those with commercially exploitable outcomes. The history of science and technology should serve as a warning of just how strong an influence these considerations can be. Ruth Hubbard, professor of biology at Harvard University, has said of the university links with biotechnology:

> The fact that genetic technology has become a major event on Wall Street has enormous and, I think, detrimental implications for people who may one day soon find that they, their embryos, or their children are candidates for 'gene therapy'. Because of direct links with the industry, the very people who are engaged in the research and practice of the new technology will be among those who reap the profits. And since recent articles on the financial pages speak of a 'Biotechnology Retrenchment', the temptation to make overly optimistic claims increases.
>
> Some scientists and entrepreneurs, as well as other observers, readily admit that scientific and medical claims already have been made with an eye on the Stock Market. . . the future of a new industry depends on the favourable outcome of clinical trials. There are enormous economic incentives for professionals with sizeable commercial interests to release overly optimistic reports about the benefits of these therapies.[12]

The effects of commercialisation of reproductive technology by Monash University were beginning to be felt in mid-1985. Monash University made a request to the Minister for Education that an exemption should be granted under an amendment to the *Freedom of Information Act*, to allow details of scientific or technical research projects carried out in the university to be withheld.

Under the *Freedom of Information Act* universities may withhold incomplete results of research of a scientific or technical nature. The proposed amendment would have protected information about research even before the work started, by covering intended research projects such as detailed proposals made in support of grant applications. In *The Age* of 26 September 1985 Philip McIntosh and David Broadbent reported on Monash arguing that if a competing research team gained access to a research proposal, it could 'steal a march on Monash in the world of scientific research'. The amendment would, of course, make it more difficult for the public to find out about controversial experiments. In particular it was a way of seeking to protect commercial interests, and of allowing those interests to dictate what the public was allowed to know.

The Attorney-General, Jim Kennan, on 25 September 1985 told Parliament that the Victorian government had not agreed to the request and that he was 'not disposed to favourably consider such a request'.[13] Yet although unsuccessful, the move by the University was a clear signal that the marketplace values which had infiltrated

US science and technology research have begun to surface in Australia.

MARKET VALUES

What are the effects of the entry of market forces and market values into reproduction? Is there any evidence of reproduction as 'commodity production' with babies seen as products? What of the value of efficiency, reliability and quality control?

Certainly in the medical journals there is a sense of babies as 'products'. In *The Mother Machine* Gena Corea quotes Dr Norman Thornton of the University of Virginia in 1986 who, in defending a phenomenal rise in caesarean sections from five per cent in 1968 to 18.5 per cent in 1982 said: 'Obstetricians today are much more interested in the product they deliver than in the caesarean section rate.' Another doctor, chairperson of the American College of Obstetricians and Gynaecologists' District, said: 'What we have to do now is concentrate on quality control . . . If more babies are surviving, we've got to make sure they are better babies.'[14]

Eugenics and surrogacy

These ideas of quality control for the breeding of better babies as 'products' are by no means new. They are expressed in the notion of eugenics, which claims to apply genetic principles to the 'improvement' of humankind. Some people speak of 'positive eugenics' which aims to increase the reproduction of especially desirable or 'fit' individuals; there is also 'negative eugenics' which aims to reduce the breeding of 'unfit' types.

Francis Galton (1822–1911), an elitist and racist, was apparently drawn to the study of human heredity and eugenics because he was particularly interested in the source of his own family's genes. He founded the eugenics movement. Galton was related to numerous luminaries, including his cousin, Charles Darwin.[15] He coined the term 'eugenics' in 1883 and advocated the regulation of marriage and family size according to hereditary endowment of parents. Because he was independently wealthy, he had the time and freedom to pursue his interest of measurement and comparison. He sought to construct a beauty map of the British Isles, to develop a method for quantifying boredom, and to study intelligence by making intensive measurements of skulls and bodies.[16] This pastime was by no means just the meanderings of a wealthy eccentric — at the turn of the century the eugenics movement had wide influence, with eugenics courses in US colleges being quite fashionable between 1904 and 1920. There were even a number of institutions devoted to eugenics research and propaganda. The eugenics movement was successful in influencing US state and federal legislation with 24 states passing sterilization laws for social 'misfits', and 30 states passing laws restricting or outlawing interracial marriages. The *Johnson Act* passed by the US congress in 1924 was an immigration law severely restricting European and Mediterranean immigrants from coming to the USA.[17] The eugenics movement was the ideological support for Hitler's social planning in Germany during the 1930s and 1940s. One might be forgiven for thinking that such an ideology would be safely dead and buried after the monumentally 'bad press' of the Second World War genocide. But strangely, this is not the case.

A modern example of the eugenics ideology can be found in an examination of the 'surrogate mother' industry in the 1980s. Readers should note that although these women are called 'surrogate mothers', they are both the genetic and biological mother of the child. It is *their* children who are sold in contractual arrangements. They may be 'surrogate spouses', but they are not surrogate mothers. Gena Corea prefers, more aptly, to call them 'breeders'. In the *Surrogate Mother Spring Directory* of 1982 produced by the Bionetics Foundation Inc., women like 'Martha' offer photographs of themselves, telling of their height, weight, IQ, college grade-point average, and language skills. Other women write of their 'proven track-record' with the 'production' of other 'gifted' children.[18] The entry of commercialisation into this area has gone hand-in-hand with nineteenth century notions of eugenics.

A service offered by another private Foundation is the provision of the sperm of Nobel Prize winning Laureates in the 'Repository for Germinal Choice'. The man who began this bank was Robert K. Graham. In 1981 he wrote a book called *The Future of Man*. In the book he refers to the middle and upper classes as 'the repositories of every nation's intelligence and wisdom', and advocates payments to married graduate students to enable them to reproduce more of their desirable genes in their children. He chides governments supporting welfare programmes because he says 'many of the programmes actually subsidise the increase of the problem-making population . . . at the very least such persons should be discouraged from producing offspring who have a strong chance of turning out like their parents'.[19] It is not surprising that Graham was interested to follow through some of these ideas by collecting the sperm of Nobel Laureates to inseminate highly intelligent women. In *The Mother Machine* Gena Corea reports that to Graham's embarrassment, the mother of the first Nobel Sperm Bank baby turned out to be a former convict who had lost custody of two children by a previous marriage after accusations of child abuse!

One of the Nobel Prizewinners donating sperm was Dr William Shockley, who won his prize for making transistors. His ideas about eugenics are clear. He once proposed a financial reimbursement for voluntarily sterilized individuals according to their number of IQ points below 100 (the 'average' score).[20] Shockley believes that the quality of the human race is deteriorating, and refers to a declining quality of intelligence in black Americans. He uses IQ tests (which have been strongly criticised for their inability to measure intelligence, and for their cultural biases) to support his position. Corea reports that Shockley donated his sperm because 'hopefully, one would be able to build more ideal human beings . . .'[21]

Organisations like the Bionetics Foundation now enable women to pay for 'higher grade' genetic material. Payment for superior genetic material is already argued by some 'new right' academics as a normal extension of market forces. In a discussion of government regulation of the supply of genetic material, Cathy Buchanan and Elizabeth Prior argue that the purchase and resale of genetic material should be seen as the prerogative of the individual and could be enhanced by a system of competitive market exchange rather than regulation by government. They recognise that individuals with sought-after genetic material (presumably high status people with intelligence, money, or power) will do better out of the market than will others.

For poor, infertile people who perhaps could not afford to pay for 'high quality' genetic material, they suggest:

> Poor people who are certified infertile could be provided with sperm and ova vouchers. By this mechanism, these individuals will be able to purchase the genetic material from which they would like their offspring to be made and will not have to rely on the generosity of individuals to make that material available. In addition, it would seem to be more equitable to call upon the taxpayer to provide the subsidy to the infertile poor than to 'tax' the suppliers of the genetic material by paying them a price less than the value of the *product* being supplied.[22] (Emphasis added.)

The logic of this statement can be extended to the situation of compulsory sterilization of the poor and the provision of 'sperm and ova vouchers' for the use of 'high quality' gametes in a market that is part of an open eugenics programme.

Carl Wood of Monash University's 'team' has said that people are already asking if they can have children with predetermined characteristics:

> A couple have one child and they have said they want a second one who is more intelligent. Because of the high level of unemployment, they want their child to have a better chance of getting a job.[23]

He tells of another couple who wrote to him defining the specifications of their desired child. The couple wished to keep the wife's 'perseverence' but to avoid her 'impatience'!

Although Professor Wood tells these anecdotes in an attempt to illustrate how the public misunderstands his work, and how they over estimate the current 'state of the art', it is obvious that there are people in our community who would welcome the use of eugenics coupled with the new reproductive technologies. These technologies can even make the eugenics applications of the surrogacy industry more straightforward. At present, eugenic screening of potential surrogate mothers for physical, intellectual and racial traits are costly for the surrogate companies. The woman contributes half the genes of the child produced. But once it is possible to engage a woman into whom an embryo is transferred and who contributes none of the child's genes, the surrogate's genetic make-up will be irrelevant. At this point the market could regulate payment for superior genetic material and generate so-called 'better' babies. The surrogate would simply be regarded as a 'vessel', selling womb space.

Critics of surrogacy who argue that it is an immoral society that allows its poor to sell off parts of their bodies for their own sustenance (for it is the poor who are forced by economic necessity to engage in providing the eggs, the womb space, the kidneys) are met with a 'new right' response that banning the trade in wombs, gametes, blood or other organs 'destroys what little wealth the poor have'.[24]

Dr Howard Adelman, a psychologist who screens surrogate candidates for Surrogate Mothering Ltd in Philadelphia, USA, believes that candidates with an element of financial need are the 'safest'. He said: 'If a woman is on unemployment and has children to care for, she is not likely to change her mind and want to keep the baby she is being paid to have for somebody else.'[25] Corea reports that when the search for Australia's first surrogate mother began in 1980, for an advertised $10,000, one applicant was an 18-year-old widow left penniless after her husband was killed in an accident.

Another was a 23-year-old woman who needed the money to provide security for her child, as her husband was dying. More than half the applicants were divorced or single, implying that they were dependent on their own resources. Another study found that more than 40 per cent of surrogate applicants were unemployed or receiving financial assistance.[26]

Surrogacy in the Third World

The extension of the surrogacy market is inevitable in this climate. While comparatively small fees are paid to women who must engage in this activity in the United States, the fees paid to women in less developed nations must be a powerful attraction for this industry. Gena Corea reports that John Stehura, president of the Bionetics Foundation, Inc., maintains that surrogacy would benefit Third World women because they would earn money with which to raise their children. With the use of IVF and embryo transfer these women could bear blond-haired blue-eyed babies for westerners. Stehura says 'the mother could have a health problem which could be quite serious . . . however, if her diet is good and other aspects of her life are OK, she could become a viable mother for a genuine embryo transfer'.[27]

Reproductive abuses of Third World women are a salient target of the feminist movement in India, Bangladesh and South East Asia. At the 1985 Women's Emergency Conference on the New Reproductive Technologies (held in Sweden), women from Brazil, Bangladesh and India told of the history of reproductive campaigns. Sultana Kamal, a Bangladeshi lawyer, spoke of makeshift sterilization camps funded by western aid agencies. Most food and economic programs have population control programmes tied to them. No population programme means no aid. Family planning organisations have 'motivators' who bring in clients and are paid on a piece rate for each case they attract.[28]

Vibhuti Patel, an Indian feminist, comments:

> Poor women are regularly used as guinea-pigs in the testing of birth control devices and drugs. Multi-national companies, assisted by local ruling classes pursuing their own economic interests, have no compunction about the introduction of drugs like Depo-Provera and EP Forte, and Asian feminists cannot afford to overlook this direct influence of the Western capitalist powers on our social and cultural life.[29]

Farida Akhtar, a Bangladeshi economist also at the Swedish conference, was concerned about the links between reproductive technologies and sterilization programmes. She said:

> Contraceptive technology applied to developing countries is creating the condition of infertility. The users of Depo-Provera are not guaranteed that they will regain their fertility. This new reproductive technology may be used to treat them.

She compared this situation to that which happened in the 'green revolution' — the introduction of high-yielding seed varieties to developing countries in the 1960s:

> The land was fertile in Bangladesh. They came with these new seeds that depended on chemical fertilisers and intensive farming. They claimed it would increase food production four-fold. But the costs of production — the energy, the fertilisers — increased at an even greater rate. The result is that our land is losing fertility and we are becoming more and more dependent on the West for fertilisers and other farming technology. Our traditional farming methods do not succeed any more because the land is so depleted. The green revolution perpetuated the food problem. And when you have a food problem, a population problem is created.[30]

Sultana Kamal says that with the origination and the projected scope for expansion of the new reproductive technologies in the West, along with the obsessive emphasis on population control in the Third World countries, international as well as national population policies need to be examined in a new light. She quotes a Population Council conference statement of 1957, which underlies much of the contemporary population programme's rationale:

> Government policies should be of a sort to equalize births between people at different socio-economic levels. They should discourage births among the socially handicapped who cannot give their children adequate opportunities. They should encourage large families among the specially fit.

But as with many programmes aimed at solving 'population problems' the proponents of the programmes are quite selective about which populations they target. While some groups of women are sterilized or used as guinea-pigs for new forms of contraception, those who are infertile and who can afford private medicine are now able to use new reproductive technologies even in Third World countries.

Pakistani professor, Rashid Latif Khan, wants to introduce IVF to his private infertility clinic in Lahore. He said that the most common cause of infertility in Pakistan was rampant and severe pelvic inflammatory disease:

> Ignorance, lack of health facilities and an inflated male ego in our strongly patriarchal society usually condemns the woman to live the life of an infertile pariah.[31]

He said that some women who attended his Lahore centre were ready to clutch at any straw to regain their fertility even if it meant resorting to unproved concoctions, with doctors or faith healers.

Setting aside the issues of balancing health care priorities between the cost of high technology IVF, and simple preventive measures in a country like Pakistan, as well as the questionable superiority of IVF compared with witch doctors or faith healers (given the poor 'success rate' of this technology), it is highly likely that the push for IVF clinics in a country with a history of reproductive abuses against women of lower socio-economic status may easily open the market place to Third World surrogates. Presumably the cost of 'breeding' western babies inside these women in their own countries is much less than the cost of bringing women to western clinics and keeping them in, say, London for the duration of the pregnancy. This practice is reportedly occurring in Europe now.[32]

'Quality control' issues — prenatal testing

When someone pays for a service or product, they expect value for money. In the surrogacy industry, where $10,000 to $20,000 changes hands, the product had better be worth the outlay. There has been an instance where a US surrogate produced a defective 'product' — a baby with a small head who was probably mentally disabled — and the surrogate and the commissioning couple each rejected the child and announced it would be put up for adoption.[33] Eugenic selection programmes aim at ensuring the quality of the potential surrogate. For ensuring the quality of the potential 'product', there is another area of 'quality control' — that of prenatal testing.[34]

The birth of a 'defective' baby is a tragedy for most people. Pregnant women have an understandable concern about their fetus, and their wishes for a healthy child. Motherhood is taxing enough in normal circumstances without the added responsibilities and emotional traumas inherent in caring for children with disabilities. So when medical technology promises relief from anxiety over the nature of the potential child, it is not surprising that a large sector of the population welcomes the intervention. In this way, technologies like ultrasound (examination of the fetus by directing sound waves into the uterus) which were introduced to diagnose certain structural problems like neural-tube defects in the fetus, or abnormal placental placement, are now used as a matter of routine. In Australia, about 75 per cent of pregnant women will have a routine ultrasound investigation during the pregnancy. Although no short-term adverse side-effects have been reported for mothers or subsequent children, there has been no long-term evalution of this procedure on the general health of the community.

Amniocentesis (examination of the chromosomes from cells from the fetus taken during aspiration of the amniotic fluid surrounding it) was originally indicated for women over 40 years of age who had some increased risk of producing a child with Down's Syndrome. The age for this procedure has dropped to 37 years in Australia and 35 in the USA. In some US states, women have been asked to sign forms stating that they were offered amniocentesis and ultrasound, and decided not to be examined, in recognition of the litigation arising from 'wrongful life' suits in the USA.[35]

The rapid expansion in knowledge about the 'environment' of the fetus (that is, the internal workings of the woman's uterus) has generated concern about the safety of the fetus. In turn, this has led to questions about the mother's obligation to provide a safe environment for her fetus. The assertion of the mother's control over her body is challenged by evidence that particular behaviours of the mother during pregnancy may endanger the life or health of the fetus.

The environmental factors designated by some as 'largely controllable by the mother' are poor nutrition, alcohol consumption, drug abuse and smoking.[36] Several of these behaviours are directly related to socio-economic status, and thus largely out of the control of the women involved. In addition, all the behaviours are supported by large industries, with obvious interests in perpetuating these behaviours.

Many of the more than half million manufactured chemicals abounding in our environment, as well as direct radiation from X-rays and other sources, cause chromosomal damage. LSD, cyclamates and other drugs: methyl mercury, benzene and vinyl chloride workplace exposure, among others, have been linked to faults in human chromosomes.

The view of the mother's responsibility in guarding the 'safe passage' of the fetus has been enshrined in the contracts that surrogates have been asked to sign in the USA and elsewhere. The surrogates must not 'smoke nor drink any alcohol [sic] beverage from the time of initial insemination until delivery'. The surrogate must not use illegal drugs. In general, any action that 'can be deemed to be dangerous to the well-being of the unborn child' constitutes a breach of contract which means that the surrogate will forfeit her fee and be subject to legal actions from the commissioning couple (where surrogate contracts are legal).[37]

Surrogacy has underlined the view of the child as a product, and the surrogate mother as merely the delivery system. She is the 'incubator' in which the product resides. Sanford Katz, professor at Boston College law school and chair of the American Bar Association's family law section, commented: 'I wouldn't consider [surrogate motherhood] buying a baby. I'd consider [it] buying a receptacle.'[38] Even advertising agencies have adopted this view. Consider a recent advertisement for the 1986 Volvo 240 wagon. A pregnant woman stands in front of the car, one hand over her ripe belly, the other touching a young toddler who, in turn, clutches a teddy. Published on billboards and in various newspapers and magazines including *The Australian* of 28 April 1986 the text reads:

> There's only one safer place than a Volvo to carry young children. Up to the age of nine months, Mother Nature does a magnificent job providing for the transportation and protection of the very, very young. After that, unfortunately, she runs out of room.

The view of woman-as-vehicle is further extended in the new area of fetal surgery—operations on the fetus during pregnancy. Fetuses have had shunts implanted in the skull to relieve the excessive pressure of hydrocephalus, or 'water on the brain'. Others have had operations to relieve or repair the effects of malformation on the urinary tracts. The results of these interventions have been mixed — some babies have died before birth or shortly after, a few have certainly benefited, and others have been born with multiple, and sometimes severe, disabilities. Although some physicians most closely involved have stated that most defects are best treated after birth, the research push is strong in this area.[39]

Arguments for these interventions have been made on economic grounds. The grounds assume the 'vehicular' nature of the pregnant woman's body, and the low cost treatment of the 'product'. Professor

Bede Morris, head of the Department of Immunology at the John Curtin School of Medical Research, Australian National University in Canberra, has spoken about surgical experiments he is conducting on fetal lambs:

> After the operation it's returned to the uterus which is in fact the very best intensive care ward that one could specify. The ward is thermostatically controlled; the temperature control, the nutrition of the fetus is completely undisturbed, of course, by the operation. It still remains attached to the mother through its umbilicus, the source of all nutrients. The uterus is sterile, there's no need for a night nurse or a day nurse — the *cost* of looking after the *patient* inside the mother is zero; as there are some real economic advantages about doing operations on fetuses, but of course, there are also some significant ethical and moral questions to be resolved when you're considering an operation that involves not only the fetus, but the mother.[40] (Emphasis added.)

SELLING THE TECHNOLOGY

Marketplace values in the reproductive sphere mean notions of quality control, babies-as-products, and women-as-vehicles being part of the means of production. A consequence of commercialisation of reproductive and genetic technologies is that markets for the use of these technologies must be sought in order for them to produce a profit. What effects do these pressures bring to bear on the reproductive technology industry?

Research and development

A recent *Medical Tribune* survey of half (54) of 108 IVF clinics registered with the American Fertility Society revealed a tendency to inflate success rates when talking with news reporters, patients and their own colleagues. Of the 54 clinics responding to a mail questionnaire, half had *never* sent a patient home with a baby. These zero success clinics have been in business for up to three years, have treated over 600 women and have collected, by conservative estimate, over $US 2.5 million in patient fees.

Gena Corea, co-author (with Susan Ince) of the study, said that each clinic in the survey collected fees averaging $US 4,084:

> Success is defined in many ways in order to give a high success rate. One common definition is the percentage of pregnancies per laparoscopy, the operation used to 'capture' eggs. But the fact that there is a pregnancy doesn't mean there is a birth. There is a very high rate of miscarriage with these pregnancies.[41]

Corea said some clinics 'massage' the figures by choosing patients who are more likely to conceive, such as young women with unexplained infertility of short duration, rather than older women whose infertility had not been cured after years of various treatments. Several clinics had no IVF babies, but claimed a 22 per cent success rate!

Gena Corea says that misreporting seems to be particularly associated with some commercial IVF clinics:

> The wide-spread practice of exaggerating the IVF pregnancy rate appears to be a marketing ploy to lure prospective infertile couples into becoming active IVF patients.

She also says that the entry of Australian 'for-profit' clinics into the US market may further influence this tendency as US clinics strive to meet the slightly higher Australian success rates.

Another danger of commercialisation of IVF clinics was raised by a Berlin IVF doctor who said that ready availability of IVF clinics was 'forcing IVF on couples who could become pregnant naturally if they waited a bit longer'. Approximately half of those infertile couples with unexplained infertility get pregnant quite independently of any IVF treatments they receive. He was referring to couples not eligible to receive IVF from his clinic as not having the required indications for IVF treatment. Commercial IVF clinics with a less careful screening and assessment component were attracting European patients away from the public system.[42]

Any discussion of the effects of commercialisation of reproductive technology must take account of the climate for scientific research in Australia and overseas. The qualitative growth of science has been studied in detail by people who looked at all the qualitative indicators available — numbers of scientists, of journals or articles published in journals. For 200 years or more science has grown exponentially, doubling in size approximately every 15 years. But the *cost* of science has tended to double every ten years — due in part to the ever-increasing use of expensive technology by scientists. With expenditure of science research and development in a typical developed country in the 1960s accounting for over two per cent of Gross National Product (GNP), there was clearly no way science could hope to maintain an exponential rate of expansion. It was beginning to be perceived as a cost as well as a benefit, and the developing community view was that scientific activity should be made to reflect 'economic realities'. Scientists are having to think about adjusting their work to considerations of usefulness. Considerations of short-term utility are receiving greater priority in universities. Science has had to adjust from the conditions of exponential expansion to a much more stable state, where it grows at a rate similar to that of the rest of the economy.[43]

This attitude is reflected in a report of the National Health and Medical Research Council (NHMRC), a body which funds public medical research in Australia. It says:

Commercial Development
Medical Research must shoulder its full responsibility in terms of the recently announced National Technology Strategy [of the federal government].

Greater awareness must be created in the Medical Research Community of the possibility of commercially exploiting ideas which emerge from basic research endeavours. These ideas can be turned into products for which there may be a need which will become obvious either as diagnostics or drugs. In Australia, there is a difficult middle ground between ideas, products on a laboratory scale, and commercial products. The problems of funding the gap, to enable this conversion from laboratory scale to viable commercial products to take place, must be addressed if the national equity in these products is to be realised.

Thus product-driven developments are common, but proper awareness of the need for a product can equally lead to its development.

The foregoing is not intended to encourage the outright commercialisation of research, but to ensure that hard won opportunities are not neglected.

The developing of guidelines for patenting procedures, models of commercial agreements, and streamlining institutional bureaucracies, together with improved incentives to inventors, would go a long way in encouraging a rally from the present inertia.

In Australia, a critical mass of intellectual property exists in several broad disciplines. Biotechnology, though internationally very competitive, may spawn unique products ... Medical research alone cannot create a commercial resurgence of this sort, but we should aim by the end of the century to produce a portfolio of new drugs, hormones, generics and vaccines, not only for the Australian community, but for the world.[44]

Certainly this stance is familiar in the areas of non-medical scientific research and engineering. But what are its implications in the area of medical care and health? Traditionally it was taken to be unethical to try to patent a medical procedure. This sort of knowledge was considered to be part of the publicly accessible and humane treatment of patients. But the time is long past when the distinction between a medical procedure and a technical procedure can easily be made. When laboratory technology intervenes in the process of reproduction, medical procedures in infertility treatment are dependent on technical procedures for their very existence. If a patent were to be sought for an associated technical procedure, instrument or drug (as it apparently can be under the licensing agreement between Monash University and IVF-Australia), the medical procedure in question would be severely restricted and, in effect, it would also be subject to secrecy and licensing.

Research priorities

What are the research priorities for the National Health and Medical Research Council (NHMRC)? In which areas does the NHMRC see a future for commercialisation? It is useful to analyse the research projects grant recommendations for 1985 in the 1984–85 NHMRC report. The grants are ordered in terms of the states and the institutes where research projects are located, rather than precise areas of interest, and the descriptions of the research projects are sometimes not very illuminating. The NHMRC certainly does not make it easy for the untutored to locate the areas of funding which are favoured. Nevertheless it is possible to carry out a rough estimate of the funding of reproductive science, technology and medicine, comparing this with funding in other areas. I have carried out an analysis and compared the funding of reproductive science to funding in the area of breast cancer (the largest single cause of death in Australian women), and epidemiology and preventive medicine. These calculations were made by allocating project descriptions to specific areas of scientific interest. Research by commercial institutions, such as chemical companies, is not of course included but would be substantial.

In 1985, the NHMRC provided grants as follows:

Funding	$AUS
Breast Cancer	270 000
NHMRC Research Unit in Epidemiology and Preventive Medicine (University of Western Australia)	373 586
Reproductive Science, Medicine and Technology	1 800 000

These emphases are further illustrated by the 1986 allocations, kindly provided to me by the NHMRC, in which breast cancer research received $AUS 332 096, whilst fertility and infertility related research received $AUS 1.417 million. Thus according to the NHMRC's own figures and categories for 1986, reproductive technology related research attracted over four times as much in funds as did breast cancer research.

The priorities are fascinating. It is apparent from these figures, and the stated policies of the NHMRC, that reproductive technologies are where the 'smart money' is being placed. Certainly there is almost nothing patentable about preventive medicine. Lifestyles cannot be 'sold' in the same way as reproductive technology.

The NHMRC clearly has the support of the Australian government in its funding priorities. The Australian government has signalled its intentions with a major commitment to demand-oriented research and development policies, particularly through the Management and Investment Companies Scheme and the 150 per cent tax concession for industrial research and development. The universities will no doubt avail themselves of these resources through industry links.[45]

In addition the report of the joint working party of the Business Council of Australia (BCA) and the Australian Vice-Chancellor's Committee calls for a stronger link between business and universities. It says better cooperation between companies and universities would provide a clearer direction to universities on research that would benefit industry.[46] What this amounts to is that an important part of industry research would largely be funded by the public research and education dollar. Even if the research done in university laboratories is not kept secret, the significance of 'links' from business into the university provides what several US business figures have called 'a very good window' — lead-time on research and first access to it — a chance to get 'know how' ahead of their competitors.

Part of the reason for the push to commercialised reproductive technology in Australia has stemmed from the criticism of universities in the 1960s and 1970s, when they were accused of 'ivory towerism' and indifference to social need. The response to this pressure was to encourage the growth of areas of more 'relevance' — energy, health and environment issues, and to look at the broader relationships between science and society. David Dickson, writer for the US journal *Science*, has said:

> The social responsibilities of scientists, however, have recently been given a new interpretation; they are now defined as the need to help private corporations achieve their economic and political objectives.

The commercialisation of research results — including acquiescence in changes in the patent system — is portrayed as a public responsibility... Paul Gray, President of MIT [Massechusetts Institute of Technology] told a congressional subcommittee that the universities had a 'responsibility' to make their research innovations available to the public through commercialisation by the private sector. The National Commission on Research states that universities, through close collaboration with industry, stand to gain 'enhanced public credibility for service to society'.

Thus, at the same time that the direct imposition of social controls, through the actions of the Federal government, are seen as a major threat to university independence, direction from the corporate sector toward the needs of the market is welcomed by both universities and their corporate sponsors as a breath of freedom and fresh air, and an act of social responsibility.[47]

Since when has social responsibility been linked to market control of science? Why does public money go to finance the education and research that will be appropriated and sold back to us at a much higher price? Who sets the priorities for research? The public control of research priorities is an issue for examination. Can we as a society afford to put money into high-technology reproductive technologies which may benefit only a few, rather than funding more mundane, less glamorous, low technology preventive health programmes which will have less easily quantifiable but more widespread effects?

EFFECTS OF COMMERCIALISATION ON THE REGULATION OF REPRODUCTIVE TECHNOLOGIES

In August 1986 parts of the *Infertility (Medical Procedures) Act 1984* (Victoria) were proclaimed. Although the Act had already taken a sluggish two years to be even partially proclaimed, that was too fast, it seems, for some of our scientific entrepreneurs.

Newspapers including *The Age* and *The Australian* reported Dr. Alan Trounson of Monash University saying that Australia could lose its lead on IVF technology in less than 12 months if the ban on unauthorised experiments on human embryos is enforced. In a rush to placate these fears, Victoria's Attorney-General, Jim Kennan, said that this section of the Bill had not yet been proclaimed and will be subject to regulatory impact assessment (that is, a legislative requirement that the economic impact of regulations be determined before their introduction).

The market for Australian IVF technology was estimated at $AUS16 billion, and the loss of the market together with the mass exodus of the researchers is apparently hanging over all our heads.[48]

The commercialisation of this technology has resulted in the use of projected market value as a lever to control our regulations. We may have used the slow process of democratic law and regulatory development, with due regard to informed public debate, but that may be cast aside in the name of economic expediency and professional self-interest. In an environment of economic depression, the faith of governments in the new hope that technologies can bring further enhances the leverage of the marketplace. The protection of proprietary information by private companies could be placed above the public's right to know, as industry and government search for new products and greater profits.

CONCLUSIONS

These issues must be urgently addressed by governments, unions, women's groups and other socio-economically disadvantaged groups.

When we allow a small group of people, who happen to control a university council, to determine the directions that reproductive technologies should take, we hand over our power to a group that is neither representative nor elected by the community.

In the absence of any form of structural social control, the pressures for secrecy and commercialisation favour control of reproduction technology by unregulated markets. It is up to us to make the case for an alternative *social* form of control. The eugenics ideology manifested within commercialisation of reproductive technologies is a bankrupt ideology because it is ultimately conservative. It preaches that elimination of the poor is the answer to poverty; that elimination of people with disabilities is the answer to a profoundly non-caring society. As the early socialists fought against private ownership and control of the means of production, so must we now examine the ownership and control of reproduction. We must avoid a future we might otherwise regret.

Endnotes

1. *Minutes of Monash University Council Finance Committee Meeting*, November 1984.
2. Philip McIntosh and Calvin Miller, "University Council Approves Sale of IVF Technology", *The Age*, 19 March 1985, p. 3.
3. *Minutes of Monash University Council Meeting*, March 1985, p. 5.
4. Advertisement, "IVF and Reproductive Technology for Sale?", *The Age*, 28 March 1985.
5. Philip McIntosh, "America to Market our IVF Technology Overseas", *The Age*, 2 July 1985.
6. Philip McIntosh, "IVF Chiefs Withdraw from Television Debate on US Marketing Scheme", *The Age*, 9 September 1985.
7. McIntosh and Miller, 1985.
8. Family Law Council, Committee on Reproductive Technologies ("Asche Committee"), *Creating Children*, 1985, Family Law Council of Australia, AGPS, Canberra ACT, p. 90.
9. David Dickson, *The New Politics of Science*, 1984, Pantheon, NY.
10. Adrienne E. Clarke *Intellectual Property — Problems and Paradoxes*, Journal of Tertiary Educational Administration, vol 8, No 1 May, 1986. pp 13-26
11. Donald Kennedy, "Who Owns Knowledge? Patents, Copyright and Intellectual Property" in *Sci-Tech Report*, J. Turney, editor, 1984, Pluto Press, London.
12. Ruth Hubbard, "Human Embryo and Gene Manipulation", *Science for the People*, May/June 1983.
13. Philip McIntosh and David Broadbent, "Kennan is Reluctant to Exempt Universities", *The Age*, 26 September 1985.
14. Gena Corea, *The Mother Machine — Reproductive Technologies from Artificial Insemination to Artificial Wombs*, 1985, Harper and Row, NY.
15. Gar Allen, "Genetics as a Social Weapon', in *Science and Liberation*, R. Arditti, P. Brennan and S. Cavrak, editors, 1980, South End Press, Boston.
16. Stephen Jay Gould, *The Mismeasure of Man*, 1981, W.W. Norton and Company, New York.
17. Allen, 1980.
18. Bionetic Foundation (Inc), California, *Surrogate Mother Spring Directory*, 1982, California.
19. Robert Klark Graham, *The Future of Man*, 1981, Foundation for the Advancement of Man, Escondido, California; quoted in Corea, 1985.
20. Gould, 1981, p. 28.
21. Corea, 1985, p. 27.
22. Cathy Buchanan and Elizabeth Prior, "Bureaucrats and Babies: Government Regulation of the Supply of Genetic Material", *Economic Record*, September 1984, vol. 60, no. 170, pp. 222–230.
23. Carl Wood, *Paper presented to the 8th International Congress of the International Society for Psychosomatic Obstetrics and Gynaecology — Hormones and Behaviour*, 12 March 1986, Melbourne, Victoria.
24. Cathy Buchanan and Elizabeth Prior, editors, *Medical Care and Markets*, 1985, George Allen and Unwin, Sydney.
25. Robert Miller, "Surrogate Parenting: An Infant Industry Presents Society with Legal and Ethical Questions", *Ob/Gyn News*, 1983, vol. 18, no. 3.
26. Philip Parker, "Motivation of Surrogate Mothers: Initial Findings", *American Journal of Psychiatry*, 1983, vol. 140, no. 1.

27. Corea, 1985, p. 215.
28. Ramona Koval, "Keeping a Watch on the Hi Tech Wonders", *The Age*, 14 August 1985, p. 26.
29. Vibhuti Patel, "Women's Liberation in India", *New Left Review*, September/October 1985, pp. 75–86. The immediately following quotation comes from the same source.
30. Koval, 1985.
31. Dan McDonnell, "IVF May Topple the Witch Doctor", *The Sun*, 19 November 1985, p. 5.
32. Jalna Hanmer, Personal communication, 1985.
33. Corea, 1985, p. 219.
34. Further on pre-natal testing, see other articles, particularly Jocelynne A. Scutt, "Women's Bodies, Patriarchal Principles — Genetic and Reproductive Engineering and the Law", this volume; and Renate D. Klein, "Genetic and Reproductive Engineering — The Global View", this volume.
35. Further on the issue of wrongful life suits, see Jocelynne A. Scutt, "Women's Bodies, Patriarchal Principles — Genetic and Reproductive Engineering and the Law", this volume.
36. Robert H. Blank, *Redefining Human Life — Reproductive Technologies and Social Policy*, 1984, Westview Press, Boulder, Colorado.
37. Susan Ince, "Inside the Surrogate Industry", in *Test-Tube Women*, Rita Arditti, Renate Duelli Klein and Shelley Minden, editors, 1984, Pandora Press, London.
38. Corea, 1985, p. 222.
39. Hubbard, 1983.
40. Interview with Professor Bede Morris, "Beyond 2000 — Babies of the 21st Centry", Reporter: Carmel Travers, Writer and Director: Bill Bennetts, Channel 7, screened (Melbourne, Victoria), 14 November 1985.
41. Gena Corea and Susan Ince, "IVF a Game for Losers at Half of US Clinics", *Medical Tribune*, 3 July 1985, vol. 26, no. 19.
42. Manfred Stauber, "Psychosomatic Care of Couples with In Vitro Fertilisation on the Berlin Programme", *Paper delivered to 8th International Congress of the International Society of Psychosomatic Obstetrics and Gynaecology*, 10–14 March 1986 Melbourne, Australia.
43. Barry Barnes, *About Science*, 1985, Basil Blackwell, Oxford.
44. National Health and Medical Research Council (NHMRC), *Report of the Ninety-Eighth Session, Canberra, October 1984*, 1985, AGPS, ACT.
45. Ron Johnson, 'Why Scientists Don't Get More Money", *Metascience*, 1986, vol. 3.
46. Robyn Dixon, "Business and Universities Told to Work for Greater Prosperity", *The Age*, 24 February 1986.
47. David Dickson, 1984, p. 104.
48. *National Times on Sunday*, 17 August 1985.

8 Women, class & genetic engineering – *The effect of new reproductive technologies on all women*

Gena Corea

Class society actively operates to divide women. Patriarchal societies actively operate to divide women. In all existing societies, women are divided by the patriarchs. Reproduction, a feature common to most women's lives, could be expected to bring women together — in joint assistance, discussion, advice and support. Yet reproduction (under the control of male technocrats) has served to divide women, particularly along class lines.

In earlier centuries, women in the higher socio-economic levels (at least, women with husbands in the higher socio-economic levels) made use of women in lower socio-economic levels as nannies and wet-nurses. Often the nannies were wet-nurses. And although nannies and wet-nurses came from 'less advantaged' backgrounds and therefore belonged to a group despised by the upper echelons, somehow their care and supply of milk was classed 'satisfactory' for nurturing children of the rich. In the American south, black American women were 'employed' as nannies and wet-nurses. Somehow, their value as childcarers overrode their blackness and the negative value set on that feature by white southern American society.

These divisions between women on class and economic lines, and simultaneous tolerance of the differences so that particular ends may be fulfilled — the nurturing of children conceived and borne by the one group — may be repeated at a different level with the application of new reproductive technologies. Today, women in the 'lower' group can 'advance' from being nannies and wet-nurses to being 'carers' or 'nurturers' of the embryo, bearing the fertilized ovum of another woman in the womb, supplying nutrients at an earlier time in the development of the child, providing care before the child is even born. Such 'advances' are being portrayed as advantaging women who no longer have to spend nine months of their own lives in pregnancy, but can have the satisfaction of owning their own child after some other woman has spent that nine month period in nurturing the fetus. This picture is *false*. Such divisions are of no benefit to women. The new reproductive technologies are detrimental to the welfare of *all* women.

CONTROL OF REPRODUCTIVE TECHNOLOGY

Medicine is depicted as a healing art, but it is not just that. It is also a means of social control or political rule. Dr. Thomas Szasz, Professor of Psychiatry at the State University of New York, warns that medicine, when allied with the state, can indeed control us. He provides a word for political rule by physicians: *pharmacracy.* It comes from the Greek work *pharmakon* for 'medicine', and is analogous to 'theocracy', rule by god or priests, and 'democracy', rule by the people.[1] In discussing such new reproductive technologies as *in vitro* fertilization and embryo transfer, physicians, embryologists and others involved can be referred to as 'pharmacrats'.

In vitro fertilization, or IVF, is the fertilization of an egg outside the woman's body, in a laboratory. This is the process by which Dr. Robert Edwards and Patrick Steptoe brought about the birth of the world's first test-tube baby, Louise Brown. They have been called Louise Brown's 'co-lab parents'.

While the new technologies are presented to the public as therapy — 'new hope for the infertile' — and as a benevolent means of expanding people's options, in fact they offer powerful means of social control. These technologies will *not* be confined to use for the involuntarily childless. According to the visions of many pharmacrats, they will eventually be used on a large proportion of the female population. They will be used to control which kinds of human beings are produced by determining which sperm comes into contact with which egg, which embryos are discarded, which are doubled, which are altered.

Is this vision paranoid? It is difficult to feel paranoid when talking with Dr. Richard Seed, for his approach gives confidence that any fears one harbours are justified. I saw Dr. Seed coming down the hall at the American Fertility Society meeting in New Orleans in April 1984 and stopped him to talk. Richard Seed is a physicist who, with his brother Randolph Seed, a surgeon, operated a cattle breeding business on a farm outside Chicago. In 1970 the brothers began transferring embryos between cows. They then moved on to experiment with embryo transfer in women. They formed a company Fertility and Genetics Research, Inc., financing the experiments of a team of physicians who produced the first flushed-embryo baby in January 1984. The physicians from UCLA (University of California, Los Angeles, USA) flushed an embryo from one woman and placed it into the womb of another in April 1983. They delivered the resulting child, a boy, by caesarean section. Fertility and Genetics Research, Inc., has applied for patents on the human embryo flushing and transfer procedure, most of them in Richard Seed's name.

So I stopped Richard Seed in the hall. Somehow our conversation got on to the genetic manipulation of embryos. With eggs being fertilized in a dish and with embryos being flushed out of women, the embryo has now become available for manipulation. I asked Seed if gene manipulation will be used for therapeutic purposes — that is, to correct genetic 'defects'. 'That's the way it will start,' he replied. 'It will start therapeutically.' He went on to say that gene manipulation would later be used to control human evolution. This, he added, was not an original idea with him; it was a common philosophical observation. Before hurrying off to his next meeting, he said to me:

> There is a very dramatic change now [in the ability to control evolution] which is not fully appreciated by the population at large.

I was not surprised at his casual mention of men's plans to direct human evolution. He had discussed it somewhat during an interview with me in his office in Chicago in 1980. Seed had told me then that he had thought a good deal about eugenics, a programme that calls for improving the human race by increasing the propagation of the 'fit' rather than the 'unfit'. He had said that people feared reproductive technology would be used for eugenics; that, in fact it could be; but that that was very positive:

> Just generally trying to improve the human race is a good thing . . .
> We have already been practising eugenics in a small way by selecting mates we consider superior and by using amniocentesis and aborting defective fetuses . . . Technology is going to provide tools to do it in a progressively larger and larger way and that's probably what will happen.

This, he reiterated, was positive and in no way the 'horror story' some made it out to be.

The idea of redirecting human evolution was not original with

Richard Seed. I had been reading the literature of reproductive technology for more than four years and had come across that idea repeatedly: in the work of the French biologist Rene Dubos, for example, and Dr. Robert Sinsheimer, as well as the late Hermann J. Muller, and Dr. Clifford Grobstein.[2] One clear example is of the ethicist Dr. Joseph Fletcher, who wrote in 1974 that in the past few years, men had indeed begun 'to take charge of their own evolution'. He looked favourably on this control over human reproduction:

> Control is human and rational; submission, the opposite of control, is subhuman ... To be responsible, to take control and reject low quality life, only seems cruel or callous to the morally superficial.[3]

We know all about 'low quality life'. We know who those in power defined as low quality life when the eugenics movement was in full swing: the disabled; the dark-skinned; the unemployed; in Germany in 1930 — the Jew. Today in the Indian cities where businesses which detect and abort female fetuses thrive, we know that female life is low quality life. We received a hint even before these businesses began thriving, when sociologists studied the record of two hospitals in a large city in Western India for a twelve month period in 1976 and 1977. Amniocentesis, a technique enabling the fetus' sex to be detected before birth, was available at these hospitals. In the first hospital, all 92 women who sought amniocentesis for sex detection wanted to abort the fetus if it were female; all wanted to retain the fetus if it were male. In the second hospital, 700 predominantly middle-class women underwent amniocentesis for sex detection. Of these, 450 were told they would have a daughter and almost all (430) aborted the female fetuses. The remaining 250 mothers were told they were carrying male fetuses and every single one of them elected to carry the babies to term, even those who were advised of a possible genetic defect in the child.[4] Of course it is not only in India that women are seen as 'low quality life'. We have evidence enough of the low esteem in which women around the world are held.

REPRODUCTION AND QUALITY CONTROL

What about the pharmacrats actually engaged in reproductive technology today? Do they think the way Fletcher thinks? Is he the only one interested in rejecting 'low quality life'? Is Richard Seed alone in finding very positive those efforts to improve the human race by controlling evolution? You decide.

ITEM: In 1982, the directors of three USA *in vitro* fertilization clinics — Dr. Richard P. Marrs of Los Angeles, California; Dr. Martin Quigley of Houston, Texas and Dr. Anne Colston Wentz of Nashville, Tennessee — predicted that in the future test-tube embryos would be screened to eliminate those with birth defects or those of a sex their parents do not want.

ITEM: At a press conference during the 1984 meeting of the American Fertility Society, Dr. Robert Edwards, baby Louise Brown's lab parent, predicted scientists would be dividing human embryos as part of IVF programmes in the near future. Besides giving a couple a better chance of pregnancy, he explained, the practice of dividing embryos would provide a bit of embryo tissue which could be examined, enabling the scientists to select the healthiest of the embryos for transfer into the woman.

It is impossible to listen to Edwards say these things without remembering what H. J. Muller wrote in 1935. The late Dr. Muller was a geneticist who won a Nobel Prize for his work on the effect of radiation on genes. Muller wrote that ectogenesis — the rearing of an embryo completely outside the mother's body from conception to 'birth' — would be a valuable advance

> in affording us a much more direct control over the development of the embryo . . . it would be even more valuable in enabling us to rear selectively—or even to multipy—those embryos which have received a superior heredity.[5]

ITEM: Professor Carl Wood of Monash University, Melbourne, Australia, IVF team has certainly thought as well about ways to eliminate human defects through IVF. He wrote:

> In the future, it may be possible for the test-tube baby procedure to reduce the incidence of, or eliminate, certain defects from the population. For example, where both partners are carriers of recessive genes that in combination would result in a major birth defect, it may be possible to select eggs and sperm cells that would avoid such a situation.[6]

It all sounds so beneficial to so many people. While it may at first appear that eliminating 'birth defects' is positive, wondrous even, keep in mind that a certain power group — males, white males — will be in charge of constructing reality and telling all of us what a 'defect' is, what a 'defect' means, what its significance should be for the mother, family, the child and society. They tend to regard a 'defect' as a unmitigated disaster, but that is *not* the only way to view it.[7]

The category 'birth defect' is capable of infinite expansion. Its meaning has indeed begun to expand and may expand further. As early as 1978 — the year the first test-tube baby was delivered by caesarean section — Dr. Randolph Seed was declaring, in testimony before a United States' ethics board, that asthma was a severe genetic defect.

Dr. Janice Raymond, a US bio-ethicist, asks us to look carefully at what is defined as a genetic disease or defect. In an interview she said to me:

> The mantle for that constantly gets enlarged. It starts off as supposed physical or biological defects. But they are not going to stop at the biological 'defects'. Geneticists have talked for years about improving intelligence and behaviour. That's not just part of the old eugenics movement at the turn of the century. It is present in all the current ethical and biomedical literature.

So it starts out benevolently: the use of reproductive technology such as *in vitro* fertilization, and embryo flushing and transfer, to eradicate disease and ease human suffering. And then, very quickly, it goes far beyond that.

In May 1984 Carl Wood announced that he, other IVF researchers and an ethics committee were discussing the future of 'genetic breeding', the selection of sperm and ova for the production of a child to desired specifications:

> Already we have had couples come and ask us if a male other than the husband could donate sperm because they were not happy with the husband's appearance or personality. Similarly women have been asking for donor eggs because they're not happy with some aspect of themselves.

Among those aspects were appearance and intellectual capacity.

Wood's team has not complied with these requests for genetic breeding, but if it received many more, the team publicly announced, it might make a submission to the Victorian Government committee examining the ethics and social implications of *in vitro* procedures. The exact nature of the submission was not specified.[8]

It sounds as though a trial balloon is being released to see how it floats. If there are no great outcries against 'genetic breeding', if people simply accept the assertion that patients are wanting this new service, and that the doctors are humble servants just trying to give the people what they want, then the team will have the licence it needs to go ahead and practice human breeding.

Infertility is the opening wedge for quality control in the production of babies. In other words, it is the opening wedge for eugenic control. Dr. Hermann J. Muller, the geneticist, believed this. In a number of papers, he advocated a voluntary programme he called 'Germinal Choice'. That is, the choice of germinal material — in this case, sperm. Child quality could be improved, he argued, if women would allow themselves to be inseminated with the sperm of 'some transcendently estimable man'. Robert Graham, a Californian who became wealthy as a result of his invention of plastic eyeglass lenses, thought Muller's idea was splendid and in 1976 set up a sperm bank which contains the semen of certain Nobel Prize winners and other transcendently estimable men. A number of Nobel Sperm Bank babies have been born.

In 1959 Dr. Muller wrote that infertility provided 'an excellent opportunity for the entering wedge of positive selection, since the couples concerned are nearly always, under such circumstances, open to the suggestion that they turn their misfortune to their credit by having as well-endowed children as possible'. He added a little later:

> Practices that today are confined to couples afflicted with sterility will be increasingly taken up by people who desire to improve their reproductive lot by bestowing on themselves children with a maximal chance of being highly endowed, and thereby to make an exemplary contribution to humanity.[9]

TOOLS FOR A EUGENIC PROGRAMME

The tools which the new reproductive technologies make available for a eugenic programme — a programme which begins simply as treatment for the infertile — are readily listed.

SPERM DONATION: A woman would bear a child conceived with the sperm of someone other than her partner. Donor sperm was used with *in vitro* fertilization only one year after the birth of Louise Brown, the first test-tube baby.

EGG DONATION: A woman would bear a child conceived with another woman's egg. The egg can be obtained by laparoscopy, an operation performed under general anaesthesia, by an ultrasound-guided procedure, or by flushing it out of a woman's uterus. Work with donor eggs was begun in 1982, only four years after Louise Brown's birth, and the first birth occurred a year later in Australia.

EMBRYO ADOPTION: The embryo would contain the genes of neither the potential mother or father, both sperm and egg having been donated.

EMBRYO FREEZING: Once embryos are frozen, they need not be transferred into the uterus of the woman from whom the egg was obtained. The birth of a child from a frozen-thawed embryo first occurred in Australia in March 1984, six years after the birth of Louise Brown.

EMBRYO SCREENING OR EVALUATION: 'Defective' embryos and those of the undesired sex could be discarded.

GENETIC ENGINEERING: Once the embryo is in the laboratory dish, it is accessible for manipulations. At the American Fertility Society meeting in 1984, at which pioneers in *in vitro* fertilization from around the world gathered, a physician from an *in vitro* fertilization program at Yale University mentioned potential gene 'therapies' for the embryo and then referred to the embryo as 'our tiniest patient'.

Today, pharmacrats frequently link use of the new reproductive technologies with sterilization. Among those who have done so are Dr. Robert Edwards, Dr. Carl Wood, Dr. Carl Djerassi, Dr. Randolph Seed, and Dr. Richard Marrs. The suggestion has sometimes been that for convenience and in order to avoid the risks of contraceptives like the Pill, women could simply be sterilized and later use IVF or other technologies to reproduce.[10]

This is just one of the many possible examples of the linkage of IVF with sterilization. When the federal ethics board in the United States held hearings on IVF, Dr. Robert Edwards wrote to the board that while he and his partner Patrick Steptoe would continue their work 'to help the infertile', with IVF:

> We equally intend to develop our methods for the reversal of sterilization. Tubal occlusion [that is, sterilization] could then be used by women to limit their fertility, relieving them of years of steroidal contraception in the knowledge that they could conceive another child in the event of remarriage or the death of their family.[11]

He made this suggestion only one year after the birth of the world's first test-tube baby.

Will *in vitro* fertilization, which offers some control over the 'quality' of offspring, become more common than natural reproduction? Already in 1976, *before* the birth of the first test-tube baby, two scientists (Dr. Laurence Karp and Roger Donahue) predicted that it would. In *The Western Journal of Medicine* they speculated that tests for evaluating the health of embryos might be developed:

> Therefore, one day, *in vitro* fertilization and embryo culture could become the preferred mode of reproduction, with transfer to the uterus of only genetically-healthy embryos.[12]

The rationale for this was, of course, that birth defects might thereby be prevented. Male-controlled procreation will be 'better', 'healthier'. With their laboratories and machines, men will produce more 'perfect' babies than these women produce with their fleshy, natural bodies. Laurence Karp, MD, now directs the IVF programme at the Swedish Hospital Medical Center in Seattle, Washington, USA.

In the spring of 1984, Professor Carl Wood announced in Australia that a study had found that test-tube children are more intelligent and superior in many ways to naturally-conceived children. This statement prepares people to look on IVF as preferable to natural reproduction. Wood's announcement was heralded in Australia with such headlines as:

> Test-tube Babies are Smarter and Stronger.
> Babies: They're Better from Glass.

Now, only eight years after the birth of the worlds first test-tube baby, who do pharmacrats see as clients for IVF? Certainly not just women with blocked or absent fallopian tubes. In fact, Dr. Cecil Jacobson, chief of the Reproductive Genetics Unit of Fairfax Hospital in the US told me, in an interview in 1980, that women with 'bad' tubes will be a very small percentage of the people for whom IVF will be useful. 'The biggest population [for IVF] are going to be men with low sperm counts,' he said. The theory is if the few sperm these men produce are placed in a lab dish with an egg, the sperm, having been spared the obstacle race through the female reproductive tract, will have a greater chance of fertilizing that egg. Jacobson told me the IVF procedure could help men with a variety of conditions: abnormal testicular development; exposure to DES (diethylstilboestrol); paralysis; war injuries. (In passing it should be noted that the procedures are not performed on such a man, but rather on the woman he married and she, rather than he, is exposed to the risks involved.)

Who, besides the wives of men with various conditions, are potential clients for IVF? If donor eggs are used, many women — not just the infertile — could be candidates for the procedure, Jacobson told me, including women with genetic diseases, endometriosis, hyperthyroid, and a history of miscarriages. IVF could also be used for older women, perhaps in their fifties, who have been 'scared off' maternity, afraid that if they bore a child of their own, it would be defective. It could help women who do not produce 'good' eggs, possibly because their eggs have been damaged by exposure to toxins in the workplace. He believes this is a large group of women, and will expand as our knowledge of the effects of workplace toxins on eggs grows. Cecil Jacobson asserts that the 'very large group of people' who produce 'poor' eggs or have genetic diseases will use the eggs of other women and will not mind doing so. 'The process of pregnancy is much more important to a woman than the origin of the sperm and egg,' he said. This scenario would mean that a large number of women would not actually reproduce. Rather than cleaning up toxic workplaces, pharmacrats suggest depriving women workers of their own children, but operating on them so they can bear the babies of other women.

NEW OPTIONS IN CHILDBEARING?

Pharmacrats present the new reproductive technologies as boons to women, providing them with new 'options' in childbearing. They depend upon the male ideology that sees women have a will to be mothers. But which women? White women? Women of certain classes in developed countries like West Germany, Australia, Britain, Canada, the United States? What about a woman in Bangladesh who has a will to be a mother? Will that prevent the local 'motivator' involved in population control programmes from offering her a sari and food-money in exchange for her submission to an operation in a sterilization camp where, according to an investigation by an international committee, surgical gloves are often not even changed between operations?[13] What about the women in Nepal who have a will to be mothers? These women, in sterilization camps, are often given five to 10 milligrams of valium as their only anaesthesia.

Infertility is prevalent in some regions of the Third World, particularly in Africa, where in some areas as many as 40 per cent of all women have never borne a child by the age of 45 years, because of the high incidence of venereal disease.[14] But the pharmacrat does not talk about the need for IVF programs in the Third World. The pharmacrat tends to talk rather about the 'population problem' there, and the need for 'effective' contraceptives like Depo-Provera and anti-pregnancy vaccines and campaigns to convince women they should undergo sterilization.

But if the pharmacrat is so concerned about the will of women to be mothers, why not promote use of barrier methods of contraception in the Third World — the only contraceptives to offer some protection against agents associated with venereal disease? The diaphragm, used with jelly or cream and spermicidal foams, and suppositories used alone, appear to offer protection against some types of venereal disease.

Two mavericks in the population control establishment, Judith Bruce and S. Bruce Schearer, write:

> ... in settings with high incidences of infertility, proper use of the condom and, possibly, of other barrier methods, can reduce the incidence of gonorrhoea which is the primary cause of the infertility.

Yet, on average in 14 Third World countries surveyed by the World Fertility Survey, only 1.1 per cent of all married contraceptive users used female barrier contraceptives. Bruce and Schearer attribute this at least partly to the failure of health delivery personnel to support, promote, and actively make these methods available to the people, while at the same time, they give 'positive attention' to the Pill, IUDs, injectable contraceptives such as Depo-Provera, and sterilization. So the pharmacrats and their associates are promoting use of the new reproductive technologies for infertile women in the West while, in the Third World, they are promoting contraceptives which provide no protection against fertility-destroying diseases; contraceptives which may indeed contribute to subsequent sterility.

If the 'wrong' women have a will to be mothers, do the pharmacrats see this? No. As the sociologist Dr Katz Rothman points out, women are socially rewarded for certain choices (for example, the choice to bear a child) and punished for others and the rewards and punishments are handed out along race and class lines. In the United States, as in Australia, black women and poor white women who choose to bear children, who have a will to be mothers, and who at some point receive public assistance (often as sole parents) are punished with social contempt, harrassment, poverty. But all the institutions of civil society go into action generating sympathy for white heterosexual married women who have a will to be mothers. How real is this sympathy? How relevant is it to the real lives and needs of women, to women's fulfilment, well-being and autonomy?

The suggestion that new reproductive technologies provide more choices for women is asinine in a society where women have no control over these technologies, where women do not control social, economic and political spheres, much less their own lives. But the proposition of 'more choices' also raises the question whether women have the option of *not* using these technologies. Will women be able to refuse them? Or will their use become compulsory as is the tendency with obstetrical practices?

Today there is a good deal of talk about 'fetal rights': about whether the fetus' right to be born physically and mentally sound should not over-ride the mother's right to refuse such operations as caesarean section. Similar talk about the right of children to be 'well-born' could also be used to manipulate a woman into accepting donor eggs which are supposedly superior to those she can herself produce.

Dr. Frank A. Chervenak of the Departments of Obstetrics and Gynaecology and Reproductive Medicine at Mount Sinai School of Medicine in New York said at a panel discussion in 1985 that he believes a woman in labour who refuses to have a caesarean section when her fetus shows signs of distress may not be thinking rationally, because of her pain and fear of labour. (He did not point out the extreme fallibility of the machines which allegedly demonstrate that 'fetal distress' or of the physicians who interpret the machine readings.) The risk of brain damage or fetal death in this situation, Dr. Chervenak said, overrides the obstetrician's obligation to respect the woman's autonomy. He said:

> If persuasion failed, I would be prepared to restrain the mother and do the caesarean section because of an overwhelming obligation to protect fetal well-being.[15]

Attorney Janet Gallagher has investigated cases in which women who have resisted caesarean sections have been compelled, under court order and police escort, to submit to this surgery.[16] Looking at these and related cases, she found that court decisions and legislative efforts throughout the United States indicate an increasing tendency to impose legal penalties and restrictions on women in the name of 'fetal rights'.

Among the cases cited by Gallagher are these:

A woman in California was involuntarily confined to a hospital for the final weeks of her pregnancy by a juvenile court judge claiming to act on behalf of her unborn child.

Women in labour in Colorado, Illinois and Georgia were ordered by judges to undergo caesarean sections because doctors said they were concerned about the health of their fetuses.

In Maryland, a man sought (and briefly obtained) a court order against his estranged wife's abortion, arguing in part that the abortion would violate the state's child abuse statute.

There are not isolated events, Gallagher writes.

Currently, risky methods of diagnosing and treating fetuses, most of which involve penetration of the woman's body, are proliferating. These methods include surgery on the fetus during pregnancy. In the name of 'fetal rights', women may be forced in the future to submit their bodies to fetal 'therapy', much of which is experimental, invasive, and unproven.[17] Dr. Ruth Hubbard, a Harvard University biologist, has pointed out that the language of 'fetal rights' is a language of social control. The aim is to control the prospective parents, particularly the mother.[18]

Dr. Margery Shaw is both a physician and an attorney. At the Third National Symposium on Genetics and the Law in Boston in April 1984 Dr. Shaw raised the question of whether child abuse laws should be extended to include fetal abuse. If the mother plans to harm the fetus, does the state have a right to control her behaviour to prevent abuse? Shaw cited several cases in which courts intervened to control the behaviour of pregnant women on behalf of the fetus. In these cases, the mothers were drug addicts.

Shaw has written that once a pregnant woman decides to carry her fetus to term, she incurs a 'conditional prospective liability' for negligent acts toward her fetus if it should be born alive:

> These acts could be considered negligent fetal abuse resulting in an injured child. A decision to carry a genetically defective fetus to term would be an example. Abuse of alcohol or drugs during pregnancy could lead to fetal alcohol syndrome or drug addiction in the infant, resulting in an assertion that he had been harmed by his mother's acts. Withholding of necessary prenatal care, improper nutrition, exposure to mutagens or teratogens, *or even exposure to the mother's defective intrauterine environment caused by her genotype* . . . could all result in an injured infant who might claim that his right to be born physically and mentally sound had been invaded.[19]

A 1980 decision by an appellate court in California held parents legally answerable for the suffering of their impaired children if they had chosen to go ahead with a pregnancy knowing the child would be impaired. Shaw commented that if this viewpoint regarding parental responsibility becomes generally accepted:

> . . . it may be recognized as a legal wrong to knowingly beget defective children . . . If conception does occur, there may not be an unfettered right to bring a defective fetus to term . . . Courts and legislatures . . . should . . . take all reasonable steps to insure that fetuses destined to be born alive are not handicapped mentally and physically by the negligent acts or omissions of others.[20]

Before fetal rights could be used as a justification for socially controlling women, the fetus had to be brought onto centre stage and defined as a patient. The embryo will come to be defined as a patient as well, following this development. This is beginning with the Yale University IVF physician referring to the embryo as 'our tiniest patient'. We can expect various manipulations of the embryo to be carried out in the name of embryo rights or, rather, in the right of children to be 'well-born', a right which could be seen as superseding the right of women to control our own persons.

GENETIC CONTROL AND MANIPULATION

The stage is now being set for laws and medical practices which would prohibit women from bearing 'defective' babies or exposing fetuses to their own 'defective intrauterine environment', or using their own eggs to reproduce if those eggs have not met the pharmacrats' quality control standards. Consider that in 1982, Dr. Howard Jones, the leading IVF physician in the United States, in answering one objection to IVF, suggested that it may be unethical for certain women not to submit to prenatal diagnostic procedures and abort 'defective' fetuses. He was answering the objection that IVF is unethical because it entails unknown risks to a potential child who cannot give consent. Jones responded that this argument could equally well be applied to a couple, the female of which is older than 35 years and has an increased risk of bearing a Down's Syndrome child. He wrote:

> The ethics of such a couple could be ever so much more questionable especially if they were unwilling to use contemporary methods of diagnosis with abortion in the event an affected fetus were discovered.[21]

As well as statements on 'ethics' from pharmacrats like Dr. Jones, and court activity around 'fetal rights', there is also a suggestion that our children will eventually blame us for not giving them the best possible genes. According to this argument, parents owe it to 'their' children to use the best possible sperm and egg in creating them. If the mother's is not the best possible, it would be selfish and mean-spirited of her to insist on using it!

Hermann J. Muller sounded the note even back in 1935:

> Mankind has a right to the best genes attainable, as well as to the best environment, and eventually our children will blame us for our dereliction [if we do not give them the best genes] . . .[22]

In 1959 Muller wrote of the goal of having each generation represent a genetic advance over the last:

As the individualistic outlook regarding procreation fades, more efficacious means of working toward this goal will recommend themselves. In time, children with genetic difficulties may even come to be resentful towards parents who had not used measures calculated to give them a better heritage. [That is, the use of sperm and eggs of persons superior to the parents.] Influenced in advance by this anticipation and also by the desire for community approval in general, even the less idealistic of the parental generation will tend increasingly to follow the genetic practices most likely to result in highly endowed children.[23]

The vision here, then, is of social pressure applied to certain segments of the population not to use their own sperm and eggs.

Joseph Fletcher, the medical ethicist, was writing much the same in 1974. After asserting that our morality should change as conditions and situations change, he wrote:

For example, moral responsibility . . . in human reproduction may be shifted from the simple matter of controlling the number of children we have to the trickier business of controlling the genetic or physical *quality* of our children . . . Our notion of avarice may have to be broadened to condemn the *selfishness* of keeping our sperm and ova to ourselves exclusively. Justice may come to mean not having large families. Arrogance might be charged against those who wish to produce children of their own image.[24]

But what about the 'right to reproduce'? Fletcher has an answer:

Humanistic . . . moralists will say, 'A right depends on human well-being, and if the parents are both carriers of a recessive gene causing lifelong pain and misery for the child they would have, then they should not conceive — the right is null and void.' The right to be parents ceases to run at the point of victimizing the offspring or society.

Some of us live in a different world than that inhabited by Joseph Fletcher. In our world, it is difficult to imagine women victimizing male supremacist society. And how would we supposedly victimize the patriarchy? By the act of bearing our own children.

But Fletcher's argument will convince many women. When told we are victimizing our offspring and the whole world by using our own 'defective' eggs, won't women believe it? Won't it confirm for us what we already know, what we are always waiting for everyone else to find out: that we are not quite good enough? Will it be any surprise to us when our eggs are found to be as inadequate as the rest of our bodies? Our hair isn't right. Our teeth aren't right. God knows our thighs and breasts are all wrong. Our eggs will prove to be as defective as our intellects are, as our characters are.

Given the low opinion we women often have of ourselves — that internalised oppression that makes us feel a deep sense of inadequacy — we can expect that the use of donor eggs could, in time, become fairly common. No force will be required to prohibit us from reproducing ourselves. Control of consciousness will do quite well.

Remember Professor Carl Wood, head of the Monash IVF team, who in May 1984 brought up the matter of human genetic breeding? He said women in the IVF programme had been asking for donor eggs because they were not happy with some aspect of themselves and he specifically mentioned appearance and intellectual capacity. Did he follow up this observation by saying: 'Look, we have a serious social problem here. All of these bright, capable women are feeling inadequate in so many ways. Why is this happening? It is an outrageous situation! What social forces are creating a climate in which women feel so bad about themselves? How can we eliminate these forces? We must do something about this because it is a horrible tragedy.' No. He did not say this. He acted as if it were perfectly appropriate to accept some women's perception of themselves as defective, and to reinforce that perception by using eggs of donors who, unlike the women themselves, *are* intelligent enough, *are* attractive enough.

Of course there will be cases when the woman does not come to the doctor and announce that her eggs 'aren't good enough' to use; the doctor will come to her. The doctor will open a file with test results in it and tell her, oh-so-kindly and oh-so-sadly, that there is a problem: she is a carrier of undesirable genetic traits. When the woman looks at the open file before her, she will find her sense of inadequacy confirmed in yet another way. For who is the woman sitting by the open file? She is a woman living in *this* culture.

In the United States, one out of three females is a victim of incest or of other sexual abuse in childhood. The wide-spread sexual assaults on children are part of what Sonia Johnson, the feminist candidate for the US presidency in 1984, calls the war against women. She points out that incestuous attacks, constituting as they do a great betrayal of trust, damage girls immeasurably. The attacks damage a girl's sense of her own worth. When she becomes an adult and is treated badly, contemptuously, how can she say: 'Don't you know *who* I am? Don't you know how valuable a human being I am? You cannot treat me this way.' No, she cannot say that because *she* does not know who she is. *She* does not know how valuable she is.

Perhaps the woman sitting by the open file was not sexually attacked as a child. Perhaps she is the one out of every two women who is at some time in her life battered in a domestic relationship. Maybe she is the one out of every three women in the USA who is raped. If she works outside the home, she is almost surely one of those who is underpaid, who receives a message on her lack of worth every week when she opens her pay envelope. So the woman sitting by the open file, a woman who lives in *this*, woman-hating, culture, is quite apt to take the 'option' the compassionate authority offers her: substitution of a donor egg for her own.

Do you think she will really feel as reassured as the developers of the embryo-flushing procedure painted her when they listed among the potential mothers of future flushed embryo babies 'women who are carriers of undesirable genetic traits or diseases' and added: 'These women should now be able to bear their husband's children without the worry of producing a child with the same genetic affliction'?

The experience of those tried in Hereditary Health Courts in Nazi Germany, found 'diseased' and forcibly sterilized, is instructive here. As physician Friedemann Pfafflin and psychiatrist Jan Gross found upon talking with a number of these victims, they suffered a great deal under the stigma of having a hereditary disease. Pfafflin and Gross wrote:

> As they were ashamed of being blemished by a hereditary disease and distressed by the uncertainty about what that really might mean, they concealed their involuntary sterilization from friends and family and, instead of protesting, drew back into isolation.[25]

We can reasonably expect a woman to react with shame when told that she is a carrier of undesirable genetic traits. We can expect her to withdraw, to remain silent, not to tell anyone, even her parents or her friends, that she used a donor egg to produce 'her' child. The silent damage to her soul will not be recorded. We can wonder about her relationship to this child, a living reminder of her own supposed inadequacy.

SELLING THE GENOCRACY AND REAPING THE REWARDS

Richard Seed plans to franchise the embryo flushing and transfer procedure — he has applied for patents — and then have a string of 20 to 30 profit-making clinics throughout the United States. His company, Fertility and Genetics Research, Inc., intends to connect the clinics through a national data base. This will help solve one of the industry's biggest problems: finding sufficient human egg donors. With the computer link-up, a clinic won't be limited to egg donors in the immediate area but will instead have access to a national pool of women. Dr. John Buster, the obstetrician/gynaecologist who headed the team producing the first flushed-embryo baby, explained to me in an interview:

> You understand that this is done in the cattle business all the time. There's nothing new in all this. It's all very feasible. It's just a case of setting it up.

An infertile or genetically 'deficient' woman in Akron, Ohio could be matched for blood type, hair and eye colour with an egg donor in, say, Baton Rouge, Louisiana. The ovulation times of the two women could be synchronized either naturally or through the administration of hormones. Sperm from the husband of the Akron woman could be flown to Baton Rouge. When the physician believed both women were ovulating (with current technology, it remains impossible to know definitely), he would inseminate the donor. The released egg would spend the next three days travelling from the ovary to the uterus through the oviduct. The sperm may fertilize the egg during this time. The egg would then float freely in the uterus for another two or three days. Five days after the insemination, the doctor would attempt to 'wash out' the egg (now an early embryo) by flushing the uterus using plastic tubing and about two ounces of fluid. The embryo would then be flown to Akron to be transferred into the recipient's body. Aeroplanes would criss-cross the country, carrying embryos flushed out of women's bodies to be inserted into the bodies of other women.

Even by expanding the donor pool to a national basis, the embryo flushing entrepreneurs have not really solved the problem of finding sufficient egg donors. But Dr. Buster listed several possible solutions in his interview with me. The infertile woman could find her own egg donor (perhaps her sister) and bring that donor into the programme. Also, brochures on embryo transfer could be left in doctors' waiting rooms where women patients could read them. 'We think that once they know this can be done, they'll come to us in large numbers', Buster said. At the time I talked with him, the brochures were being written.

Richard Seed had another solution to the problem when I talked with him in 1980:

> We try to set up a system similar to a blood bank's [system] in which every recipient must provide one or two donors for the [egg] bank.

So a woman is infertile. She learns that she can be accepted into the embryo transfer programme only if she delivers two egg donors to its bank. She asks her best friend and her sister to do this for her. They do not want to. But they know how she suffers. If they refuse, they feel, they will be denying her a child. She feels this way too. She would be angry at them and not at the embryo transfer industry. So, feeling violated, the woman's friend and sister lie on gynaecological tables, feet in stirrups, and allow doctors to artificially inseminate them and later flush embryos out of their bodies.

In 1984, when I asked Buster about Seed's idea, Buster said that he and his team thought it could be done and that they might put the plan into effect once the clinics were begun. At some point, the embryo transfer pioneers hired a California public relations firm which, in its press release, gave out a telephone number for those women interested in giving or receiving eggs, to call. The last four digits of the exchange spelled B-A-B-Y. Presumably that number, too, will bring in more egg donors. Seed told me in 1984:

> We would expect in five to ten years time to have a potential donor bank of several thousand women. That's exactly what we're looking for.

I have heard some critics of the new reproductive technologies say, in effect: 'I'm not worried when physicians from university medical centers use these technologies to help the infertile. In fact, I applaud them. But what if an evil tyrant like Adolph Hitler or P.W. Botha of South Africa uses them to create a slave class or to clone an army?'

Yet this criticism misses the point. As a friend said to me when we discussed it: 'It's not P.W. Botha we have to watch out for, or a reincarnation of Hitler. It's P.W. Botha-Smith, MD'. She meant that the technologies will be used by physicians for seemingly benevolent purposes. These kindly physicians may even use a feminist or a liberal rhetoric, passionately defending a woman's right to choose these technologies and 'control her own body'. It is these good doctors working to reduce human suffering, to create a 'healthier' populace, more in line with the choices of parents, who are the danger.

Words of wisdom from some of the most respected and prestigious people in our society — scientists, lawyers, physicians, ethicists, must be noted and remembered:

> . . . it may be recognized as a legal wrong to knowingly beget defective children.

> . . . exposure to the mother's defective intrauterine environment [caused by her genotype] could result in legal action [against her] . . .

> [Infertility provides] an excellent opportunity for the entering wedge of positive selection.

> Mankind has a right to the best genes attainable . . . and eventually our children will blame us for our dereliction . . . [if we do not take measures calculated to give them a better heritage] . . .

> Our notion of avarice may have to be broadened to condemn the selfishness of keeping our sperm and ova to ourselves exclusively . . .

> Arrogance may be charged against those who wish to produce children in their own image.

And finally:

> To be responsible, to take control and reject low quality life, only seems cruel or callous to the morally superficial.

The new reproductive technologies are *not* all about helping the infertile. That is the sugar-coating on the pill. The technologies are about controlling women, controlling child production, controlling human evolution. They are also about making money, setting up corporations which sell women's reproductive services and women's body parts — eggs and wombs. When the pharmacracy controls child production, women become a collection of interchangeable body parts — eggs, ovaries, uteri, bits of fallopian tube which can be added to the culture fluid to aid the fertilization process in the dish. These body parts are the raw material IVF technologists use in producing babies. Pharmacrats understand all this. We had better, as well. The 'morally superficial' among us, as well as those of us who feel they are 'low quality life', need urgently to act now in defence of the lives of the women who will be born — or decanted — after us.

Endnotes

1. Quoted in Janice Raymond, *The Transexual Empire — The Making of the She-Male*, 1979, Beacon Press, Boston.

2. See for example Clifford Grobstein, *From Chance to Purpose: An Appraisal of External Human Fertilization*, 1981, Addison-Wesley Publishing Co, Reading, Massachusetts;
    H.J. Muller, *Out of the Night: A Biologist's View of the Future*, 1935, The Vanguard Press, Inc., NY;
    H.J. Muller, "The Guidance of Human Evolution". *Perspectives in Biology and Medicine* III (2), 1959;
    Rene Dubos, *Man Adapting*, 1965, Yale University Press, New Haven.

3. Joseph Fletcher, *The Ethics of Genetic Control: Ending Reproductive Roulette*, 1974, Anchor Press/Doubleday, Garden City, NY, p. 157.

4. A. Ramanamma and Usha Bambawali, "The Mania for Sons: An Analysis of Social Values in South Asia", *Social Science and Medicine*, 1980, vol. 148, pp. 107–110.

5. Muller, 1935.

6. Carl Wood, *Paper presented to the 8th International Congress of the International Society for Psychosomatic Obstetrics and Gynaecology — Hormones and Behaviour*, 12 March 1986, Melbourne, Victoria.

7. See Anne Finger, "Claiming All of Our Bodies: Reproductive Rights and Disabilities" in *Test-Tube Women*, Rita Arditti, Renate Duelli Klein and Shelley Minden, editors, 1984, Pandora Press, London and Boston, p. 281;
    Marsha Saxton, "Born and Unborn: The Implications of Reproductive Technologies for People with Disabilities" in *Test-Tube Women*, 1984, p. 298.

8. See John Schauble, "Babies: They're Better from Glass", *Sydney Morning Herald* (Australia), 17 May 1984;
    Fiona Whitlock, "Test-Tube Babies are Smarter and Stronger", *The Australian*, 17 May 1984;
    Karen Milliner, "Invitro Babies Better Adjusted: Team xxxx", *Canberra Times* (Australia), 17 May 1984.

9. Muller, 1959, p. 35.

10. George J. Annas, "Artificial Insemination by Donor: Beyond the Best Interests of the Donor", *The Hastings Centre Report*, August 1978.

11. Robert G. Edwards, *Correspondence with Patrick Steptoe and R. G. Edwards, Appendix*, 1979.

12. Laurence E. Karp and Roger P. Donahue, "Preimplantation Ectogenesis", *The Western Journal of Medicine*, 1976, vol. 124, no. 4, p. 295.

13. See for example Betsy Hartmann, *The Population Fix*, forthcoming, Food First: Institute for Food and Development Policy, San Francisco, Ca.

14. See generally Judith Bruce and S. Bruce Schearer, "Contraceptives and Developing Countries: The Role of Barrier Methods", *International Symposium on Research on the Regulation of Human Infertility*, February 1983, Stockholm, Sweden. The immediately following quotation comes from the same source.

15. Quoted in Sally Koch, "Treatment of Gravida Against Her Wishes Debated", *Ob/Gyn News*, 1 May 1985, vol. 20, no. 9.

16. Ruth Hubbard, "Some Legal and Policy Implications of Recent Advances in Prenatal Diagnosis and Fetal Therapy", *Women's Rights Law Reporter*, 1982, vol. 7, no. 3;
    Ruth Hubbard, "'Fetal Rights' and the New Eugenics", *Science for the People*, March/April 1984;

Henry M. Sondheimer, "The Fetus is the Only Patient", *The Hastings Center Report*, August 1983, p. 50;

17.   Hubbard, 1982;
        Ob/Gyn News 15 March 1984;
        New York Times 27 July 1981;
        Harold M. Schmeck, "Frozen Mice Embryo Banked", *New York Times* 10 August 1981;
        H. M. Schmeck, "Pre-Natal Adoption is the Objective of New Technique", *New York Times* 14 June 1983;
        H. M. Schmeck, 'Births to Monkeys without ovaries may offer hope to Infertile Women", *New York Times* 28 October 1983;
        Robin Marantz Henig, "Saving Babies before Birth", *New York Times Magazine*, 28 February 2982;
        Robert P. S. Jansen, "Spontaneous Abortion Incidence in the Treatment of Infertility: Addendum on *in vitro* fertilisation" *American Journal of Obstetricians and Gynecolgists*, 1982, vol. 144, no. 6, pp. 738-739;
        David Rorvik, "The Test tube Baby is Coming", *Look* 18 May 1971;
        John C. Hobbins *et al*, 'How Safe is Ultra Sound in Obstetrics?' *Contemporary Ob/Gyn*, 1979, vol. 12.
18.   Hubbard, 1984, p. 27.
19.   Margery W. Shaw, "The Potential Plaintiff: Preconception and Prenatal Torts" in *Genetics and the Law*, 1980, vol 2, A. Milunsky and G. J. Annas, eds, Plenum Press, NY, pp. 225-232. Quoted in Hubbard, 1984, p. 345.
20.   Quoted in Hubbard, 1984.
21.   Howard M. Jones, "The Ethics of *in vitro* Fertilisation", *Fertility and Sterility*, 1982, vol. 37, no. 2, pp. 176-179.
22.   Muller, 1935, p. 113.
23.   Muller, 1959, p. 19.
24.   Joseph Fletcher, 1974, pp.xiv–xv. The next immediately following quotation comes from the same source, p. 125.
25.   Friedemann Pfafflin and Jan Gross, "Involuntary Sterilization in Germany from 1933 to 1945 and Some Consequences for Today", *International Journal of Law and Psychiatry*, 1982, vol. 5, pp. 419–423.

9 Disturbing connections –
Artificial & natural conception and the right to choose

Jocelynne A. Scutt

> Freedom to have sex without reproduction does not guarantee
> freedom to have reproduction without sex.   John A Robertson*

Women have a long history of seeking to gain control over their own
bodies. In *Hypatia's Heritage* Margaret Alic reports that women
have 'always been healers, surgeons and midwives'. Women discovered the medicinal properties of plants when they fulfilled their
role as gatherers, learning how to 'dry, store and mix botanicals'.
Women discovered 'which herbs provided effective treatment for
various ailments', using their learning for the benefit of women in
childbirth and for limiting childbearing through contraception and
abortion. As civilisation developed, women retained this knowledge, passing it down by word of mouth, from generation to
generation:

> In Athens in the fourth century BC women doctors were accused of
> performing abortions and were barred from the profession. Abortion
> was common among the ancients but was periodically declared
> illegal, especially during outbreaks of misogynist sentiment.[1]

The advent of christianity also threatened the right to abortion. Alic
comments that Tertullian the Carthaginian, a Father of the
Christian church during the third century AD, 'vented his wrath on

---

*"Procreation, Liberty and the Control of Conception, Pregnancy and Childbirth"
(1983) 69 *Virginia Law Review*, pp. 405, 406.

women physicians and midwives, accusing them all of being abortionists.'

In the nineteenth and twentieth centuries the struggle continued. Women like Louisa Lawson in Australia, Elizabeth Wolstenholme, Elmy and Frances Swiney in Britain, and Lucinda B. Chandler and Elizabeth Cady Stanton in the United States recognised the need for women's rights to sexual freedom, encompassing control over the sexual function for both childbearing and choice of sexual partners. Speaking on marriage reform in 1888 at the Washington meeting of the International Council of Women, Lucinda Chandler reported:

> Man's legal institution of marriage was based upon the idea that woman's office in social economy is chiefly that of childbearing . . . How shall a woman be educated to know she has the right to control her own person? By listening to the voice of her own soul, and setting aside every inbred idea that has come down from male theology and statute.[2]

Others, including Annie Besant, Margaret Sanger and Marie Stopes lobbied for practical measures to gain for women some reproductive control, demanding access to safe contraception for women, whatever their economic standing. Each ran into problems with the law, being persecuted on grounds of 'immorality'.

The fight for legal access to contraception was fundamentally won by the Women's Movement in the 1970s. In Australia, for example, the first measure taken by the incoming Whitlam Labor Government in 1972 which could be described as part of a 'women's rights platform' was the removal of high import duty on the Pill. Women were now relatively free to obtain this form of contraception economically as well as legally. Yet rights to safe contraception and abortion continue in the list of Women's Movement demands. At the July 1984 federal conference of the Australian Labor Party (ALP), women within the party gained a significant win through the inclusion in the platform of the statement that Labor 'supports the particular right of women to choice of fertility control and abortion'.[3]

With the advent of the new reproductive technologies women and the Women's Movement are confronted with questions about the 'right' (or lack of it) to control sexuality by becoming pregnant through artificial means. Early this century Margaret Sanger wrote that no woman could 'call herself free until she can choose consciously whether she will or will not be a mother'. As Naomi Pfeffer and Anne Woollett point out in *The Experience of Infertility* this right to choose is defined in terms of the right *not* to have children:

The right to have children and what this entails both in practical terms and in terms of attitudes towards women with children is much less considered. Even further down this list of 'priorities' are the rights of infertile women whose experiences and needs remain largely invisible.[4]

One of the women interviewed by Pfeffer and Woollett is quoted as saying:

> It was brought home to me. I think that everyone has the right to choose, to have an abortion, to be sterilised or whatever. It's just that you're very vulnerable when you're infertile. I don't want to make women have more children. It's just being surrounded by women all of whom have got a choice whereas I don't have a choice. The ones that don't want to be pregnant are having abortions, or being sterilised. I feel as though I'm the only one who doesn't have a choice.

The framing of the problem in terms of 'choice' and 'choices' raises a possible conundrum for women's liberation: in stating that women have 'the right to choose' an abortion (however real or unreal that choice may be), is the Women's Movement logically, and in all conscience, bound to support a right for infertile women to choose pregnancy and childbirth using the new reproductive technologies?

Looking at the matter sociologically, medically and politically, the question of 'choice' really does not arise in any meaningful way. As Barbara Katz Rothman says:

> Most discussions of the new technology for the treatment of infertility have welcomed it as giving new choices to the infertile. But here too there is a negative side to consider: all of the new treatments for infertility have also created a new burden for the infertile — the burden of not trying hard enough. Just how many dangerous experimental drugs, just how many surgical procedures, just how many months — or is it years? — of compulsive temperature-taking and obsessive sex does it take before one can now give in gracefully? When has a couple 'tried everything' and can finally stop? All of the technology still leaves many couples . . . without a pregnancy. At what point is it simply not their fault, out of their control, inevitable, inexorable fate? At what point can they get on with their lives? If there is always one more doctor to try, one more treatment around, then the social role of infertility will always be seen in some sense as chosen: they chose to give up. Did taking away the sense of inevitability of their infertility and substituting the 'choice' of giving up truly increase their choice and their control?[5]

Infertility is not 'cured' by the new reproductive technologies. Few women going into these programmes will become pregnant, even fewer will give birth, and in fewer cases again will the infants live.[6] Access to *in vitro* programmes may result in *more* infertility rather than less through either infertility caused by medical intervention or infertility caused by technology 'going wrong'. (As a result of side-effects with contraceptive technology many women are now on *in vitro* fertilization programmes, or seeking entry to them.)

Katz Rothman adds:

> For those who are successful with the new technology, those for whom the drugs and surgery are a success ... [f]or those whose choices meet the social expectations, for those who want what the society wants them to want, the experience of choice is very real.

The social and political structures in which choices are made cannot be ignored, nor can the medical structures within which women exercise 'choice', whether it be for or against conception, for or against pregnancy, for or against birth. Women's 'choice' becomes a question of more medical control.

And from a legal point of view, the question of choice should concern all women who have fought for the right to control our own bodies. Parallels in the laws relating to abortion and laws newly passed to regulate developments in reproductive and genetic engineering crystallise the dilemma facing women and women's rights. This legislative development forces a closer look at the feminist philosophy underlying demands for access to contraception and abortion.

Women have struggled against laws preventing legal abortion; for the right to gain an abortion; for the right of women to choose without interference from the father of the fetus; and for control over the abortion process. In each of these areas laws relating to the new reproductive technologies may be relevant, or so closely parallel the abortion laws as to give rise to legitimate concern about the preservation of our tenuously held rights to control our own fertility.

ABORTION LAWS

In most countries procuring an abortion is unlawful. Legal restrictions against it are not lifted unless the life or health of the mother-to-be is in danger, or in some countries where fetal indications supporting an abortion on diagnosis are present, where conception has come about as a result of rape or incest, or where there are 'social or economic' indications justifying abortions.[7] 'Health' is often defined to include psychological as well as physical health.

Legal abortion is generally available for one or other or all of these reasons, the world over, although in no instance is it available unconditionally. For example, in the Netherlands which has one of the most liberal abortion laws a compulsory delay must occur between the decision to abort, and the abortion operation. (The implication is that the law has to ensure that the woman *really* knows her own mind, and has not been carried away on some instantaneous whim to request an abortion.) In essence, laws do not give autonomy to the woman involved. The age or development of the fetus are generally relevant to the 'right' to have an abortion. The decision as to whether an abortion will go ahead rests with the doctor or doctors concerned, once a woman has made a decision to approach the medical practitioner seeking the operation. Generally, laws require that two or more doctors certify the abortion is within the strictures of the law: that the continuing pregnancy is a risk to the life of the mother; that it is a risk to her physical and/or mental health; it is a risk in terms of fetal indications (that is, congenital or other deformities present in the fetus); in some cases rape or incest; and in some, social or economic reasons.

In some jurisdictions time limits are placed upon performing the operation. Under the law in South Australia, for example, an abortion is lawful if carried out within 28 weeks of conception; in the Northern Territory of Australia, the operation is lawful for 'broad indications' in 14 weeks after conception, and for 'grave physical and mental risk' up to 23 weeks after conception. In Britain the *Infant Life Preservation Act* governs the limit, requiring that the operation be carried out within 28 weeks of conception; a 'voluntary agreement' (between doctors and hospitals, of course, not with women seeking abortion) limits abortion to less than 24 weeks. In other jurisdictions 'viability' is taken as the limitation — which is, traditionally, about 28 weeks — as for example in Victoria, Tasmania and Western Australia. In the United States, viability of the fetus is an important benchmark. On the other hand, sometimes no legislative or common law time limit or benchmark exists (for example, in New South Wales or the Australian Capital Territory).

Fetus' rights?

In common law no fetus possesses 'human rights'. In certain places, however, provisions now exist providing that the killing of a fetus, capable of being born alive but unable to exist independently of its mother, is unlawful. It is labelled 'child destruction'. Fetuses are not generally considered by the law to have any right to reach 'full human potential'. Indeed, the right of a woman to undergo an abortion directly eliminates any such right on the part of a fetus.

The idea that a fetus has rights that should be preserved through the application of abortion laws has been rejected in Australia by the High Court. In 1982 *In the Application of Kathleen May Harrigan* the High Court was asked for an injunction to prevent a woman from seeking an abortion. The application was brought on behalf of the unborn child. Counsel for the applicant stated:

> . . . we appear for the applicant who was before the New South Wales Supreme Court as next friend or tutor for an unborn child and address the questions raised by the Court of Appeal's decision refusing an injunction and rejecting that the unborn child had any status to be heard in those proceedings.[8]

The High Court held that the applicant had no standing to appear before the court, because there was no individual of any status to represent. That is, an 'unborn child' is not a person with status to bring any action before a court, nor a person upon whose behalf any action can be brought. Thus it is clear that the legal reasoning supporting abortion laws is not connected with any rights in the fetus, nor to the possibility of future life. This is emphasised in some laws, as for example the *Criminal Code* of Queensland, Australia, which in section 282 states:

> A person is not criminally responsible for performing in good faith and with reasonable care and skill a surgical operation upon any person for his [sic] benefit, or upon any unborn child for the preservation of the mother's life, if the performance of the operation is reasonable, having regard to the patient's state at the time and to all circumstances of the case.

Similarly in the United States no human rights attach to a fetus. In 1976 Dr Kenneth Edelin, chief resident in obstetrics and gynaecology at Boston City Hospital, was convicted of manslaughter for performing a late term abortion. The conviction was overturned by the Massachusetts Supreme Judicial Court on 17 December 1976 on grounds of insufficient evidence of the viability of the fetus or of life outside the womb. These findings were necessary if the case was to go to a jury on a charge of 'wanton' or 'reckless' conduct resulting in death.

One month later, on 19 January 1977, Christian S. White and Gary K. Potter, representing the Catholics for Christian Political

Action, filed a petition with the Inter-American Commission on Human Rights on behalf of the 'Baby Boy' (as they termed it) aborted in the *Edelin case*. This petition alleged violation of rights recognised by the *American Declaration of the Rights and Duties of Man* [sic] — namely, article I, the 'right to life', article II, 'all persons are equal before the law', and article XI, 'every person has the right to the preservation of his [sic] health . . .' (In relation to all persons being equal before the law, the article provides that equality should be without distinction as to race, sex, language, creed, or any other factor, and the petitioners claimed the 'any other factor' relevant to 'Baby Boy's' case was age.)

With two members alone dissenting, the Inter-American Commission on Human Rights resolved that the decision of the US Supreme Court and the Supreme Judicial Court of Massachusetts in the case did not constitute a violation of the articles.[9] Similarly the European Commission of Human Rights has held that article 2 of the *Human Rights Convention* adopted by the European states does not grant any 'right to life' to a fetus. Article 2(1) provides 'everyone's right to life shall be protected by law'. The term 'everyone' was considered to apply only to persons already born, and not to a fetus. As far as the word 'life' was concerned, the Commission considered that although 'life' may be interpreted variously in various situations, regard should be had to the context, and thus to the article as a whole. 'Life' would be related, therefore, to persons already born and not to a fetus. The Commission commented:

> The 'life' of the fetus is intimately connected with, and cannot be regarded in isolation of, the life of the pregnant woman. If Article 2 were held to cover the fetus and its protection under this Article were, in the absence of any express limitation, seen as absolute, an abortion would have to be considered as prohibited even where the continuance of the pregnancy would involve a serious risk to the life of the pregnant woman. (This would mean that the 'unborn life' of the fetus would be regarded as being of a higher value than the life of the mother.)

The Commission pointed out that granting any 'right to life' to a fetus would be in conflict with other provisions of the very same article of the Convention, namely a clause permitting the death penalty in restricted circumstances:

> No one shall be deprived of his life intentionally save in the execution of a sentence of a court following his conviction of a crime for which this penalty is provided by law.

Further:

> Deprivation of life shall not be regarded as inflicted in contra-vention of Article 2 when it results from the use of force which is no more than absolutely necessary in three cases —
> * defence of any person from unlawful violence
> * to effect a lawful arrest or to prevent the escape of a person lawfully detained
> * in action lawfully taken for the purpose of quelling a riot or insurrection

Granting a fetus a 'right to life' would subject the woman in whose uterus the fetus was developing to a further implied limitation on her own right to life. It would grant the state an additional ground upon which to end her life, or let her life come to an end (without abortion intervention being allowed). Thus, if an abortion is to be carried out to save the life and health of the mother, refusing the right to an abortion under the Convention would violate the article of the Convention dealing with the conditions under which a state may commit a person to death, or upon which a killing may be con-sidered lawful. The Commission therefore refused to acknowledge any 'right to life' of a fetus.

Fathers' rights?

What of the rights of the father — the man whose sperm has ferti-lised the woman's ovum — where the mother seeks an abortion? Legally, the father has no rights in relation to a fetus. In 1982 the High Court of Australia held in *Attorney-General for Queensland and Another* v. *Miss T.* that there is no right in a boyfriend or lover of a woman to prevent her from having a legal abortion. There, the court held that the man failed in an application to prevent a woman from seeking an abortion on both grounds upon which he argued his case:

* the argument was that if she had an abortion, the woman would be engaging in a criminal act, and should be pre-vented by way of an injunction from doing so. This ground failed.
* the argument was that the fetus 'is to be regarded as a person whose existence can be protected by the courts'. The court said that 'a fetus has no right of its own until it is born and has a separate existence from its mother'. Therefore, this ground also failed.[10]

In Australia, no case has arisen before the courts where the husband of a pregnant woman has argued that he has a right to protect his child from destruction under abortion laws, or in relation to any other law. However, the arguments used in the *Miss T* case would be equally applicable, whatever the relationship between the man and woman involved: a husband would be in the same position as a *de facto* husband, boyfriend, lover, with no right in law to interfere.

Indeed, this issue has been argued out before the courts in England. In Britain in 1976 an application by the husband, Mr Paton, for an injunction to prevent an abortion being performed upon his wife, Ms Paton (who had requested the abortion) was heard and decided by the President of the Family Division of the High Court of Justice. The President dismissed the application, stating that an injunction could be granted only to restrain the infringement of a legal right; that in English law the fetus has no legal rights until it is born and has a separate existence from its mother; and that the father of a fetus, whether or not he is married to the mother, has no legal right to prevent the woman from having an abortion. The court went further to say that the father has no right to be consulted or informed about a proposed abortion, if the provisions of the *Abortion Act* 1967 (United Kingdom) have been complied with. On appeal to the European Commission of Human Rights, the English decision was upheld.[11]

Fetus viability

As earlier pointed out, some jurisdictions have referred to the viability of the fetus in looking at abortion rights. In 1973 the United States' Supreme Court in *Roe* v. *Wade* debated this issue. A pregnant single woman, known as Roe for the purpose of reporting the case, brought an action as one of a class of women seeking an abortion, but constrained by the existence of the Texas criminal abortion laws which forbade procuring or attempting an abortion, except on medical advice for the purpose of saving the mother's life. The woman, who lived in Texas, was not in danger of death, but for other reasons wished to procure an abortion.

The argument of those opposing the charge that the Texas law was unconstitutional and against the woman's legitimate interests, was that the fetus is a 'person', and therefore has a right not to be 'put to death' through abortion. The Supreme Court stated:

> In areas [as well as] criminal abortion the law has been reluctant to endorse any theory that life, as we recognize it, begins before live birth or to accord legal rights to the unborn except in narrowly

defined situations and except when the rights are contingent upon live birth . . . [Such cases] however, would appear to . . . vindicate the parent's interest and [be] consistent with the view that the fetus, at most, represents only the potentiality of life. Similarly, unborn children have been recognized as acquiring rights or interests by way of inheritance or other devolution of property, and have been represented by guardians *ad litem*. Perfection of the interests involved, again, has generally been contingent upon live birth. In short, the unborn have never been recognized in the law as persons in the whole sense.

In view of all this, we do not agree that, by adopting one theory of life, Texas may override the rights of the pregnant woman that are at stake.[12]

However the Supreme Court recognized 'an important and legitimate interest' held by the state 'in preserving and protecting the health of the pregnant woman, whether she be a resident of the state or a nonresident' who seeks medical consultation and treatment there, and that it has 'still another important and legitimate interest in protecting the potentiality of human life'. The court went on to say that these interests 'are separate and distinct':

Each grows in substantiality as the woman approaches term and, at a point during pregnancy, each becomes 'compelling' . . .

The pregnant woman cannot be isolated in her privacy. She carries an embryo and, later, a fetus, if one accepts the medical definitions of the developing young in the human uterus . . . [I]t is reasonable and appropriate for a state to decide that at some point in time another interest, that of health of the mother or that of potential human life, becomes significantly involved. The woman's privacy is no longer sole and any right of privacy she possesses must be measured accordingly.

The Supreme Court divided the term of a pregnancy into trimesters: In the first trimester, the first three months, the privacy rights of the woman override any interest of the state in the developing life in the womb. She has a right to an abortion during that period. During the second trimester, three to six months, the interests of the state come into play in accordance with requirements that the health of the mother be preserved: this means that the state has a right to require abortions to be carried out in a hospital designated for that purpose with the state controlling the procedures carried out. In the third trimester, six to nine months, the preservation of the fetus' life is the legitimate interest. The court said:

With respect to the state's important and legitimate interest in potential life, the 'compelling' point is at viability. This is so because the fetus then presumably has the capability of meaningful life outside the mother's womb. State regulation protective of fetal life after viability thus has both logical and biological justifications. If the state is interested in protecting fetal life after viability, it may go so far as to proscribe abortion during that period, except when it is necessary to preserve the life or health of the mother.

This decision was hailed as a victory for the Woman's Movement, and a boon to women faced with unwanted pregnancy. There was a predictable backlash from organisations such as the Right to Life and the Moral Majority. Although the decision was directly relevant only to United States' laws, anti-abortion crusaders in other countries such as Australia, Britain, Canada and New Zealand were spurred into further action against women's rights. Joan Evans Gardener of the National Organisation of Women in the US reported that the church had contributed 'over $400,000 from 1971 to 1974 either directly or indirectly to finance anti-abortion programs'.[13] In Australia, reports of massive funding to organisations to fight against women's rights to abortion are readily available,[14] and in the United States funding has increased rather than lessened in ensuing years.

By 10 August 1977 the federal Congress had passed the Hyde Amendment relating to the 1977 Department of Health, Education and Welfare appropriations, banning Medicaid funds for abortion. The Supreme Court decided that the states do not have to pay for abortions for poor women — unless choosing to do so. In Australia this approach was tried at federal level by an attempt to disallow abortion refunds under the (then) Medibank ('national health') scheme. The motion was lost in the House of Representatives, as was a similar motion put forward sometime later in the Senate. In America in 1978 Claudia Dreifus in *Seizing Our Bodies* reported that the backlash:

> . . . isn't a backlash at all, but a well-organized campaign by one religion's hierarchy to inflict its dogma on a whole nation. While Catholic clergy and laity were confronting the bishops on true issues of conscience, the hierarchy responded by turning abortion into The New Crusade. From the pulpit abortion was called murder, and though Catholic women, in large numbers, availed themselves of legal abortion, the Church threw its resources into an effective national campaign to nullify the Supreme Court's decision [to allow abortion, in *Roe* v. *Wade*, and *Doe* v. *Bolton*] . . .

Well financed, using the Church as an organizational backbone, the Right-to-Lifers were and are everywhere, with their self-righteous lectures and their magnified photos of dead fetuses and their biased facts . . .

Since Carter's ascendency [as President], all three branches of the federal government have become activists in their opposition to abortion. The Right-to-Lifer's next goal is to eliminate abortion for all women, rich and poor . . .[15]

With the failure of Jimmy Carter to win endorsement for another term as President, and Reagan's inauguration, threats to woman's control over her own body in the United States did not lessen. Indeed, they intensified.

Exemplifying the United States' President's attitude, on 8 October 1985 the *Sydney Morning Herald* reported a three-year legal battle over the disposal of 16,433 aborted fetuses. These fetuses were found immersed in formaldehyde, in sealed plastic bags, stored in a steel bin outside the home of the owner of a defunct medical laboratory which 'routinely examined aborted fetuses for clinics and hospitals'. A suit was filed by the feminist Women's Health Centre to prevent the fetuses going to the Catholic League for religious burial. Eventually the fetuses were given a non-religious burial with a eulogy written by President Reagan:

I am confident that your memorial service will touch many others, as you proclaim the inviolability of human life at every stage of development. From these innocent dead, let us take increased devotion to the cause of restoring the rights of the unborn.

Although actions in the United States appear to be more exaggerated than in Australia and other countries, antipodean anti-abortion organisations have picketed abortion clinics and hospitals, hurled abuse at women entering the precincts seeking an abortion, ruthlessly lobbied Members of Parliament at state and federal level, and adopted crude, invasive (and sometimes violent) tactics at all levels of government and community operations. Opinion polls appear to be strongly in favour of women's rights to abortion. Yet an analysis of the laws now being passed in various states or countries to regulate the field of the new reproductive technologies shows clearly that the anti-abortionists, and more particularly those opposed to woman's right to control her own sexuality and her own body, are now presented with a new means of working against women's rights. The serious implications which arise have not yet been fully debated and analysed by the Women's Movement, if at all.

NEW REPRODUCTIVE TECHNOLOGY LAWS

Debates taking place on the formulation and passage of laws relating to the new reproductive technologies usually conform to the 'gee whiz' style, with a few obligatory comments about the need to pay significant attention to these medical developments, and to take care that the law not unreasonably limit them. Simultaneously politicians recognise that a growing community awareness about *in vitro* fertilisation and other forms of reproductive technology has 'led to growing community concern which has been reflected in the types of comments that have been made to members of Parliament from so many different people'. During legislative debate on the *Infertility (Medical Procedures) Bill* 1984 one member of the Victorian Parliament said:

> As the implications of the programme have begun to strike home to many people, it has led them to look further down the track and to become alarmed at the possible implications of the type of work being done in [these programmes] . . .
>
> Many people, because of deeply-held religious or moral views, cannot accept the fact that life can be created other than through the natural process that human beings have been using for thousands of years. They cannot countenance the view that one should be able, through medical techniques, to create an embryo outside the womb and to interfere with the conduct of nature. The people who hold those views are totally opposed to the programmes currently being conducted.
>
> Other people do not hold such views about the conduct of the programmes and have no objection to scientists developing genetic engineering. A range of views exist between those two extremes. The duty of Parliament is to provide legislation for the community as a whole and to try to discover a policy that is representative of the views of the general public.[16]

The representative views of the general public are difficult to fathom, particularly where little information is available about the nature of the programmes, the 'treatment' involved, the implications for those intimately involved with the programmes, and the implications for us all. The laws being developed and passed are potentially opposed to feminist ideology.

Fetus' rights

On 8 September 1985 the *Good Weekend* news magazine accompanying the *Sydney Morning Herald* and the *Canberra Times* commented upon a proposed private member's Bill to be presented in the Australian Senate. Senator Harradine's intention to introduce the Bill, seeking to ban the creation of human embryos for experimentation and aiming to outlaw 'any dabbling with fertilised human cells left by *in vitro* fertilisation researchers', was reported on. Margaret Rice writes:

> [Senator Harradine's] concern grows from his belief that full rights begin at conception and, because conception has occurred, the cells have the same claim to survival as a full-grown adult.
>
> As he puts it: 'It is based on the fact that human beings, whether born or unborn, deserve the protection of a legal framework. There is absolutely no argument about when human life begins. No one has suggested that it begins at any time other than at conception'.

The immediate reaction to Senator Harradine's *Human Embryo Experimentation Bill*, at least from medical specialists and scientists involved in *in vitro* programmes in Australia, was to deplore the 'halting of IVF in Australia' through the operation of the Bill, should it become law. The Senator's response was to deny the charges:

> It is unfortunate that in the public debate this threat [of the use of technology for self-cannabalistic purposes by the use of embryos in suspended animation to repair parts of a person's body as they wear out] has been clouded by a smokescreen of unfounded assertions that my Bill would halt IVF in Australia. IVF raises many questions which have not been answered and which go beyond the specific scope of my Bill.
>
> The ink was hardly dry on my Second Reading Speech when, ignoring my open invitation in that speech for reasoned suggestions, Dr. Ian Johnston and Professor Warren Jones convened a press conference in Melbourne at which they made the false assertion that my Bill would halt IVF in Australia.[17]

The Bill was then referred to a Select Parliamentary Committee for review and report to the Senate.[18] Yet whatever the truth or otherwise of the assertions, the provisions of the Bill have worrying implications, should they or measures akin to them become law, for women asserting the right to control our own bodies. Clause 5 of the Bill is titled 'prohibited experimentation', and provides:

> (1)For the purpose of this Act, but subject to sub-section (2), any experimenting that is undertaken on, or that involves the use of, a relevant human embryo before the embryo has been implanted

in the womb of a woman, including, but without limiting the generality of the foregoing —
(a) any manipulation of a relevant human embryo;
(b) any procedure undertaken on, or involving the use of, a relevant human embryo;
(c) any dissection of a relevant human embryo; and
(d) any process by way of testing reactions to a drug involving the use of a relevant human embryo,
before that embryo has been so implanted, is prohibited experimenting.

Sub-clause (2) provides that any experimenting referred to in the foregoing is not prohibited under the proposed Act if it is undertaken 'primarily for a benefit consistent with the development of the relevant human embryo's full human potential'. Sub-clause (3) reinforces the ideology that any embryo created must be granted the right to develop its 'full human potential' in stating:

The creating of a relevant human embryo in anticipation that the development of the full human potential of the relevant human embryo will be interrupted, or of using the embryo, or having the embryo available for use, in any experimenting, manipulation or procedure that is prohibited experimenting by virtue of sub-section 1 [outlined above] shall be deemed to be prohibited experimenting . . .

for the purposes of the proposed Act. Any embryos created by *in vitro* fertilisation must be created only for the purpose of bringing them to their 'full human potential' — that is, to term, as fully developed fetuses which will become human babies on birth.

The human embryos to be covered by Senator Harradine's Bill are 'relevant human embryos' defined in the Bill to be human embryos 'created by means of *in vitro* fertilization' and including 'tissue obtained from such an embryo'. Offences are listed in clause 6, prohibiting experimenting with 'relevant embryos' on pain of penalties in the range of $20,000 or four years' imprisonment for some offences, $50,000 for others. Under sub-clause 6(8) no one is entitled to 'wilfully destroy a relevant human embryo', nor to 'wilfully allow a relevant human embryo to die'.

Although these provisions relate only to embryos created by way of *in vitro* fertilisation, contradictions in the existence of this proposed legislation and existing laws relating to abortion are readily apparent. If an embryo created artificially, through *in vitro* fertilisation, cannot be 'destroyed' or 'allowed to die', can it be argued that naturally created embryos should continue to be allowed to die, or be destroyed, through operations sanctioned by the state, namely, abortions? Certainly the *Human Embryo Experimentation Bill*, were it to become law in its present form, could not be interpreted to preclude destruction or allowed death of naturally conceived embryos. Yet the logical conflict between this legislation and abortion legislation would be readily apparent.

And what of the imprecation that if an embryo is to be created artificially, that is by *in vitro* fertilisation, it should be created only in 'anticipation that the development of the full human potential will not be interrupted'? Looking again at naturally conceived and 'created' embryos, would the argument then arise from those opposed to women's right to abortion that the 'full human potential' of the former should not be interrupted either? Again, the legislation proposed by the *Human Embryo Experimentation Bill* does not cover naturally conceived embryos. However the logical conflict between the idea that naturally conceived embryos have no right to 'develop their full human potential', but that artificially created embryos do, is obvious.

Similar problems arise in the proposals put forward in the United Kingdom parliament by Enoch Powell, in his *Unborn Children (Protection) Bill*, which was introduced into the House of Commons in February 1985 and was passed on Second Reading by a majority of 238 to 66. (The Bill later lapsed on a procedural ground.) Although this Bill did not have the obvious implications of the *Human Embryo Experimentation Bill*, that legislation could be proposed to provide 'protection' for embryos created by *in vitro* fertilisation, but not be intended to provide 'protection', ultimately, for embryos created by natural fertilisation is difficult in the circumstances to believe. The UK Bill prohibits the creation of any embryo, artificially, for purposes other than implantation into a woman's uterus for developing into a child.

Fetus viability

Already existing laws have implications which should have been seen at the time those laws were formulated. The danger in the concept of fetus viability as a measure of a woman's right to an abortion was clear at the time of the *Roe* v. *Wade*, *Doe* v. *Bolton* Supreme Court decision. In the early 1970s experimentation and scientific 'advances' in the field of reproductive technology were advancing apace. Although no human embryo had, to our knowledge, been successfully created outside the uterus, that potential was in the air.

By 1955 Shettles in the United States had discovered the possibility of *in vitro* fertilisation for infertile women, but was hampered in going further in his experimentation by the failure of the collected oocytes to fertilize.[19] The probability that a method would be discovered for preserving live embryos outside the womb, at least for a viable length of time until transfer into the same womb, or another, could be arranged, was real in 1973. Yet the Supreme Court went ahead to determine that a woman's right to an abortion was contingent, from viability of the fetus, upon the state's right to step in to protect the potentiality of human life. 'Viability' was defined as the time when the fetus is 'potentially able to live outside the mother's womb, *albeit with artificial aid* '. Certainly the court went on to state that viability is 'usually placed at about seven months (28 weeks)', but even at that time recognised that viability could be measured at a time less than that traditionally considered as the benchmark: it 'may occur earlier, even at 24 weeks. . .'[20] It was predictable, then, that the time span for viability would lessen and lessen.

In the 1980s, the viability of the fetus exists from conception, as an embryo, so long as there is a uterus ready to harbour it. An embryo can be created in a petri dish, kept alive by artificial means. It can then be transferred into the biological mother's uterus — or into the uterus of another woman. It has also been suggested that the transfer could be into the body of a man: 'The technical difficulties would be enormous,' said the director of the Institute of Early Human Development at Monash University, Dr. Alan Trounson, in a feature article appearing in *The Australian* of 17–18 May 1986. 'And,' he continued, 'so would the ethical difficulties. But it could be done by getting an embryo to implant on the bowel.' 'It can be done,' asserts another of these wondermen, Dr. John Parsons, a senior registrar and lecturer at King's College Hospital, London: 'Undoubtedly, someone will do it.' Others, including the pioneering Dr. Patrick Steptoe of Britain, are quoted as being 'more sceptical'. But whatever the case, if a woman's right to abortion is predicated upon the inability of a fetus to be maintained outside her womb, the implications are clear: what logical argument can be used against the preservation of an embryo, after abortion, for implantation into another body? If the state has an 'interest in protecting the potentiality of human life' and thereby a right to prohibit abortion or make special rules covering abortion when the fetus is viable, how can it be argued that a woman has a right to have the aborted embryo destroyed?

These problems do not arise only out of the United States' Supreme Court decision. They arise in all places which relate access to abortion to the lack of viability of the fetus. Under the newly existing conditions where embryo flushing and embryo transfer are readily spoken of and used in some new reproductive technology programmes, at least, the sole indication for legitimate destruction of the embryo would be where the 'fetal indication' (damage, injury, disease or defect of the fetus) is the reason for the abortion. That would be the only case in which it might be rightly said that the fetus is not 'viable'. Or, though viable, it might be argued that the embryo or fetus should not live, because the defects from which it suffers are such as to warrant ending its life. With proposals that genetic engineering might 'correct' defects and deficiencies of various genetically damaged embryos, even this becomes uncertain.

Fathers' rights

Under the *Infertility (Medical Procedures) Act* 1984 (Victoria) 'certain procedures for the alleviation of infertility or to assist conception' are introduced into the law existing in Victoria, Australia. Sections 11 and 12 deal with the *in vitro* procedure where male and female donors are concerned, in almost identical language. If semen is used which is produced by a man other than the woman's husband, that semen must come from a donor who has consented to the use of the semen in this way. Subsection 11(5) states:

> A person shall not use semen produced by a man (in this section called 'the donor') for the purposes of [*in vitro* fertilization] unless—
> (a) the donor has consented in writing to the use of the semen in such a procedure and has not withdrawn that consent;
> (b) where there is a spouse of the donor, the spouse has consented in writing to the use of semen in such a procedure and has not withdrawn that consent; and
> (c) the donor and the spouse (if any) of the donor have received counselling from an approved counsellor.

Subsection 12(5) provides:

> A person shall not in [an *in vitro*] procedure . . . use an ovum removed from a woman (in this sub-section called 'the donor') unless, before the ovum was removed —
> (a) the donor consented in writing to the use of the ovum in a procedure to which this section applies, being a procedure to be carried out in relation to another woman, and has not withdrawn that consent; and
> (b) the husband (if any) of the donor consented in writing to the use

of the ovum in such a procedure and has not withdrawn that consent; and

(c) the donor and her husband (if any) received counselling from an approved counsellor.

The penalty laid down for contravention of either section is '25 penalty units', or imprisonment for one year.

These provisions were probably drafted and passed by the legislature with fond thoughts in mind of the need to encourage 'partnership marriage', or simply to recognise marriage as a partnership, just because the law says so. This incorporates the idea (and the ideal) that each partner to a marriage should have equal rights and obligations, and should be seen as equally involved in the life and well-being of the other. Yet the real nature of the legislation has to be taken into account in the context of the world as it is. These provisions grant a married man rights over his wife's bodily appurtenances (her ova) at a time when women are fighting to ensure that the law enshrines the idea that a woman's body (every part of it, including her sexual organs) is her own, and not her husband's property. Conversely, the provisions grant a married woman rights over her husband's body parts — at least, over his sperm, as he over her ova.

Although the idea that a man might have rights over his wife's ova is abhorrent to feminists, and that a woman might have a right to her husband's sperm is simply foolish, the implications for abortion rights are dramatic. As previously noted, it has never been the case under common law that a man has any rights over an embryo or fetus to whose creation he has contributed the sperm. Yet if a man now is granted rights over what a woman will do with her ova, how can it be asserted that the right a woman has held indisputably over her determination to abort or not to abort a fetus exists without any corresponding right in the 'father-of-the-fetus' (or of the embryo) to grant or withhold his consent to its removal from her womb? After all, ova consist of bodily material created by the woman alone. An embryo or fetus consists of bodily material created by the woman *and* by the man.

That anti-abortionists have not seized upon this legislation as a mechanism for lobbying for 'father-right' is extraordinary. All who believe in a woman's independent right to abortion must realise that the implications will soon be recognised by such groups, and used as leverage. Just because the *Infertility (Medical Procedures) Act* provides for marital consent to ova give-away and sperm-dispersal, does not mean that legislation must or will be passed granting men rights to determine the fate of embryos fertilised by their sperm. Yet women have rightly feared regulatory legislation by male domi- nated parliaments. There may well be cause for acting either to change the laws or to repeal them effectively by lobbying action. But which lobby will be most powerful? Which lobby will win? At least, the Act does not require those living in *de facto* relationships to give consent in writing to the donation of sperm or ova. Will Right to Lifers confine their agitation for the extension of a husband's right to grant or withhold consent to the 'giving away' of an embryo by abortion, to those legally married only, or will *de facto* husbands be deemed to benefit from their efforts to ensure that women's determination to seek an abortion is trammelled by 'father right'?

MEDICAL CONTROL

The medicalisation of women's lives, and the passing of control over women, from individual men to men collectively through the medi- cal model has been commented upon by Barbara Ehrenreich and Deidre English,[21] Barbara Seaman,[22] and Ann Oakley,[23] amongst others. As Janice Raymond says of these new reproductive technologies:

> At first glance, reproductive technologies seem to offer a positive vision to women, that is they appear to give so-called infertile women the ability to reproduce. At second glance, however, another not-so- positive vision looms large, and this is the persistent *medicalization* of women's lives. . . . But many accept only the first vision as truth and dismiss the second as reactionary . . . [But] medicalization of life means more and more areas of living have been colonized by medical intervention, and staked out as medical territory ... The medicalization of female existence rests on the availability of female bodies to be analyzed, quantified, qualified, and integrated into the sphere of medical practice on the grounds of a male-perceived path- ology said to be intrinsic to women, that is, ability to reproduce.[24]

Laws now being passed to cover *in vitro* fertilisation and other new reproductive technologies are generally clear in their requirements that these procedures should take place only in hospitals or clinics authorised for that purpose. For example, section 5 of the *Infertility (Medical Procedures) Act* 1984 (Victoria) provides that no 'fertiliz- ation procedure' can take place unless in accordance with the Act. A fertilization procedure means:

- *in vitro* fertilization
- any other procedure (other than the procedure of artificial insemination) for implanting in the body of a women

— an ovum produced by that woman or by another woman, whether or not it is fertilized outside the body of the first-mentioned woman

— an embryo derived from an ovum produced by that woman or by another woman whether or not it is fertilized outside the body of the first-mentioned woman.

Hospitals in which these procedures can take place must be approved under the Act. This approval is made by the committee of the hospital seeking it, through an application to the Minister administering the *Infertility (Medical Procedures) Act.*

Medical control of these technologies means more than simply maintaining health standards. (And here, women have little to hope for, from the medical profession, which traditionally has been less than concerned with maintaining women's well-being, and more concerned with imposing their analysis of 'women's troubles' onto their patients.) It ensures that social control is exercised over those coming onto the new reproductive technology programmes. Under the law in Victoria, for example, married women only are welcome to participate; those living in *de facto* relationships are excluded. (Those *de facto* couples already in a programme at the time the legislation was passed through parliament were allowed to remain in the programmes.) Barbara Burton lists the types of characteristic important to be exhibited by a woman hoping to enter a programme. Women the medical profession has labelled 'deviant', and women living unconventional lives in terms of traditional society, are generally precluded from participating. Burton and Brown point out that although 'counselling' of those entering programmes may be said to be supportive, and 'for their own good' this is not demonstrably the case. Rather than operating to give supportive counselling and advice through the process, counsellors attached to IVF programmes are seen by participants to be 'gate keepers' to those programmes. Women (and couples) who are keen to be admitted to a programme receive 'tips' from those who have been accepted, about what to wear to a counselling session; how to talk, act, conduct themselves generally. Women act in what they believe to be a 'typical female' manner, projecting an image of 'good mother to be', or 'demure wife and mother', to 'pass' the interview. They complain that after having been admitted to a programme and gone through the IVF procedure, there is little or no support from the medical teams or the counsellors.[25]

The medical profession 'captured' gynaecology and obstetrics, staking out its claims on women's health, women's lives, women's bodies. Similarly the medical profession has 'captured' abortion through the intervention of the legislature or the courts. In requiring IVF operations, however simple, to be carried out in hospitals or clinics and therefore under the control of the profession, new reproductive technologies have been captured. There is a clear parallel between women seeking abortions and those seeking access to new reproductive technologies. Where special procedures must be followed to comply with abortion laws (for example in the Australian Capital Territory, some USA states and Canadian provinces and New Zealand), women must 'go through the hoops' to find a 'friendly' medical practitioner to perform the abortion, or gain the approval of a medical committee. So women seeking access to the new reproductive technologies are obliged to conform to the standards of the medical profession, operating in accordance with existing legislation, and in accordance with their views of whom it is appropriate to admit. If this is a question of 'choice', then whose choice is it? If it is a question of control over women's bodies, then who has that control?

THE FETUS VERSUS WOMAN APPROACH

In Adelaide, South Australia in 1986 a judge of the Family Court of Australia issued an injunction to prevent a young woman from going overseas with her parents. The basis of the order was that she was pregnant to a man whom she had earlier married, but had decided to leave upon the breakdown of the marriage. It was he who brought the action against her in the court. His argument was that because she was pregnant, his former wife should not be allowed to remove herself from the country.[26] This court order flew directly in the face of earlier High Court decisions. It also ran counter to an earlier Family Court decision, where it was held that a fetus is not a 'child of a marriage', and therefore no arrangements can be made upon divorce, by the court, for maintenance or custody of the fetus. Justice Lindenmayer touched directly on the question in the earlier decision:

> ... whilst opinions may differ as to the desirability of [the legal] consequences . . . of adopting an interpretation of the word 'child' as including an unborn child, . . . my own view is that they would be most undesirable. The law of domestic relations is complex enough without inviting or encouraging conflicts between spouses as to the custody etc. of their unborn children with all of the implications and complications which that might entail. For example, could a woman desirous of leaving her husband, and intending to travel overseas be restrained from doing so unless and until she underwent a pregnancy

test to ensure that she was not secretly, or even unknown to her, carrying a 'child' over whom the court might wish to seek an order as to custody?[27]

The judge concluded that this might 'sound a fanciful proposition', but that the 'ingenuity of lawyers and the deviousness of litigants, particularly in [the family jurisdiction], cannot be under-estimated'.

The view that a husband has a right over his wife's or former wife's body by reason of a pregnancy does not only conform to patriarchal notions of male-right. It promotes a fetus-centred ideology. This ideology is becoming entrenched in particular debates, and is as dangerous to women as its patriarchal precursor.

The notion has its beginnings in the abortion argument, as well as in the newly developing medical approach to 'the tiniest patient' — the embryo. Organisations such as the Right to Life join forces with medicos who see their role as anchored firmly in the care of the fetus, with the woman as a mere receptacle carrying that fetus. The concept has found its way into child abuse terminology and practice, with the newly developing field of 'fetus abuse'. Now, women are accused of being fetus abusers by drinking alcohol or smoking cigarettes when pregnant, and even deliberately beating their own bodies solely for the purpose of abusing the child *in utero*.[28] Demands are placed on women to look after their health during pregnancy not for their own sakes, but for the sake of their expected children. Medical practitioners see the health of the child as all important, and the mother's health and well-being as relevant only to the health and well-being of that child.

This ideology is directing the IVF debate, also. As Janice Raymond points out in 'Fetalists Versus Feminists : They are Not the Same':

> Fetalists are concerned with what they express as the 'violence' done to the conceptus, embryo, or fetus in such procedures as IVF [just as they are in abortion]. For example, Leon Kass states that 'The human embryo is not mere meat; it is not just stuff; it is not a thing. Because of its origin and because of its capacity, it commands a higher respect'.[29]

If only women were accorded the same respect, writes Raymond:

> Kass and other fetalists offer no critique of the *reality* that the NRTs [new reproduction technologies] impose on women and on real women's bodies. It is almost as if real women don't exist in their view,

or that the only real women are those who are willing to bear any pain and manipulation to become mothers.

Their major objection, she writes, 'is how the technologies affect fetal *potentiality* for personhood. For fetalists, the real person here is the fetus.'

For women who are fighting for the right to control our own bodies, the language of the fetalists is dangerous, adding to the danger of their actions and the actions they seek to thrust upon women seeking an abortion. Yet the danger is added to by the language the women's movement itself has selected to embody our demands for personal autonomy and access to contraception and abortion. The language of 'choice', which the women's movement has adopted as its own, is increasingly being used against women and women's rights.

THE RIGHT TO CHOOSE

In the early 1970s, the Women's Movement was loud in its demands. One of the primary demands, if not *the* prime demand, was the right to 'free abortion on demand'. As the 1970s wore on, the demand was toned and tempered down to meet the 'threat from the right'. Many women then believed that continuing with an overwhelmingly aggressive demand, an all out, give-it-to-us-or-we'll-take-it approach, was bad tactics. This strand of the women's movement believed it was important to formulate the demand as 'the right to choose an abortion'. While this view won out, even that slogan was too strong for most. It was then tempered further by the removal of the word 'abortion', leaving only 'the right to choose' (abortion was implied).

Surveys in the United States, Britain and Australia show that, overwhelmingly, a majority of the populations of each country favour the right to an abortion. In 1980, a survey reported in *Time* magazine showed 82 per cent of Americans favouring woman's right to seek — and gain — an abortion. Between July and August 1977 the *Pregnancy Termination Control Bill*, a draconian piece of legislation limiting abortion to rape or incest (proved to the satisfaction of a member of the police force); serious risk of death; serious risk of suicide of the putative mother; or serious risk, 'clearly demonstrated, of major fetal abnormality or disease' was before the Queensland parliament. A survey at that time, conducted by personal house to house interview, found:

- respondents overwhelmingly agreed that support for legal abortion on wide grounds was acceptable and necessary

- there was no link between views on abortion and religious or political views, nor age or social, educational or financial background
- 61 per cent of respondents supported the right to an abortion during the first three months of pregnancy[30]

Compared with a survey carried out by Wilson and Chappell in 1967 it was clear that attitudes toward abortion had changed substantially, so that the predominant trend was towards its acceptance. In 1967, the Wilson and Chappell survey found:

- 92 per cent of respondents supported the legality of an abortion to save the life of the putative mother
- 75 per cent of respondents supported the legality of an abortion in the case of danger of deformity of the child
- 27 per cent of respondents supported the legality of an abortion for social/economic reasons[31]

Was the change contingent upon adoption of the slogan 'the right to choose' and the movement away from the direct demand for women's right to abortion? In early 1985 a survey carried out nationally in Australia showed 72 per cent of Australians favouring a right to abortion. Earlier in the 1980s, the Anglican Church in Australia officially condemned abortion after supporting liberalisation of existing laws, during the 1970s — when the Women's Movement was at its most vocal on this demand. The church's position of change against women's rights has taken place at a time when women are more subdued about those rights.

The patterns are not clear. On 30 May 1985 when the Queensland Attorney-General apparently orchestrated a raid on the Greenslopes Fertility Control Centre in Brisbane and confiscated 18 000 patient files, public outrage was generally expressed throughout the country, including Queensland. Public figures who had consistently taken the stand of opposition to abortion rights, often on religious grounds, spoke out *against* the raid. In *R.* v. *Peter John Bayliss and Dawn Cullen*[32], the court case which followed the raid, the Queensland County Court upheld the law in a land-mark decision, interpreting the provisions of the Queensland *Criminal Code* in accordance with the relatively liberal Victorian and New South Wales' approaches: that so long as the doctor has a reasonable and honest belief that the physical or mental health of the mother is threatened, then abortion is legal.

Groups such as the Right to Choose Coalition might assert that public acceptance has been dependent upon the 'played down' approach of 'right to choose' versus 'free abortion on demand'. Yet by adopting a small 'l' liberal terminology, women are now trapped in a bind which places those asserting 'the right to choose' *in vitro* fertilisation and other new reproductive technologies in a position of self-righteousness if feminists declare there *is* no right to choose these technologies.

We must not confuse 'choice' with the demand of women to the right to control our own bodies. We need a well-thought-out position governing our policies and demands where women's bodies, women's lives and women's health are in question. The threat placed before women and humanity by the new reproductive technologies is not limited to the ravages that technology can wreak in itself. The threat goes beyond to questions of self-determination for all women. As Robyn Rowland has said:

> It is the life-force in women which men have always sought to control. How powerful we have always seemed; we who can bleed regularly and not die, we who can grow another human being inside our own bodies. Obvious though it has been in real terms, this has since 'primitive' times been a source of mythical power for women when all else was kept from them. For many women it is the *only* experience of power they will ever have. And men have coveted that last of powers. Men's myths have continuously expressed their fear, awe, and envy of it, and they have repeatedly tried to control it.[33]

Rowland comments that men originally renounced midwives and made a profession out of studying women's bodies:

> . . . they frequently express their anger, resentment, and hatred of women through violence against our bodies; they have controlled and regulated our choice with respect to our bodies, controlling contraception, controlling abortion. Now, with the possibilities offered by technology they are . . . taking control of conception, fetal development, and birth . . .

The threat posed by the new reproductive technologies goes to the very essence of feminist demands. Without regulation of the new reproductive technologies, we are left in a state of *laissez-faire*, and the laws already existing will operate to govern our reproductive lives, anyway. Yet any demands we have for regulation must be clearly centred not in the fetus, or men's rights, but in our demand to acknowledge our bodies as our selves, our reproduction and reproductive capacity and organs as integral to our bodies, not parts to be dealt with or demeaned. Any laws must be based on a woman's needs and interest at the centre. It is not a question of any 'right to 'choose'. It is an assertive demand for bodily and personal freedom, not for further incursions of the technodocs into our bodies and our lives.

Endnotes

1. Margaret Alic, *Hypatia's Heritage*, 1986, Women's Press, London.
2. Sheila Jeffreys, *The Spinster and Her Enemies*, 1986, Pandora Press, London, p. 23.
3. Australian Labor Party, *Federal Platform*, 1984, "Women", p. 26.
4. Naomi Pfeffer and Anne Woollett, *The Experience of Infertility*, 1983, Virago, London, p. 2. The immediately following quotation is from the same source.
5. Barbara Katz Rothman, "The Products of Conception: The Social Context of Reproductive Choices", *Journal of Medical Ethics*, 1985, vol. II, p. 188. also Barbara Katz Rothman, "The Meaning of Choice in Reproductive Technology" in *Test-Tube Women*, 1984, p. 23. The immediately following quotations are from the same source.
6. A six year study released on 19 November 1985 showed that IVF babies were more likely to be born pre-term and seriously underweight than naturally conceived children. More than 40 per cent were delivered by caesarean section, compared with 19 per cent in the general population. Babies resulting from *in vitro* fertilization were found to be four times more likely to be stillborn or die soon after birth. There was also a high miscarriage rate with *in vitro* fertilization pregnancies. The study was coordinated by Dr. Paul Lancaster, director of the National Perinatal Statistics Unit in the School of Public Health and Tropical Medicine at the University of Sydney.
   See Philip McIntosh, "In Vitro Technique Needs Perfecting, Says Scientist", *The Age* 20 November 1985, p. 15.
7. See generally the Max Planck Institute study on abortion laws throughout the world, available from the Max Planck Institute, 73 Gunterstalstrasse, Freiburg im Breisgau, D-7800, West Germany.
8. *In the Application of Kathleen May Harrigan*, 1982, High Court of Australia.
9. *Edelin case*, Inter-American Commission on Human Rights, 1976. The immediately following quotation comes from the same source.
10. *Attorney-General for Queensland and Another* v. *Miss T*, 1982, High Court of Australia. But this is certainly no time to be sanguine. For the idea that men *should* have some legitimate rights over women's bodies, simply on the basis that they are/may be carrying an embryo having sperm from the man as the fertiliser, see Max McManus, "Abortion: Another View — How Men Cope with the Final Sentence". *The Age*, 26 November 1986. (This large article was given prime place in the Accent page, a page purportedly designed to deal with women's issues.)
    See also Valerie Colyer, "With an Estimated 85,000 Abortions each Year in Australia (27,000 in Victoria) Some Men are Protesting that their Rights to Fatherhood have been Overlooked", *The Age*, 26 November 1986, p. 26.
11. *Paton's case*, 1976, European Commission of Human Rights.
12. *Roe* v. *Wade*; *Doe* v. *Bolton*, 410 *U.S.* 113, 93 *Supreme Court* 705, 35 *Legal Education* 2d 147 (1973). The immediately following quotations come from the same source.

13.   See for example Maureen Anderson, 'Catholic Hierarchy Escalates Anti-Woman Campaign Against Reproductive Rights', *National NOW Times*, May 1985, p. 4. On 8 June 1985 a national rally — Witness for Women's Lives Rally and March — was held in Washington, D.C. to 'protest the catholic hierarchy's anti-woman campaign to end birth control and abortion'.

14.   See Tim Duncan, "Anti-abortionist 'Shock Troopers' to Close Clinics", *The Bulletin*, 3 September 1985, p. 52.

15.   Claudia Dreifus, *Seizing Our Bodies*, "Introduction", 1978, Vintage Books, NY pp. xvii-xxi.

16.   *Hansard*, Victoria, October 1984.

17.   Press Release, Senator Harradine, Tasmania.

18.   The Senate Select Committee reported to the Australian Parliament in 1985. Michael Tate, chairperson.

19.   See Gena Corea, *The Mother Machine*, 1985, Harper and Row, NY:
      A. Milunsky and George Annas, *Genetics and Law*, vol. II, 1980, Plenum Press, NY, pp. 345–346.

20.   *Roe* v. *Wade, Doe* v. *Bolton*, 410 *U.S.* 113, 93 *Supreme Court* 705 (1973).

21.   Barbara Ehrenreich and Deidre English, *Complaints and Disorders: The Sexual Politics of Sickness*, 1973, Feminist Press, NY;
      Barbara Ehrenreich and Deidre English, *For Her Own Good: 150 Years of Experts' Advice to Women*, 1978, Anchor Press/Doubleday, Garden City, NY.

22.   Barbara Seaman, *Free and Female: The Sex Life of the Contemporary Woman*, 1972, Coward, McGain and Geoghegan, NY.

23.   Ann Oakley, *The Captured Womb* 1986, Basil Blackwell, Oxford.

24.   Janice Raymond, Paper presented to *Liberation or Loss'. Women Act on the New Reproductive Technologies*, Conference, May 1986, Canberra, ACT, Australia, 1986, p. 427.

25.   Barbara Burton, Paper presented to *Liberation or Loss? Women Act on the New Reproductive Technologies* Conference, May 1986, Canberra, ACT, Australia; Patricia Brown, "IVF and the Simple Case", paper presented to *Liberation or Loss?* Conference, May 1986, Canberra, ACT.

26.   See report *Adelaide Advertiser*.

27.   *In the Marriage of Diessel (J.E. and C.G.)*, 1980, 44 *Federal Law Reports* 1, pp. 5–6. The next following quotation comes from the same source.

28.   One session at the International Congress on Child Abuse, Sydney Australia, 11–14 August 1986 was devoted to this issue, gaining more press and other media coverage than almost any other session of the congress.

29.   Janice Raymond, "Fetalists vs. Feminists: They Are Not The Same", paper presented at *Liberation or Loss?* Conference, 1986; to be published in Heather Dietrich, Janet Ramsey and Robyn Rowland, *Liberation or Loss? Women Act on the New Reproductive Technologies*, forthcoming.

30.   Beryl Holmes (Children by Choice) and Janet Irwin (Australian Family Planning Federation), 1983, Brisbane, Queensland.

31.   Paul Wilson and Duncan Chappell, in Wilson and Chappell, *The Australian Criminal Justice System*, 1967, Butterworths Australia, Sydney.

32.   *R.* v. *Peter John Bayliss and Dawn Cullen*, Queensland County Court, 22 January 1986.

33.   Robyn Rowland, "A Child at Any Price?", *Women's Studies International Forum*, vol. 8, no. 6, pp. 339–346. The next following quotation comes from the same source.
      See also Joanne Finkelstein, "Women, Pregnancy and Childbirth", this volume.

10 Women's bodies, patriarchal principles – *Genetic and reproductive engineering & the law*

Jocelynne A. Scutt

There is no right to a child as property.[*]

Traditionally, the law has concerned itself with property and property rights. This is so in Britain, Australia, Canada, New Zealand and the United States with legal systems based on English common law. Property concepts are prevalent where the law deals with reproductive technology and genetic engineering, whether the law operates as it already exists, without special rules being devised to cover these developments, or whether the legislature steps in to regulate this 'new' area.

'Ownership' and 'proprietorial rights' arise often in the debate. Ownership of knowledge — scientific knowledge, and that developed out of the examination of, and experimentation on, women's bodies, particularly in the realm of reproduction — underpins the medico-scientific approach to reproductive and genetic engineering. 'Science' has traditionally been a male domain, which legitimises the 'boys' invading women's bodies for the purposes of scientific 'advancement'. They then possess rights over the information gained through scientific dominance and the subsequent exploitation of that knowledge. These rights are bolstered within the legal system, through the application of copyright, patents and commercial laws.

The law has been slow to change, but where new laws have intervened or old laws have been clarified, the legal status of children

[*]*Resolution, Women's Emergency Conference on the New Reproductive Technologies*, Sweden, 1985.

produced as a result of IVF and AID programmes is the prime target. Interpretation of the law cannot adequately take into account women's claims for autonomy and consideration as individuals, despite its ostensible purpose of assisting infertile couples, and enabling women to bear children. The principles of the law also conflict with feminist calls for an end to ownership rights over children — despite an apparent concern of the laws and legal system for children. The laws are outwardly designed to assist the children born by new reproductive technologies, by clarifying their parenthood and legal standing; analysis shows different concerns.

Just as women do not have control of the new reproductive and genetic engineering technology or its application, through scientific and medical expertise, women do not control genetic and reproductive engineering through the law. New laws are firmly held within a patriarchal tradition of property and ownership. The supposed battle lines appear to be drawn between men believing it is important to regulate new reproductive technologies (as long as the regulations accord with their beliefs about who should own what), and those proclaiming the value of a *laissez-faire* approach (leaving ownership and control as it is). Concerns for women's autonomy, for children's essential human needs for care and love, and recognition of an adult human capacity for loving and consideration are currently remote from the legislative palette.

REPRODUCTIVE TECHNOLOGIES

Existing laws

If reproductive technologies involve surgery of some kind then the procedure will be lawful only if carried out for the good health and wellbeing of the patient and with the patient's consent. With artificial insemination by donor (AID) or artificial insemination by husband or partner (AIH) there appears to be little to offend existing laws on medical operations — so long as the sperm is obtained through non-surgical methods, and insemination conducted without surgical intervention. That is, the sperm being obtained by masturbation and introduced into the woman's vagina and uterus by means of a syringe or other similar mechanism not requiring surgical intervention. However, if the sperm are obtained by surgical means, for example where the man has an obstruction which prevents emission of sperm, the legality of the method appears to become a little tenuous — unless patriarchal notions of women's fulfilment and role apply, and men's desire for biological immortality.

The question is whether the operation is performed on the man to remove sperm *for his own benefit and well-being*. The direct affirmative answer could be given that unless he is able to father his own progeny a man feels less than a man and that his psychological well-being is disrupted or at risk. A more circuitous way of making the operation legal is to argue that as the sperm is to be used to make his partner pregnant, and therefore is for her well-being, his well-being is indirectly affected in a positive way. If she did not become pregnant he might suffer psychologically through *his* inability to supply sperm naturally, preventing his partner from having their child. Yet the question could equally be asked: why is it important that *his* sperm be extracted and used? Couldn't the woman's well-being be secured by the use of sperm from a man other than the partner? Why does he need to biologically father a child in order to feel 'a man'? The estimation of well-being for the man through extracting his own sperm for fertilization of the woman's ovum is centred upon a patriarchal concept of 'well-being'.

Consider also the position of the woman undergoing medical treatment to become impregnated where ova have to be obtained from the woman to enable *in vitro* fertilisation to go ahead, and this is done by way of a medical operation, the argument would have to be made that the operation and the procedure prior to it — such as stimulation of multiple ova shedding by way of hormone injections — are for the benefit of the woman concerned. To conform to the legal standard, the well-being of the woman is defined in accordance with her ability to give birth to a biological child, or at least to give birth to *a* child. Where her partner's infertility causes the problem, but his sperm can be used to fertilize her ovum *in vitro*, her well-being has to be premised upon the psychological stability she will gain from giving birth to *his* child, rather than the child of another — through, for example, AID. Even where the woman is impregnated with the ovum of another woman, fertilised by her partner's (or another's) sperm, there is some idea that it is vital to her psychological health that she physically gives birth to a child.

The legality of *in vitro* programmes rests upon patriarchal notions of woman's place and man's rights. A man's well-being is centred upon notions of a right to immortality through progeny. A woman's well-being is determined in accordance with whether or not she can become pregnant, and beyond that, whether or not she can become pregnant *to her husband*.

Although this is the way existing law requires the problems of *in vitro* fertilisation to be dealt with, in order that the treatment comes within legal standards, the reality is somewhat different. The evidence does not support the idea that women's well-being is served through IVF programmes. In a study of women in IVF programmes in New South Wales and Victoria, Barbara Burton reports upon their reactions to the treatment. Her overall assessment is that all the women whom she interviewed were aware 'that for the majority of them IVF would not result in a child'.[1] She also asserts that all the women 'had an overriding positive attitude to IVF and IVF personnel'. Any negative reactions are assessed as 'minor irritations' while 'Most of them expressed minor irritations about the IVF procedures'. But the women's views speak for themselves. One is quoted as saying:

> It's embarrassing. You leave your pride at the hospital door when you walk in and pick it up when you leave. You feel like a piece of meat in a meat-works. But if you want a baby badly enough you'll do it.

Of the IVF cycle for one treatment, a participant in the research study summed up:

> What makes IVF so dreadful is that you're living in your own private emotional hell for four weeks. Everyone is nice and kind but they just don't know what you're going through. It makes you focus on that part of your life which makes you unhappy. I can only just cope day to day.

A third said of the treatment:

> Honesty is the most important thing. There are a lot of things to handle and you can handle them if you've got good information.
>   I think it's dishonest to give a success rate based on the number of positive pregnancy tests per number of women who have embryo transfer. I think we need to know how many women are treated, how many pregnancies occur, how many deliveries occur over a period of time. I think it should be readily given out to patients from the outset.
>   I think a lot of women drop out of IVF because they just can't handle the hassles because they're unprepared. I think a lot of women feel cheated because it is so financially expensive and disruptive of our lives.

Apart from the direct IVF treatment (the extraction of ova and insertion of the fertilised egg) women's views of the preliminaries — for example, the hormonal treatment stimulating ovulation — similarly raise doubts as to the promotion of well-being. Burton notes that a problem perceived by the women on IVF programmes was the short and long term effects of hormone treatment. One said:

I wasn't aware of the tremendous and immediate emotional effects which can occur. When you start having the injections very often I just find myself getting extraordinarily emotional, which is something I've always been able to control. It was a new sensation for me to have this emotional turmoil and I recognised it was not so much related to the distress of the treatment cycle but to the increased hormones I was getting.

Another woman is quoted as commenting:

I sometimes get concerned what's going to happen to us in 10 to 15 years time. Our generation were guinea pigs for the Dalkon Shield, and now we're guinea pigs for a new form of modern technology. I think it is really, really important that some research is done on the long term effects of the hormonal treatment we're getting.

Her final comment was: 'Even if there were an increased incidence of ovarian cancer I'm sure a lot of women would still want to be involved with the [IVF] programme but it would be necessary to have increased surveillance.' Yet how can this approach be fitted into existing legal standards of medical treatment and wellbeing? If a treatment were found to increase the likelihood of early death for at least a defined percentage of those undertaking the treatment, this seems disproportionate to the positive end said to be sought through that treatment. A life threatening condition is likely to be created to 'deal with' a non-life threatening condition — infertility. Women who are infertile or who have infertile partners, will not die as a direct cause of *that* medical condition. If the treatment they undergo to gain a child is likely to cause death from ovarian cancer for some of them, how can that treatment be justified as promoting their well-being?

If the criterion is applied that the woman's well-being is affected because her partner's well-being is affected, because he is infertile and unable to produce biological progeny, why take the drastic step of subjecting *her* to surgical treatment through an IVF programme? Surely the wider boundaries of the issue have to be looked at. Why not counsel the man to enable him to come to terms with not being able to gain biological immortality? Why not spend time considering the ramifications of living in a world where manhood is, at least in some men's minds, premised on the biological imperative?

If the woman undergoing treatment has psychological concerns as a result of her own infertility, it is almost as difficult to assert that IVF contributes to her well-being. Causes of infertility are not treated by IVF. Even if a woman bears a child as a result of IVF, the cause of her infertility remains. She remains essentially an infertile woman, albeit one who has borne a child. Ultimately, when research shows that the stated aim of the treatment — the birth of a baby — is in reality rarely achieved, it is questionable whether 'well-being' is serviced by IVF. Already women who have been diagnosed as 'infertile' describe their feelings as 'a life crisis', affecting self-esteem, causing depression, affecting sexuality, bringing feelings of powerlessness, shock, disbelief, anger, guilt and jealousy:

> I keep thinking why me, why is this happening to me? What have I done, it's such a simple thing, I feel like lashing out at everyone, it's not fair.[2]

Will these feelings go away through placement on an IVF programme? The infertility remains. Rarely is a child born to those on IVF programmes. Participants are caught in a round of treatments, surgical intervention, hormonal stimulation, rising hopes, apprehension, disillusionment and upset: 'I just wanted to sit in a corner and die, but life goes on, there's beds to make and meals to cook'. And their family relationships do not improve at each treatment cycle failure. One woman comments:

> My husband went to pieces [after the treatment cycle failed]. I felt I was dying. I was really crook, but I didn't let any pent-up emotions come out; I had to look after him.

Another woman said:

> I spent the day scrubbing the shower recess. I just wanted to be alone. A friend had decorated the house with pink balloons and streamers when I came home from hospital. When I got my period and told my husband he busted the balloons and tore the streamers down.

And the well-being argument is not enough to make the operation legal. Consent of those entering the programmes must be valid. The importance of patient autonomy in medical decision-making has been accepted in courts in Canada, Britain, the United States, New Zealand and Australia.[3] This is framed in the rulings that a medical operation performed without consent of the patient (or a guardian in certain circumstances) will be unlawful. Indeed, it is an assault, or infliction of unlawful wounding, or commission of grievous bodily harm. Informed consent to medical treatment is preserved through the mechanisms of the criminal law relating to bodily integrity and the unlawfulness of acts done to a person without consent, and rules governing professional competence. Ordinarily when a person presents herself to a doctor for treatment, this implies consent. However with more complex procedures, particularly where they invade bodily integrity, as in surgery, express or explicit consent will be required.

Generally there is no legal requirement that consent to medical treatment or surgery should be in writing, but writing shows voluntary agreement of the patient to be treated, and implies that the patient has been given sufficient information about the treatment or surgery to make the consent real. First, consent must be given by the patient. Then if legal action is to be taken against a doctor for improper or inadequate treatment, the action will be for negligence (for professional incompetence). There could be a legal action against the doctor, also, for breach of a contractual agreement. That is, that the doctor and patient have contracted together that the treatment should be carried out according to professional standards, and that it will be treatment of the nature the patient requested.[4]

To secure consent, the doctor must advise the prospective patient of what the treatment is, and of the risks, consequences and implications of that treatment. The extent of disclosure to the patient varies between countries. England, Australia and New Zealand take a somewhat more restricted view of the responsibilities of disclosure by doctors than do courts in Canada and the United States. The more restrictive view is highly paternalistic. The basic rule is that there is no duty to warn a patient of every risk involved in a treatment or operation. In *Chatterton* v *Gerson*[5] it was accepted that in England a doctor must warn the patient of all material risks. The doctor is the judge of what is material, and the standard by which the doctor will be judged is that of what a reasonable doctor would regard as material risks. In New Zealand in *Smith* v *Auckland Hospital Board*[6] it was said that the scope of the duty to advise was 'governed by the practice of competent and prudent doctors'. In *Bolam* v *Friern Hospital Management Committee*[7] the principle was endorsed that a doctor is entitled to 'play down' the risks in the reasonable belief that this is in the best interests of the patient, so long as in doing so the doctor is acting in accordance with the practice of the medical profession. That line was further approved in *Sidaway* v *Board of Governors of the Bethlem Royal Hospital and the Maudsley Hospital*[8] in England, an approach generally in line with the Australian, New Zealand and Canadian approaches.

In the United States, the early line was akin to that taken in other common law countries where the physician's duty of disclosure was judged by prevailing standards of medical practice. The test applied by the courts was whether the information as to the specific risk in undergoing the operation or treatment was routinely disclosed by reasonable members of the medical profession under similar circumstances as those in question in the particular case: *Natanson* v *Kline*.[9] However beginning in the 1970s several courts rejected this standard as being inconsistent with the ideal of patient autonomy which 'informed consent' is supposed to promote. In *Canterbury* v *Spence*[10] and *Cobbs* v *Grant*[11] the court judged the doctor's duty to disclose information by its 'materiality' to the patient's decision: that is, is the information something which would or could affect materially the patient's decision to go ahead with the operation or to refuse the treatment? Some courts have said that materiality should be judged in accordance with the standard of the particular patient: would disclosure of the information have affected that particular patient's consent or not? Other courts have determined materiality in accordance with what a 'reasonable' person in the position of the patient would consider significant in deciding upon the treatment agreed to.

It may appear that the standard applied to the particular person in the particular case (was information disclosed to *this* person, undergoing the operation, in relation to *this* treatment?) is more appropriate, and less paternalistic, than the standard of the reasonable person (was the information disclosed such as a *reasonable* person, in these circumstances, would require to make an informed decision?) However patriarchal attitudes are inherent in law and medicine. As the House of Lords revealed in its judgment in *Sidaway's case*[12] these attitudes permeate decision-making even where the particular person in the particular circumstance is being looked at, or even more so. In that case one of the judges said:

> ... when it comes to warning about risks, the kind of training and experience that a judge will have undergone at the Bar makes it natural for him [sic] to say (correctly) it is my right to decide whether any particular thing is done to my body, and I want to be fully informed of any risks there may be involved of which I am not already aware from my general knowledge as a highly educated man of experience, so that I may form my own judgment whether to refuse the advised treatment or not.

The elitist nature of the law, at least with regard to medical treatment, is evident in his and the other judges' opinions that if the patient *asks*, then information should be given:

> No doubt, if the patient in fact manifested this attitude [of wanting

> to decide about treatment] by means of questioning, the doctor would tell him whatever it was the patient wanted to know . . . (Lord Diplock)

And:

> Ms Sidaway could have asked questions. If she had done so, she could and should have been informed that there was a . . . risk . . . [t]he patient cannot complain of lack of information unless the patient asks in vain for more information . . . (Lord Templeman)

Are women undergoing IVF treatment fully informed of the risks? Are they fully informed of the nature of the treatment and its possible — or probable — outcome? Similarly, are women in IVF programmes in a position to question the risks, the nature of the treatment, its likely outcome, and the expertise or assumptions of those dispensing the treatment? Are they likely to ask?

Generally, women have been socialised into being submissive, particularly in authority situations. Women's passivity or meekness is often enforced by those with whom they conduct relationships. The evidence indicates it is very difficult for women to obtain information about IVF from those running IVF programmes. This is true even of women with an assertive disposition. Research shows that women and men are dealt with in a patronising way by the medical profession. For women, the problem is doubled in that not only are women patients, and therefore in the less powerful situation *vis-à-vis* the doctor, but women as women are in an unequal situation, exacerbated by the professional nature of the relationship and the fact that the medical practitioner will (mainly) be male. Although some women medical practitioners work in the new reproductive technologies, few do.

In her study of women on IVF programmes, Burton found:

> The majority of women interviewed felt that not enough information was given to them about their treatment, that IVF teams did not have the time necessary to talk to their patients and explain what was happening. Most of the women felt unable to ask questions as they saw the staff as being too busy. They were reluctant to jeopardise their treatment by being seen as 'making waves' or 'being pushy'.[13]

She cites one woman as saying:

> I'd like the doctors to participate more, they just pick up the eggs and put them back. The rest of the time you never see them. It's rush, rush

all the time. You don't like to ask questions. Even when they inform you, you don't take it all in. You don't like to phone them and make a nuisance.

Even if women did ask questions, telephone, 'make a nuisance' of themselves, would they obtain correct and full information? If success of the treatment is measured in accordance with likelihood of conceiving and bearing a child, then the answer would be 'rarely', if ever. Of the 'success rate' in the United States, Gena Corea writes:

> I became interested in the issue of IVF success rates in June 1983 when visiting a newly opened IVF clinic in New Jersey. I sat with a young woman going through the program as she had one of her many hormone shots and, days later, waited in the hall for one of her many ultrasound examinations. The woman . . . explained to me that she had about a 20 per cent chance of success. Her statement shocked me because, in fact, her chances were much closer to zero.
>
> While the most established and successful IVF clinics in the world were reporting success rates of 20 per cent (and that rate is only as high as 20 per cent because of the tricky way clinics tend to define what constitutes 'success'), a brand new clinic with no experience could not reasonably claim to have the same rate. If its experience was anything like that of other clinics, it would produce *no* IVF babies in its first year. (In fact it was in June 1985, exactly two years after . . . that this clinic announced its first expected IVF birth.)[14]

In the subsequent study of IVF success rates, conducted by Corea and Susan Ince, the probability of having a baby on the programme was between five and seven per cent. In the survey, they inserted one definition of success which they had not noted being used by any clinic. It was 'percentage of live births per laparoscopy'. A respondent, Dr. James Homan, former head of the IVF programme at Duke University in North Carolina, wrote that this was actually the most important criterion of success, but no clinics use it. He explained:

> Realistically, when you first get started, [IVF] is very difficult. Many clinics go for 20, 30 and more attempts before they even have a pregnancy of any sort. In fact the Jones [a wife and husband medical team who established the first US IVF clinic] went for 60 attempts before they had their first pregnancy. Any kind of positive feed-back you get for yourself, for the morale of the team, and also positive feedback for patients who are interested in it, is a big plus. So when you first start getting pregnancies of any sort, that's what you report.

As Gena Corea concludes, the success rate, whilst giving women a deceptively positive picture of their chances of an IVF baby, 'is serving the purpose of keeping up the spirits of physicians who are, by and large, failing at IVF'.

Although the 'success rate' in Australian programmes appears to be higher than in the United States (calculated by Carl Wood of the Queen Victoria–Monash University programme at 15–25 per cent) it is doubtful that women on the programmes are properly informed of the likelihood that they will not emerge with an 'IVF baby'. Burton's research affirms this, as does the research conducted by Christine Crowe.[15] Burton found that women did not receive full information about other aspects of IVF, also:

> Most of the women had suggestions as to how IVF treatment could be improved. One major perceived need was the provision of information prior to treatment so that women entered the treatment cycle with realistic expectations. One said: 'I think people come on to the programme thinking it's going to be a bed of roses. I think they're in for a terrible shock. I think people need to be warned it's a hard thing, it's not going to be an easy trail. If you're made aware how tough it's going to be, it's only going to get easier.'

Other aspects of the informed consent debate in relation to the new reproductive technologies cannot be ignored. Of informed consent generally, Erica Bates and Helen Lapsley in *The Health Machine* state:

> The debate about informed consent is directly related to increased technology. It is generally thought that people have a right to understand what is being done to them, and should agree to it: but how much can the average person really understand about a very complicated treatment? How can a patient choose between several alternative treatments when doctors themselves do not agree, or know the possible consequences of each treatment? Will patients be able to sue doctors, hospitals and manufacturers if the results of the technology are not satisfactory or indeed are damaging?[16]

Yet the problem does not relate only to debates between varying types of technology, their value or otherwise. The problem lies in that 'choices' may be made in absence of information about all or some alternatives, particularly alternatives which do not involve the same level of 'high tech', with its consequent glamour and attraction for research grants and expertise. Many of the problems now confronting women in terms of infertility were in fact developed out of the high tech 'solution' to contraceptive needs. Corea draws parallels between the 'sale' of contraceptive measures such as DES and the Dalkon Shield, and the current 'high sell' of new reproductive technologies:

> . . . the IVF life cycle shows much in common with the IUD life cycle: selling the technology as 'new hope for the infertile', a wonder technology that will help women achieve pregnancy; basing the sales pitch on deceptive success rates and on data interpreted to put IVF in the best possible light; using the technology on women without having adequately tested it beforehand. IVF researchers did not verify the safety of IVF in primates before attempting it on women.[17]

She cites federal ethics board hearings on IVF in 1979:

> Experts appearing before the Board agreed that there has been insufficient controlled animal research designed to determine the long-range effects of IVF and embryo transfer. The lack of primate work is particularly noteworthy in view of the opportunity provided by primate models for assessing subtle neurological, cognitive and developmental effects on such procedures.

The validity of consent must also be seen in its social, political and economic context. We live in a world which predicates women's very humanness upon the products of her womb. Those women who choose not to bear children run a strong risk of being classified 'abnormal': the theme is that most women are mothers; women (generally) have a biological capacity to reproduce; therefore all women *should be* mothers. Women without children may be greeted with sympathy or with horror, or with simple assertions that they cannot 'know' what it feels like to 'really be a woman' until they have borne children. Strong assumptions exist that 'true' mothering is connected with giving birth. Adoptive parents may be placed in a 'special category', with comments like 'they're not her/his *real* parents'; 'but it's not really so important that his father's dying — after all, it's not his *real* father'; 'she's not her *daughter*, you know, she was adopted . . .'. For many women who are infertile, that infertility is part of their identity as women; unable to produce offspring biologically, their perception, influenced by the dominant ethos, may be that they simply are 'not women'.

Doctors and others running or involved with IVF and other new reproductive technology programmes may protest that women *choose* to go on the programmes; that they *beg* for a place and are devastated at not being able to be placed immediately at the 'top of the list'. Yet patients have defined themselves 'patients' in the past and clamoured for operations which today would generally be recognised as unethical and unacceptable. These were based upon a concept of femininity which is not now so common or if it is, other means of social control have been discovered which are less blatant. Thus in the nineteenth century, as Barker-Benfield[18] reports, women were said to 'beg' surgeons to remove their clitorises, or womb and ovaries, on the basis that these organs were interfering with 'proper' conduct becoming to a woman. In 1904 one doctor noted 'the power of social beliefs in spreading these operations'. Female patients "were fully convinced that directly or indirectly, all their grief emanates from the pelvis, and oftentimes this idea is fostered and materially augmented by their friends".' But friends alone do not foster the 'wanting'. Medical 'fashions' do.

And what of women being defined by doctors as 'wanting' particular treatment, when it is the doctors who define the 'wanting'? Deborah Larned describes the approach taken in some United States' hospitals to a particular form of female 'treatment', hysterectomy:

> Dr Bernard Rosenfeld, a Californian physician who is currently studying sterilization practices in the United States, describes one doctor's tactic . . .
> 'I remember treating a young black woman with several children who was having trouble with her IUD. She was interested in trying another type of device and was referred to the family planning clinic of the hospital to have her present IUD removed. About two weeks later I accidentally ran into her at the hospital. She looked upset and I asked her why. She said, "They just told me I needed a hysterectomy." I knew from having examined her that she did not *need* a hysterectomy, so I went and looked up her file. On her medical chart the doctor had recorded, "Patient *requests* hysterectomy".'[19]

This approach is not isolated. Larned comments:

> Black women have long been aware of this kind of medical practice. In the old days it was called a 'Mississippi appendectomy'. You'd go into the hospital to have a baby and come out minus your uterus. Now doctors are more subtle, but the results are the same. When the doctor decides you've had too many children, he tells you that you 'need' a hysterectomy and then writes down that you 'asked' for it.

Women may go down in their medical records as 'asking' for tranquillisers where they attend a practitioner seeking help for bashing, beating and abusing by their husbands: the most common 'treatment' appears to be doling out the librium, valium or other analgesics.[20] But this does not mean women's approach to the problem is so simplistic; rather, it means that doctors see tranquillisers as a 'solution' to the problem of 'whining women' turning up in their surgeries. Women may be registered as 'begging' for hormonal treatment to ward off old age, or to take themselves through menopausally induced minor hot flushes and other irritants. But this does not mean that women make a free choice about this form of treatment.

The choices medical practitioners make about 'good' and 'bad' treatment, or 'appropriate' and 'inappropriate' treatment for all manner of ills, including infertility, have a direct relationship with the treatment 'sought' by their patients. A patient attending a doctor who specialises in preventive medicine will receive different treatment from a patient attending a doctor believing in, and practising, the 'high tech' solution. Patients may deliberately seek out a doctor renowned as 'preventative' or publicised as high tech. But many patients chance upon a particular medico and adopt the medico's approach to illness and well-being. If the high tech solution receives publicity, patients may not be aware that other treatment options exist.

With IVF, Christine Crowe in the *Australian Left Review*[21] points out that participation in the programmes requires certain prerequisites — an adherence to the dominant ideology of motherhood; a focus on fertility; the dynamics of medical science; and the maintenance of male power relations over women. In her view, the new reproductive technologies are socially shaped and designed to contain and maintain specific social values. She writes:

> 'Choice' is always mediated by social circumstances. In a situation where women experience personal condemnation and social stigma because of their infertility and in which the social definition of motherhood necessitates a biological relationship the question must be asked what *real* 'choices' do infertile women have? To participate in an IVF procedure, with its low 'success' rate, or to remain without children, with all its negative implications, seems to represent very little choice.

Where technology is male owned and administered, and legal concepts are male defined, what validity can 'choice' or 'informed consent' have where women are the 'actors'?

The women interviewed by Christine Crowe regarded motherhood as 'an integral part of marriage' and essential for maintenance of social relations and standards. Most rejected the idea of adoption due to long waiting lists, their own age, and partner disapproval. The male spouses often expressed the view that they would rather have no children if they could not produce a biological child. On the other hand the female spouses regarded social motherhood as more important than the transfer of genetic traits consistent with biological motherhood. This indicates the entry of women into IVF programmes can be a result of male coercion in many forms — for example, possible rejection by the husband; his necessity to produce biological children; the husband's rejection of adoption as an alternative; and the woman's own sense of being, seen in terms of 'wife' and biological motherhood. These factors reflect the patriarchal strategies of domination and exploitation of women, backed by a legal system which defines 'consent' with no regard to power relations between men and women.

The social pressures from spouses and external sources cause women to enter IVF programmes and to suffer the pain, risks and indignities of the procedures, likely 'failure' and possible marital breakup anyway. All suffer from some form of anxiety and depression, as the programme invades every aspect of their lives. As Crowe reports:

> Once a women has decided to undergo an IVF procedure, participation in the programme seems to have a momentum of its own. For various reasons women found it very difficult to 'give up' the programme. Those who initially set a time limit to how long they would participate, or how many attempts they would have, found it very difficult to adhere to their initial resolve.

Having lost control over her body and been socialised into accepting the dictates of the programme, little wonder that women remain to 'consent' to further treatments. Their very being depends on it. The woman must produce to satisfy male ego — her husband's, the scientists', and that of the medical man. And if anything 'goes wrong', the patriarchal legal model is there to absolve the doctors from responsibility, on the basis that the woman was a fully, freely consenting party to the treatment meted out. This is in spite of the truth that these programmes remain experimental. In common with the technology which has been used on women's bodies in the past (also with their 'full, free consent') we will have to wait to see the full extent of the damage rendered, both to the women, and to the children whom they bear.

New reproductive technology laws

On 10 August 1981 *The Age* editorialised about the failure of the law to keep pace with events surrounding the development of the new reproductive technologies:

> Like the hare and the tortoise, science and the law run a permanently unequal race. While science moves in dazzling leaps and pirouettes, weaving wonder and miracles, the law plods sedately behind and collects the dust. It is sometimes a very long plod.

Those human beings and human bodies caught up in science's 'dazzling leaps and pirouettes', 'wonder' and 'miracles' might have a different assessment now, or in the future. The daughters of women who were given DES 'on cue' by doctors are a case in point.[22] Those doctors were trained into believing that what the drug companies told them of the miraculous nature of that drug (and any other) was true. The place of the law and attempts at regulating the new reproductive technologies are instructive in themselves.

In 1977 the Australian Law Reform Commission recommended to the federal government that it should be given a reference on questions relating to the new reproductive technologies. This call was ignored, and state governments began legislating. In the late 1970s moves were made to introduce uniform legislation to cover the status of children born through AID. The Standing Committee of Attorneys-General agreed to introduce laws based on a model Bill. It was not until 1982 that advisory committees or similar bodies were established to look at broader questions. In March and May 1982 committees were set up in New South Wales and Victoria, with Queensland, Western Australia and South Australia following in 1983, and Tasmania in 1984. In July 1982 in England the Warnock Committee of Inquiry into Human Fertilisation and Embryos was established to examine the social, ethical and legal implications of recent and potential developments in the field of human 'assisted reproduction'.

Europe was more swiftly off the mark. In March 1970 the Council of Europe published *Draft Recommendations on Artificial Insemination of Human Beings*. This followed approval in 1969 of a 'model code' of laws relating to transplantation of human tissues and organs, excluding gametes. The model code has not yet, however, been approved by all the 20 members of the Council. Those few member states with legislation on the issue deal solely with questions of status of children, or affiliation — that is, with paternity.

In the United States, in 1973, the National Conference of Commissions on Uniform State Laws approved, with recommendations for adoption by all states, the *Uniform Parentage Act*. This also has the approval of the American Bar Association. In the late 1970s the federal Department of Health, Education and Welfare (HEW, as it then was) by administrative restrictions placed a moratorium on IVF processes and the funding of IVF projects through federal government sources. The Ethical Advisory Board later reported that it was acceptable for HEW to support or conduct research, under certain conditions, into IVF and embryo transfer (ET). However there has effectively been a continuation of this moratorium although this does not affect experimentation and programmes where private funds are used. About 13 states have adopted the uniform parentage legislation, although moves relating to aspects of artificial reproductive technologies apart from AID are not yet in train.

In other developments, France established the Centre d'Etude et de Conservation du Sperme Humain (CECOS), which controls 14 or 15 AID clinics in that country. Donors are restricted to married men with at least one healthy child, and a wife who consents to his participation; payment is not allowed. The theory behind the consent requirement is that a couple, not a man alone, has donated sperm to an infertile couple so that they may produce a child by AID. In 1984 Sweden passed comprehensive legislation dealing with artificial insemination, coming into effect on 1 March 1985. The legislation provides:

- the prospective parents' psychosocial circumstances and medical suitability must be examined
- AID is to be performed only at public hospitals under supervision of medical practitioners with specialist qualifications in gynaecology and obstetrics
- the husband is deemed to be the child's legal father where he has consented to insemination of his wife
- an oath is taken that the best interests of the child are to be safeguarded
- as adults, AID children will have a right of access to identifying information about the sperm donor which is not available to the child's parents or to any third party

The purposive provisions of the Swedish legislation emphasise that parental honesty is important and frankness toward the child is stressed: the idea that the child should be told by the parents of her or his origins is seen as vital.

The legislation which has been passed, apart from the *Infertility (Medical Procedures) Act* 1984 (Victoria) and the *Surrogacy*

Arrangements Act 1985 (United Kingdom) (both covering surrogacy and experimentation with embryos, amongst other matters), universally deals with questions of paternity: who is the legal father of a child created through artificial conception? The legislation in the various jurisdictions takes one of two approaches. The first approach, adopted, for example, in the *Family Law Act* 1975 and *Marriage Act* 1961 at federal level in Australia, in the United States under the *Uniform Parentage Act*, and in the *Status of Children Acts* in New South Wales and Victoria, is to deem the child born by AID or *in vitro* fertilisation the child of the husband of the woman who so conceives, so long as the husband has consented. (Alternatively the husband is deemed to be the father of the child.) The second approach is that taken in Tasmania under the *Status of Children Act* 1974, where in section 10 C(1) it is provided that for legal purposes the social father of a child created by artificial conception shall be 'treated as if he were the father' of that child. The Tasmanian legislation recognises the reality: that there is in fact a social father of the child and a biological father of the child (the person donating the sperm). The former jurisdictions introduce artificiality at an additional level, by 'deeming' the social father to be the natural or biological father. The federal legislation and Tasmanian legislation differ from that of the other jurisdictions, however, in that they date the social father's paternity from birth, rather than from conception. Thus, if parties gained a divorce prior to birth of a child conceived by artificial conception, the husband would have no rights to custody or access upon birth of the child. The *Family Law Act* provides that any child 'born . . . as a result of the carrying out . . . of a medical procedure [artificial insemination or the implantation of an embryo] . . . is deemed to be a child [of the husband] . . . of the marriage . . .' The vital word is 'born', not 'conceived'.

In terms of the flurry of legislative activity, rather late in the day considering the estimated thousands of children being produced as a result of artificial insemination by donor in the 1970s, the argument has generally been made that it is to the benefit of the children that their legal status should be clarified. Who is the father of the child? was the question asked. This was translated in the popular mind to 'who will be responsible for the child?' or 'to whose name does the child have a right?' In New South Wales the *Artificial Conception Act* 1984 provides:

Where a married woman, in accordance with the consent of her husband, has undergone a fertilisation procedure as a result of which she has become pregnant, the husband shall be presumed, for all purposes, to have caused the pregnancy and to be the father of any child born as a result of the pregnancy: s.5

Where a woman becomes pregnant by means of —
(a)   artificial insemination; or
(b)   the procedure of implanting in her womb an ovum (whether or not produced by her) fertilised outside her body,
any man (not being, in the case of a married woman, her husband) who produced semen used for the artificial insemination or the procedure shall, for all purposes, be presumed not to have caused the pregnancy and not to be the father of any child born as a result of the pregnancy: s.6.

Thus the legislation was designed not only to answer the question 'who is the father?' but also 'who *is not* the father?' The man providing the sperm as a result of which the child is born is irrefutably presumed not to be the father of the child. No argument can be made in law that he is in any way paternally responsible for the child's well-being, upkeep or any other aspect of its existence.

Although the accepted philosophical outlook is that the legislation was passed to benefit children born from artificial conception, there is another way, more pertinent in the social and economic circumstances, of looking at these new laws. Rather than being concerned about who is responsible for the child's well-being, the laws could be interpreted as ensuring that particular persons — namely, sperm donors — are *not* responsible. For this is the one assurance the legislation gives. The laws conclusively state that sperm donors have no responsibility: no one, mother or child or state, can bring an action against a sperm donor for maintenance or paternity in relation to a child he has biologically fathered. Thus men who act as sperm donors have all means of perpetuating their biological immortality, but no responsibility for the products of their spermatozoic nepotism. Children have no rights of inheritance or of child support from them. Certainly in the past men were always in a position of being able to perpetuate themselves as often as they wished, so long as women with whom they had sexual intercourse did not avail themselves of contraception or abortion, or suffered 'accidents' in the application of contraception. But men engaging in extramarital sex, if they did harbour thoughts of populating with as many of their own kind as possible, always ran at least a theoretical risk of having paternity suits brought against them. They ran the risk of being financially responsible (at least in theory), for the products of their desire for biological immortality.

The laws give no such cast-iron assurance as to who *is* responsible financially and morally for the upkeep and care of children born by way of AID or IVF. Theoretically, the 'social father' is responsible. Yet how much is this theoretical assurance worth? These laws simply reiterate the position of a biological and social father, where a child is born by way of natural conception. A review of the responsibilities taken up, in practice, by natural fathers gives little confidence that those men deemed to be natural fathers of artificially conceived children, or stated to be responsible as social fathers of artificially conceived children, effectively will be held responsible for care or upkeep of those children.

Where maintenance provisions are sought to be put into effect by a custodial parent (in the main, mothers) against a non-custodial parent (in the main, fathers), the record shows the effort is more likely than not to fail. In Australia in 1984 the *Report of the National Maintenance Enquiry*, established by the federal Department of the Attorney-General, reported that the maintenance enforcement provisions of the *Family Law Act* and regulations 'are, from time to time, criticised for their apparent lack of effectiveness'. This could only be described as an understatement. Although there are many complaints about various aspects of the *Family Law Act* and its operations, and the operations of the Family Court of Australia, many researchers confirm that complaints are strongest with regard to lack of maintenance payments and ineffectiveness of enforcement procedures.

A mid-1980 survey of Victorian magistrates' courts in Prahran, Frankston, Ringwood, Preston, Moonee Ponds, Sunshine, Williamstown, Geelong, Bendigo, Hamilton, Mildura and Sale recorded payment performance of respondents to 1981 and 1982 maintenance orders. Of the 1982 orders, 41.5 per cent were currently being paid; 19.5 per cent were paid intermittently; 39 per cent were not paid at all. Of the 1982 orders, 51 per cent were being paid; 10 per cent were paid intermittently; 39 per cent were not paid at all.[23] In Western Australia, where it is often said enforcement procedures are superior to those in other states (apart from South Australia) because a state mechanism exists for enforcement, figures convey little real joy. Thelma Bessell-Browne surveyed divorcing couples who obtained a *decree nisi* for divorce in March 1979. Of a total of 229, some 75 per cent had 'arranged some form of maintenance' at the time of divorce. What 'form' it took is apparent in that 73 per cent of orders obtained did not affect eligibility to social security: obviously, reasonable amounts of maintenance were not ordered! Some twelve months after the orders were made, 41.2 per cent of those with orders were receiving moneys through the office of the collector of maintenance. The *Report of the National Maintenance Enquiry* concludes that 'no doubt a further number would have been receiving partial payments' — though how often, and how much, is not speculated upon. Evidence available from other studies would support the view that it would not be often, and not be much. In 63.7 per cent of cases where there was evidence of default of payment of an order, court action by way of enforcement resulted. Examination of 16 of these cases showed:

> ... of the 16, 25 per cent had a 'good' incidence of success of enforcement action, 50 per cent had a 'fair' incidence of success and 25 per cent had little success.

So what price provisions deeming 'social fathers' of artificially conceived children responsible for those children?

Does the legislation give any assurance that men will act responsibly as parents during the course of the marriage, and ongoing fatherhood? Studies of fatherhood say otherwise. Where naturally conceived children are in question, there is little evidence that fathers play a participatory role in child care and child rearing. In *The Changing Role of Fathers?* Graham Russell found there are four different types of fathers:

- the *uninterested and unavailable father*, rarely at home and, when there, spending little time with the children
- the *traditional father*, with a strong but nevertheless traditional commitment to the family, taking little responsibility for day-to-day care of the children but being available and playing with the children regularly
- the *good father*, more involved than traditional fathers, it being more common to perform basic child care tasks such as bathing, feeding, and changing nappies; classified 'good' through being willing to help mothers, but not having equal status with mothers
- the *non-traditional, highly participant father*, from shared care-giving families, carrying out 46 per cent of child care tasks each week, considerably more than the average for fathers in traditional families, which was nine per cent in Russell's study

In 'traditional families', Russell found all mothers were primary caregivers or primary caretakers, spending an average of 40 hours each week as the *sole* caregiver. Traditional fathers spend 'an average of only one hour each week as the primary caregivers for their children'. In those families classified as 'shared-caregiving', distribution of responsibilities was in the order of fathers spending an average of 26 hours as primary caregivers, with mothers spending an average of 16 hours each week in this way. However, Russell says:

> On current standards, the fathers in shared care-giving families were highly participant indeed. Nevertheless, on average they were not as highly participant as their own spouses and were significantly less participant than mothers in traditional families. There was little evidence of role reversal: of fathers taking on the same roles as traditional mothers, and mothers taking on the roles of traditional fathers. Many mothers and fathers in shared care-giving families also agreed that mothers were still more likely to take overall responsibility for the children, even though fathers contributed nearly as much to their day-to-day care.[24]

Further, Russell found that those men who take on the participatory role do so for a limited period of time. His study showed men playing this role whilst on leave from university or for some similar reason and reverting to the traditional or more traditional role upon conclusion of 'time out'.

Status of children legislation passed to cover the case of artificially conceived children might give an appearance of care and concern for the children, but the realities of patriarchal society contradict the facade. In a society where men have traditionally escaped responsibility for the products of their sexual activity, the passage of laws relating to AID and IVF children assists the sperm-givers to escape conclusively, and the 'social fathers' to take the option of living up to responsibilities — which in current Family Court terms in the realm of $15, $25 or $30-$40 per week maintenance for each child. And Australia is not alone in this. In the United States it has been found that child maintenance orders generally cease being paid, where any payment at all is made, within three years of the date of the original order.[25] Similarly in the United Kingdom low maintenance orders and difficulty of enforcement is recognised as a continuing problem located in the real world, however egalitarian and responsible legislation might appear at face value.

Legislation also emphasises the need for the male partner of the marriage to consent to the procedure being carried out on his wife.

If his consent is not obtained, then he is not deemed to be the father of the child, nor legally responsible for that child. This again places the option in the hands of the male partner. If he chooses to take up the option, he is in a position to enforce legal rights to custody and/or access to the child. If he reneges on his responsibilities, the woman is left with the burden of being financially responsible, without a practical means of ensuring the father plays a financially responsible role. Men's bargaining position at the end of a failed marriage may be increased by the existence of children. Many women who have children conceived by natural means testify to threats on the part of fathers and husbands that unless the woman agrees to a particular property settlement, the man will take action for custody. Access actions are sometimes used by men to gain leverage in property disputes. Julia Brophy, commenting upon the situation in the United Kingdom with regard to custody generally, points out:

> ... campaigns and trends ... are likely to have a significant effect upon an increasing number of mothers who will have to fight for the custody of their children. Perhaps the most significant area of impact will be experienced at the level of pre-court practices (sometimes referred to as bilateral bargaining). Here, for example, it is probable that the impact of the father's rights campaigns will be experienced at the level of the relative bargaining powers of the men and women involved in proceedings ...
>
> What this means in effect is that on divorce, husbands and wives negotiate over issues of housing, money and children against a backdrop of what may happen if they ultimately cannot agree and they make an application to the court for a decision on the areas of dispute ...
>
> While the legal system itself does not sanction trade-offs between money and children, nevertheless the negotiating process does provide opportunities for parties to link money and custody ... Hence, men's bargaining powers on many questions (financial resources, property, maintenance) have ultimately been increased — and this has been achieved whatever the reality of responsibility for childcare within a marriage.[26]

As Brophy says, this increase in men's bargaining power has also been achieved 'without any necessary transformation in the sexual division of labour within the domestic economy . . .'

Finally, new reproductive technologies have given rise to a perceived need to clarify, in law, the meaning of 'motherhood'. Biological motherhood has never been in question in the past. The woman giving birth to a child prior to the introduction of new reproductive technologies was the woman whose ovum created that child. Biological fatherhood, on the other hand, has always been in question. A man has never had complete assurance that the child he calls 'son' or 'daughter' has in fact developed from an ovum fertilised by his sperm. The common law developed to provide that a naturally conceived child born during marriage would automatically be assumed to be the child of the husband of that marriage, unless otherwise proved. For inheritance purposes, the common law rule was adopted that a child born up to a certain time after the death of the husband of the other (and the time could extend beyond nine months) would be, unless otherwise proved, considered to be the child of that man. Due to biological reality, no rules of any similar nature had to be devised to cover motherhood.

With the introduction of *in vitro* fertilisation and other procedures where an ovum from one woman can be introduced into the uterus of another, there to develop into a child to which the latter ultimately gives birth, the law has seen a need to clarify who is the 'mother'. Thus, under the *Status of Children Act* 1974, by way of amendment in 1984, in Victoria it is provided:

> Where a married woman, in accordance with the consent of her husband, has undergone a procedure as a result of which she has become pregnant —
> (a)   the married woman shall be presumed, for all purposes, to have become pregnant as a result of the fertilization of an ovum produced by her and to be the mother of any child born as a result of the pregnancy;
> (b)   the woman who produced the ovum from which the embryo used in the procedure was derived shall be presumed, for all purposes, not to be the mother of any child born as a result of the pregnancy . . .

A need for such a provision was seen to exist, in that there were conflicting views about who would be the 'mother' in such circumstances. In Victoria, the Waller Committee *Report on Donor Gametes* concluded, without supporting argument, that 'the mother of a child born as a result of the use of donor ova is the donor of the ova'. The *Report by the Senate Standing Committee on Constitutional and Legal Affairs on National Uniformity in Laws Relating to the Status of Children Born through the use of In Vitro Fertilisation* in 1985 stated:

> Commentators are divided on whom the common law would regard as the mother where the child was born as a result of IVF using donor

ova. Some regard it as an open question. It can be argued that courts would rely on the primary dictionary meaning of 'mother' and regard the woman who gave birth as the mother. On the other hand [it could be said] that 'the mother of a child born as a result of the use of donor ova is the donor of the ova'. It might be argued that, in choosing between the woman who supplied the genetic material and the woman who gave birth, the former has the greater role in the make-up of the child and therefore ought to be regarded as the legal mother.[27]

The Committee concluded that a court 'taking a less legalistic, more policy-oriented, approach' would hold that the woman giving birth, not the woman donating the ovum, was the mother:

> To hold otherwise would establish legal links to a person (the donor) with whom the child would not normally be expected to come into contact and whose identity the child may not even be able to discover, if record-keeping procedures are such as to permit the preservation of anonymity.

Debates on this issue so far have been framed within the context of *married* women. (Single women, whether heterosexual or lesbian, are not within the 'legitimating' legislation.) The Victorian legislation talks of a *married* woman undergoing a new reproductive technology procedure *with consent of her husband* being deemed to be the mother of the child, whether or not the ovum involved was produced by her. For Australia generally, the Standing Committee of Attorneys-General and all the various state committees of enquiry into the use of donor ova in new reproductive technology programmes have accepted this approach and, as the Senate Standing Committee points out, have 'concluded that the appropriate policy is for the woman who gave birth to be the legal mother, *at least if she is a married woman* who has undergone IVF *with the consent of her husband* '. Thus what appears to be of concern is not simply 'who is the mother', but 'who is the mother of the child in relation to *a man*' — the husband/father! The aim is, apparently, to confirm parenthood in terms of *who is the father*, through the indirect means of declaring upon motherhood.

The laws and the committees have either little or no concern, when a 'generic mother' might be in the offing in addition to a 'birth mother', but there is no legal marriage and thus no man legally involved. This again confirms the view that laws are not truly concerned about the well-being of children produced on new reproductive technology programmes, but are, in reality, concerned about the *rights of fathers*. A man is perceived as having a right to a child born into his marriage, if he chooses to exercise this right. That right exists whether the sperm is produced by himself or not. Concomitant responsibilities, ostensibly provided for through the legislation, are theoretical only. As a matter of practice, it is father right without responsibility — just as in terms of natural conception, fathers have rights to *their* children, but can escape responsibility for their care and financial upkeep, should they choose to do so.

SURROGATE MOTHERHOOD

On 30 June 1985 the *Sunday Independent*, a newspaper published in Perth, Western Australia, reported that women who offer or 'rent' their wombs to become pregnant for childless couples 'are prostitutes', according to the Association of Relinquishing Mothers:

> 'Both prostitutes and surrogate mothers are exploited', said Mrs Shirley Moulds, co-ordinator of the association, this week.
>
> Mrs. Moulds' opinions were sparked by the *Sunday Independent*'s recent article describing a Melbourne couple's search for a surrogate mother in Western Australia.
>
> Likening surrogacy to the selling of livestock, she added: 'Their bodies are rented out for a price, and it's usually men who act as go-betweens. People who advertise for surrogate mothers have no thought, care or knowledge of the long term psychological damage that they may cause for some gullible woman who may act out of compassionate or financial reasons.'
>
> She said research on adoption showed that the child's natural mother continued to grieve for her lost child for the rest of her life. 'Pain intensifies over the years for 50 per cent of relinquishing mothers,' she said. 'Some have committed suicide.'

In Australia, various committees have recommended that surrogate motherhood should be banned or regulated — including the *Report to the Health Commission of South Australia* in 1984, the Demack Report in Queensland in 1984, and the Waller Committee Report in Victoria, also in that year. In the United Kingdom, the Warnock Committee Report, produced in June 1984 recommended regulation of surrogacy.

As a result of the reports, legislation has been passed in Victoria and the United Kingdom to cover the case. In the United States, it appears that no legislative action has yet been taken, as in Canada apparently. The United Kingdom legislation prohibits the recruitment of women as surrogate mothers, the negotiation of surrogacy arrangements by agencies acting on a commercial basis, and the advertising of or for surrogacy services. In Victoria, the *Infertility (Medical Procedures) Act* 1984 defines a surrogate mother as a woman:

> ... who has entered into, or enters into, a contract, agreement or arrangement with [another] person or ... persons, whether formal or informal, and whether or not for payment or reward, under which the woman agrees — .
> (a)   to become pregnant, or to seek or attempt to become pregnant, with the intention that a child born as the result of the pregnancy become and be treated, whether by adoption, agreement or otherwise, as the child of that other person or those other persons; or
> (b)   being pregnant, that a child born as the result of the pregnancy become and be treated, whether by adoption, agreement or otherwise, as the child of that other person or those other persons: s.30(1).

A punishment of 50 penalty units or two years imprisonment is provided for if a person contravenes the provision that a person shall not:

> (a)   publish, or cause to be published, a statement or an advertisement, notice or other document that —
>   (i)   is intended or likely to induce a person to agree to act as a surrogate mother;
>   (ii)   seeks or purports to seek a woman who is willing to agree to act as a surrogate mother; or
>   (iii)   states or implies that a woman is willing to agree to act as a surrogate mother;
> (b)   make, give or receive, or agree to make, give or receive, a payment or reward for or in consideration of the making of a contract, agreement or arrangement under which a woman agrees to act as a surrogate mother; or
> (c)   receive or agree to receive a payment or reward in consideration for acting, or agreeing to act, as a surrogate mother: s.30(2)

Section 30(3) provides that any contract or agreement under which a woman agrees with another person or other persons to act as a surrogate mother is void. That means that any contract or agreement purported to be made between parties for the 'supply' of a child in accordance with surrogate motherhood cannot be enforced through the courts whether there is any money or other financial reward involved or not.

When the Warnock Committee reported in England, the London *Times* of 21 September 1984 commented, under the heading 'Ultimate Values' upon surrogacy:

There is a real risk that surrogate motherhood arranged through organised agencies may be on the edge of rapid growth in Britain. Sympathy for the plight of childless couples might make the development seem tolerable. The practice is in some forms something that people can and will do whether it is legal or not and it would be wrong to punish or obstruct medical care to those directly involved. But as an organised transaction it should be discouraged, because of the insecurity of the child's position, because the hiring of sexual services of any kind is repugnant, and because the practice is likely to grow if people have a financial interest in promoting it. Even on an ostensibly non-profit basis, the sanction of respectability would be encouragement.

In Victoria, when the *Infertility (Medical Procedures) Act* 1984 was debated, one member of the Legislative Council, the Hon. Caroline J. Hogg referred to examples of surrogacy arrangements related in the *Bible*, namely the cases of Abraham and Sarah and Rachel and Jacob. She noted Rachel's comment to her husband Jacob: 'And she said, Behold my maid Bilah, go in unto her, and she shall bear upon my knees that I may also have children by her.' Hogg comments:

> I suppose it is no coincidence that the surrogate in each case was a slave, and that there are potential overtones of slavery in the idea of surrogacy . . . In mentioning slavery I am no doubt overstating the case, but there is a potential for it. It has been suggested by some women's groups that were surrogacy to be widely practised in the community, it might lead women of means, who found it inconvenient to sustain a pregnancy, to exploit the bodies of women who needed extra money or extra resources. That would be morally objectionable under any circumstances in this community and utterly unacceptable ethically.[28]

A different approach has been taken in Canada. In 1985 the Law Reform Commission of Ontario published a two volume report entitled *Human Artificial Reproduction and Related Matters*. Although the recommendation was made that surrogacy legislation should be enacted, it was not contemplated that surrogacy should be outlawed. On the contrary, the proposal was that surrogacy should be allowed in certain defined circumstances. The approval of the Provincial Court (Family Division) or the Unified Family Court should be obtained prior to any surrogate motherhood arrangement being entered into. All such arrangements should be in writing, the court approving the terms of the agreement 'to ensure that they adequately protect the child and the parties and are not inequitable or unconscionable'.[29] No payment should be made without prior approval of the court. Other matters which the Commission said should be legislated for include:

- the court should be required to assess the suitability of the prospective parents for participation in such an arrangement
- the prospective parents should be required to satisfy the court that there is a medical need that is not amenable to alleviation by other available means, including artificial conception technologies
- the courts should be required to be satisfied that the intended child will be provided with an adequate upbringing, factors being relevant including the marital status of the prospective parents, the stability of their union, and their individual stability
- surrogate mothers should have reached the age of majority at the date of application
- the court should be required to assess the suitability of the prospective surrogate mother
- in assessing a surrogate mother's suitability, the court should consider, among other factors, her physical and mental health, her marital and domestic circumstances, the opinion of her spouse or partner, if any, and the likely effects of her participation in a surrogate motherhood arrangement upon existing children under her care
- the surrogate mother should receive separate legal representation
- to minimise uncertainty concerning a child's parentage upon birth, the court should require that information relating to the blood type and other relevant biological characteristics of the surrogate mother, her husband or partner, if any, and the persons who produced the gametes involved should be placed before it prior to approval of the surrogate motherhood arrangement
- the appropriate children's aid society should have standing in the case
- anonymity of the prospective social parents and surrogate mother and confidentiality of court records pertaining to surrogate motherhood proceedings should be preserved; the application should be heard and determined in closed court, the court records should be sealed, and access to records granted only upon judicial approval for good reason.

The Ontario Commission considered that regulations should provide indisputably that a surrogacy arrangement, once entered into with the approval of the court, should be enforceable:

> A child born pursuant to an approved surrogate motherhood arrangement should be surrendered immediately upon birth to the social parents. Where a surrogate mother refuses to transfer the child, the court should order that the child be delivered to the social parents. In addition, where the court is satisfied that the surrogate mother intends to refuse to surrender the child upon birth, it should be empowered, prior to the birth of the child, to make an order for transfer of custody upon birth.

Legislation, or proposals for legislation, thus lie at two extremes: either complete prohibition of surrogate motherhood arrangements, whether for money or not; or allowance of such arrangements, with a possibility of reward being given in exchange for a child, so long as the legal system has complete control over the arrangement through the Family Court or another similar court. In the light of evidence now available about the psychological consequence of adoption, for both the relinquishing mothers and the children, it is questionable that any government body should contemplate setting up a government scheme for the provision of children through surrogacy. Simultaneously, in view of existing economic and social conditions under which women labour, it is instructive that governments should see banning of surrogate motherhood through laws as a viable option.

Although at first glance the Ontario Commission approach and that of the Victorian and United Kingdom governments might be seen as directly in opposition to each other, on further reflection they have disturbing similarities. They aim to take control over surrogacy arrangements — and monetary reward for any such arrangement — out of the hands of the women who might be involved. The parallel with prostitution, and the legislative response to prostitution, is dangerously obvious. With prostitution, governments generally outlaw the sale of sex for money. That is, women are prohibited from exchanging the sexual use of their bodies for monetary reward. Where prostitution is regulated, laws generally force women into working for brothel owners who control the prices charged and take a generous cut of the proceeds. Women working as prostitutes, whether within a system which prohibits solicitation for money, or regulates that solicitation, do not have control over the trading of their bodies for money. (In the 'non-regulated' system, *de facto* regulation takes place, with brothel owners or pimps policing their charges' income-earning capacities.)

With surrogacy arrangements (where the trade is prohibited), if there is a call for the service, women will be available but they will not have control over the rent of their wombs as incubators. Because the trade is illegal, control will be exercised by those with entrepreneurial skills who are able to buy off the regulators (or the enforcers of these regulations, the police). Where surrogacy is regulated, as suggested for Ontario, the courts have control over who will be allowed to receive money in exchange for womb-rent; the owner of the womb again loses control.

Why should any women be available to rent their wombs in this way? The parallel with prostitution again surfaces. Women have been socialised into an acceptance of their bodies as useful for two purposes; child-bearing and heterosexual activity. Prostitution and surrogate motherhood appeal to these roles. But beyond socialisation, women are economically driven into using their bodies in this way. Marriage and motherhood has been held out as a valid (indeed *the* valid) career option for women. Women have been trained to be dependent upon the economic viability of the husband's career in the world of paid work. In those trades and professions to which women have been given access, monetary rewards are at all times lower than the monetary rewards available to men in the same trades or professions, or in their (more lucrative) traditional trades and professions. Yet the irony is that within the areas of prostitution and surrogate motherhood, although these may appear to (some) women to be relatively highly rewarded in monetary terms, in fact the pay is not worth the effort. With prostitution, women run the risk of contracting venereal diseases from customers or, more often, being physically attacked.[30] Their activities are policed either by law enforcement agencies with state backing, or by 'private police' — their pimps, managers, madams (the latter who, in turn, are policed by the 'big boys'). With surrogate motherhood, policing is a natural part of the contract, whether the contract is legally approved and enforceable, or not.

If a woman wishes to enter into a surrogacy contract, she will be required to conform to standards laid down by the agency through which she secures the arrangement, or by the person or persons organising the arrangement privately. In the Ontario Law Reform Commission proposals, it is provided that legislation should state that the parties should be 'free' to include in the agreement terms of 'their choosing'; however, they should be required to consider, and to agree upon a resolution of, the following issues:

- health and life insurance protection for the prospective surrogate mother
- arrangements for the child should the intended social father
  or mother, or both, die before the birth of the child
- arrangements for the child should the intended social
  parents cease to live together as a couple
- circumstances regarding the particular manner in which
  immediate surrender of the child to the social parents is to
  be effected
- the right, if any, of the surrogate mother to obtain information respecting, or to have contact with, the child after
  surrender
- prenatal restrictions upon the surrogate mother's activities
  before and after conception, including dietary obligations
- conditions under which parental screening of the child may
  be justified or required, for example, by ultrasound,
  fetoscopy or amniocentesis.

If a woman enters into a surrogacy arrangement and fails to live up
to these requirements then she may well be left 'holding the baby'.
For example, she may continue to smoke in contravention of a stipu-
lated term of the agreement, or refuse to undergo prenatal screening
for personal reasons. If she is simply not in a position to undertake
the care of the child, and would not have chosen to bear it apart
from the surrogacy arrangement, she is in a dilemma and cannot
enforce the agreement. If a woman enters into a surrogacy contract
where such contracts are unenforceable (as under the Victorian
legislation) this does not entirely protect her if she decides to keep
the child. Although it has traditionally been the law that a woman
giving birth to a child when not living in any marital relationship
has custodial rights, current emphasis upon men's allegedly developing capacities in terms of non-traditional fathering could well
change this.

Although the courts would not enforce a surrogacy arrangement
under the Victorian law, a question arises beyond this, of what is in
the 'best interests of the child'. In marriage relationships, it has been
considered in England, as in other common law countries that:

> It is quite clear that detrimental factors such as a wife's behaviour in
> breaking the marriage or leaving home, her inability to provide suit-
> able accommodation for the children, her mental instability, inad-
> equate personality or her choice of cohabitee play a much larger part
> where the father gets custody.[31]

Now in *de facto* relationships men are more likely to be seen as having custodial rights over children born of that relationship. What of the case where a man (and his wife) enter into a contract with another woman to provide a child, which is produced of his sperm? It is not beyond the bounds of possibility that a court confronted with an action brought by the biological father for custody might decide that the surrogate mother wishing to retain the child cannot provide the most suitable homeground. The 'best interests of the child' might better be served by custody of the child being granted to the biological father: he, after all, is living in a traditional nuclear family situation, which courts in the United States, Canada, England, New Zealand, Australia . . . see as primarily the more satisfactory living arrangement for any child who is the subject of custody proceedings.

Indeed it was this sort of question which in fact confronted the English court in the celebrated *Baby Cotton case*. There, the mother had agreed to bear a child to an American couple, did so, and wished to hand the child over in exchange for 6,500 pounds Sterling. The courts intervened on the basis that the child's best interests had to be served. The issues were should the child be forced to remain with her biological mother, or be given to her biological father (and his wife), or be made a ward of the state? *The Guardian* reports:

> The court drama dragged on behind closed doors, and Kim [Cotton, the mother] had no idea what was happening, even when a social worker made her sign a paper renouncing all rights to the baby, without telling her if it would go to its father or into care. Finally, the judge gave the child to the father, and by the time Kim read about it in the press, the baby had already been flown out of the country . . .
>
> The judge said he was assured the parents could and would tell [Baby Cotton] of her true origins . . . [32]

That the mother wanted to give up the baby in this case does not interfere with the basic premise: if the biological father wished effectively to enforce the surrogacy arrangement against the wishes of the mother, the way to attempt this would be by invoking the 'best interests of the child' argument. He would at least be given a hearing and might be successful. But a woman seeking to enforce such an arrangement would certainly not have a court support her right to any monetary gain, nor indeed to any maintenance payments in terms of the pregnancy and associated expenses. What she would get, no doubt, would be a stern lecture from the court, a penalty in terms of abrogating the law against surrogacy arrangements — and the child to the care of the state. [33]

GENETIC ENGINEERING

Committees and commissions have not generally taken up the challenge of genetic engineering and the law. As a rule, laws in the United States, Canada, Britain, Australia and New Zealand are taken to prohibit genetically orientated population control: that is, none of these legal systems would today (openly) tolerate the ending of lives of persons on the basis that they suffered from particular genetic defects. Nonetheless the attitude towards sterilisation of those classed mentally defective is not so clear: cases have been fought involving the right of propagation (or lack of it), where a state agency has contended that a young person should be sterilised on grounds that she is incapable of caring adequately for herself where sexual encounters are involved.[34]

Hospitals and doctors also effectively end the lives of some newborn children by not taking active steps to preserve life, where the fetus is born with severe handicaps or is too premature to ultimately live, in the assessment of the hospital or doctor.[35] This is not generally taken to be the application of eugenicist philosophies, however. Nonetheless, scientific exploration and experimentation has gone on, designed to fathom the genetic make-up of human beings. The discovery of the DNA molecule, developments of synthetically produced hormones, and synthetic and natural hormone treatment have led to various treatments to prevent or correct genetic defects or weaknesses in humans. Embryo experimentation has been both praised and condemned. Some scientists believe this experimentation could prevent the birth of any children suffering from genetically related diseases such as thalassemia or haemophilia. Others consider that the embryo has 'a right to life' which is immutable, and should be defended against all manner of intervention.

In 1971 the retiring president of the American Association for the Advancement of Science, Bentley Glass, stated:

> In a world where each pair must be limited, on the average, to two offspring and no more, the right that must become paramount is . . . the right of every child to be born with a sound physical and mental constitution, based on a sound genotype. No parents will in that future time have a right to burden society with a malformed or a mentally incompetent child.[36]

How do men such as Bentley Glass intend to enforce their authoritarian views? It has been suggested that the continuing development of prenatal screening can alert childbearers to defects in a fetus, thus providing the women with a choice to abort. In Bentley Glass' terms, there would be no choice: once alerted to a genetic defect, presumably the woman would be under a legal duty to terminate that pregnancy.

Ruth Hubbard comments upon the growing use of various types of fetal screening, including amniocentesis and the relatively new technique of *chorionic villi* sampling. With the latter, cells of fetal origin are taken out through the cervix of the pregnant woman in the eighth to tenth week of pregnancy, and examined for chromosomal and other genetic defects. Hubbard points out the advantages of such screening, but adds a warning:

> One of the reasons I am concerned about the widespread use of genetic screening is because it focuses our attention on our genes at a time when environmental hazards are on the increase and need much more attention than they are getting.[37]

Amniocentesis involves withdrawing a small amount of the amniotic fluid surrounding the fetus. This occurs during the sixteenth to twentieth week of pregnancy. Fetal cells are cultured over approximately four weeks. Using the technique, a variety of abnormalities can be detected, including Down's syndrome, sickle cell anaemia, thalassemia, Tay Sachs disease; and neural tube defects such as hydrocephalus and spina bifida.

Hubbard identifies other problems with the practice of routine screening:

> ... I worry about many of the other prenatal manipulations, including amniocentesis ... because usually at some point they involve the use of ultrasound ... It took twenty to thirty years before epidemiological studies linked prenatal X-ray examinations to the production of leukemias and cancers. No reason to think that the health effects of irradiation with ultrasound can be evaluated more quickly. There is no question that exposure to higher doses of ultrasound than are usually used for diagnostic purposes can damage chromosomes, cells and tissues. As with other forms of radiation, the question is whether there is a threshold dose below which there are no destructive effects. If there are risks, they clearly are long-term and they may be subtle. Is it really a progressive health measure to expose large numbers of healthy women and fetuses to unnecessary ultrasound examinations in the hope of detecting a relatively small number of problem pregnancies?

As Hubbard points out, because of family, personal or environmental health history of one or other or both partners, particular women may be concerned about the health of a fetus:

To some of them it may seem preferable, on balance, to undergo examinations by means of ultrasound and perhaps further tests, such as amniocentesis. Yet at present, ultrasound has become such a widely used tool in obstetrics that it is used as though it were known to be safe. Indeed, it forms the technical basis of the newly designated speciality of 'fetal medicine'.

But the number of people in this situation does not justify the universal use of prenatal testing which is now practised in younger and younger age groups. When amniocentesis for diagnosing Down's syndrome was first introduced, the test was restricted to women over the age of 40 years. Now, in the United States the age has dropped to 35 years, and younger women are more and more being advised to undergo such testing. In Australia, the age appears to have fallen from 40 years to 37 years. For a woman at 40 years, the chances of having a Down's syndrome child are one in 100; they are one in 350 at 35 years, and approximately one in 1000 for a woman aged 30 years.

Once a fetus has been detected as suffering from a particular problem, the option is to have it aborted. However, in the future it will be possible to 'correct' genetic defects by replacement of the defective gene. (Those working in the field are not inclined to estimate when.)[38] Beyond the correction of defects, however, it is also suggested that it will be possible to 'improve' 'ordinary' fetuses: that is, to make 'more perfect' a fetus' genetic make-up, change the colour of eyes, hair, make better other features. Legal implications arise in correction of genetic defects. They may equally arise in relation to 'bettering' a normal, everyday fetus or embryo.

Pre-natal testing and genetic defects

What is the legal situation, or what might it be, with fetal testing and the responsibility of a pregnant woman to undergo such testing? What is the legal position of a woman who persists with an 'unhealthy' lifestyle (smoking, drinking, drug-taking) during pregnancy, and who produces a child suffering from some genetic or other defect which is attributed to that lifestyle, or the refusal to abort a fetus which testing has shown to be genetically or otherwise defective?

In Australia, as in England and New Zealand, it is accepted in law that a child born with a handicap as a result of an injury before birth has an action in tort against the person causing the injury. For example, if the child is injured in the womb, where the pregnant woman is involved in a car accident, and as a result is born with a disability, that child can sue for damages the person who caused the accident.[39] Additionally in the United States the action for 'wrongful birth' has developed: the claim lies in the mother (or parents) that, as a result of some negligence on the part of the physician, genetic laboratory, or hospital a defective child is born. Alternatively, where a vasectomy, tubal ligation or other sterilisation operation has 'gone wrong' and a child has unexpectedly been born (whether healthy or not) parents may claim damages against the doctor responsible for the bungled operation. Damages contemplated include pain and suffering, emotional distress, cost of raising the child. The United States has generally gone further in recognising such claims, but other jurisdictions also may provide an avenue of action.

However, it is not generally considered there is any action available for 'wrongful life': a claim by a child to damages for being born with features conventionally labelled as 'defects' (although some lawyers and academics see this as an area which the courts will eventually come to accommodate). Thus, in *McKay and Another* v *Essex Area Health Authority*[40] a child was born disabled as a result of an infection of rubella suffered by her mother while the child was in her womb. The child and her mother argued that but for the negligence of the health authority and the medical practitioner, the mother would have had a legal abortion (under the *Abortion Act* 1967), and the child would not, therefore, have 'suffered entry into a life in which her injuries are highly debilitating, and distress, loss and damage'. The English Court of Appeal held that there was no claim in law:

> . . . because a doctor can lawfully by statute do to a fetus what he cannot lawfully do to a person who has been born, it does not follow that he is under a legal obligation to a fetus to do it and terminate its life, or that the fetus has a legal right to die . . . We have no exact information about the extent of this child's serious and highly debilitating congenital injuries — the judge was told that she was partly blind and deaf — but it is not and could not be suggested that the quality of her life is such that she is certainly better dead, or would herself wish that she had not been born or should now die . . .

The court said that to hold that the doctor or health authority were under a duty to end the child's life would 'make a further inroad on the sanctity of human life which would be contrary to public policy':

> It would mean regarding the life of a handicapped child as not only less valuable than the life of a normal child, but so much less valuable

that it was not worth preserving, and it would even mean that a doctor would be obliged to pay damages to a child infected with rubella before birth who was in fact born with some mercifully trivial abnormality. These are the consequences of the necessary basic assumption that a child has a right to be born whole or not at all, not to be born unless it can be born perfect or 'normal', whatever that may mean.

The court added that an objection to accepting such an action

must be the opening of the courts to claims by children born handicapped against their mothers for not having an abortion . . . [T]hat is . . . a graver objection than the extra burden on doctors already open to actions for negligent treatment of a fetus . . .

But what if the mother's own actions had caused the child to be born with a defect, as in *In re D* (where the mother was addicted to hard drugs and took them knowingly throughout the pregnancy),[41] or refused to take positive steps — say through submitting the fetus, whilst still *in utero*, to genetic engineering — to ensure the child was born free of some detected defect?

It is important that *McKay's case* related to a claim by the child that a right to be aborted exists in law — that is, to have her life brought to an end, as a fetus, so as not to have to come into the world damaged. If the argument was that if particular treatment had been undertaken whilst the child was *in utero*, and the child would not have been born with the handicaps, the conclusion might have been different. In the United States, the courts are more ready to accept the 'wrongful life' thesis. Robert H. Blank debates the issues, commenting that while the child's life is not 'wrongful', neither is it 'as it should be'. To reject an action for wrongful life shows adherence to a policy denying 'a clear case of meritorious cause of action . . . because of its ill-chosen label'.[42] To succeed, the child (or child's representative) would have to prove a duty of care on the part of the doctor or hospital, and a breach of that duty. Damage caused to the child must relate to the failure to exercise care:

What the infant plaintiff alleges is that the breach of duty led proximately to his birth — the maturing of the harm — and, thus, he is forced to endure life with defects which he would not be forced to do but for the defendant's breach of duty.[43]

Courts in the United States may be ready to accept an argument that the child has a right of action against the doctor, hospital and even the mother, where a defect should have been detected (and was not) and could have been corrected by genetic therapy or other treatment, or that the defect was detected but appropriate treatment by genetic therapy or other means was available, but was not applied.[44]

Indeed, it has been suggested that claims by siblings might be entertained, both in the United States and in England. (Probably the English situation would be more akin to that in Australia, although Australian courts are becoming more adventurous in accepting United States' decisions, at least in some areas of the law.) In *Cox* v *Stretton*[45] two older children laid a claim against a medical practitioner for failing to carry out a vasectomy operation sufficiently carefully, as a result of which a third child was born, unexpectedly, into their family. The children alleged they had been 'deprived, and in the future [would] be deprived, of a portion of the care, affection, training and financial support which each would have received except for the birth of their unplanned brother'. The claim was rejected on the basis that children under the law of New York, where the case was heard, have no valid action for loss of society and services; and also that while the children might 'expect future care and affection from parents there was no 'proportion' to which they were entitled, and while the law certainly forbids abuse and abandonment, it does not compel devotion'. Horton Rogers contends that siblings may nonetheless have a claim:

> [The latter] reason is not . . . a sufficient answer to a sibling claim, for the whole law of fatal accidents compensation (which, of course, extends in favour of children) proceeds upon the basis of reasonable expectations not legal entitlements.[46]

Rogers goes on to say that such claims should be rejected on the basis that 'the very assertion of [them] is offensive'.

Yet would it be 'offensive' (or whether offensive or not, legally unable to be entertained) if siblings complained that positive action had not been taken to correct the defect leading to the handicapped sibling being born? Where parents are concerned, damages may be obtained for failure of a duty of care on the part of a doctor who does a vasectomy operation badly, or does not warn the patient of the chances that the operation may not be 100 per cent effective, and as a result the party fathers another child. In *Thake* v *Maurice*[47] a husband and wife received damages for, amongst other matters, loss of the mother's wages from the date of birth of the child (as a result of a failed vasectomy operation), until the child reached school age. The court also said that although in assessing damages arising from the birth of a healthy child any sum in respect of the future 'trouble and care involved in the upbringing was to be set off against the joy occasioned by the birth', an award for normal ante-natal pain and suffering 'should not be extinguished by the happi-ness of post-natal events'. With the court extending rights of recovery of damages in this way, failure to take positive steps to ensure that a child is born without defects that might have been corrected by genetic engineering might open up avenues of 'redress' for other siblings, where care and attention has to be diverted to the new child. This would create 'special circumstances' beyond the normal distribution of time and attention effected between children in a family, which might have been averted if only the woman had submitted herself to advanced medicine.

Standards of professional care are not static. Where improve-ments in medicine have brought about higher standards of care the legal system adjusts to require higher standards to be applied. If it becomes the accepted norm of professional medical practice to advise a woman to undergo particular prenatal tests, then for a medical practitioner to fail to advise the woman and enable her to undergo the testing would appear to offend the 'reasonable pro-fessionalism' requirement. This concern is important to medical practitioners involved in intensive birth technology. Carl Wood in *Test Tube Conception* says that the number two priority for legal clarification of the 'test-tube baby programme' is: 'The right of a child to bring an action against a clinician who fails to detect fetal abnormality.'[48] The number one priority for Wood is 'the area of compensation for pre-conception and pre-birth injuries':

> The legal rights regarding compensation for a child born disabled as a result of the [IVF] procedure are not clear. And if compensation is to be made available, who should bear the burden of payment?

Plaintively he asks: 'If [the burden of payment is] placed upon [medical] teams, would medical initiatives in this area cease?'

If the practitioner advises of tests which can be taken to detect abnormalities, and makes available procedures to correct those abnormalities but the woman refuses to participate in the treat-ment, the practitioner could possibly absolve himself from any possible legal responsibility simply by making that treatment avail-able. In such a case, a woman must decide whether to submit to treatment which she may not, for reasons related to her own beliefs in her health rights or those of the child to be, wish to undergo. Veitch reports already that in Britain some physicians have urged that some tests be made mandatory at least once or twice during pregancy.[49] Robertson contends that woman's biological 'destiny' requires her to abide by certain conduct:

In terms of fetal rights, a fetus has no right to be conceived or, once conceived, to be carried to viability. But once the mother decides not to terminate the pregnancy, the viable fetus acquires rights to have the mother conduct her life in ways that will not injure it ... [a woman] is free not to conceive, and free also to abort after conception and before viability. But once she chooses to carry the child to term, she acquires obligations to assure its wellbeing. These obligations may require her to avoid work, recreation, and medical care choices that are hazardous to the fetus. They also obligate her to preserve her health for the fetus' sake or even allow established therapies to be performed on an affected fetus. Finally, they require that she undergo prenatal screening where there is reason that this screening may identify congenital defects correctable with available therapies.[50]

This appears to be just a more sophisticated version of the argument which was used against women in the battle for access to tertiary education: the medical profession of the nineteenth and early twentieth century argued that women and girls needed to conserve their energies for reproduction, whether they were pregnant at the time or not; this precluded them from using 'brain power' in intellectual work, and denied them the right to participate in energetic sporting activities. In the late twentieth century women are now told that we must live exemplary lives not for our own sake, but for the sake of our fetuses. The legal system moves toward a fetal rights position, by apparently granting women rights: a woman may have a right to abort a fetus, but if she chooses not to do so, then she assumes an obligation to the fetus' health and well-being which ensures that fetus' rights take precedence. The language of rights is thus a minefield for women: grown used to the denial of rights on the one hand; eager to show our responsible use of 'rights' if only we are granted them, on the other; women fall into the trap of seemingly gaining rights which bring in their wake responsibilities containing the seeds of rights of 'others' — potential children grown from the fetuses which, after all, we have freely exercised our choice not to abort.

Barbara Katz Rothman contends that the new technology of reproduction 'encourages and reinforces the commodification process'. Genetic counselling, she says, 'serves the function of quality control, and the wrongful life suits are a form of product liability litigation'[51]. The technology and possible mechanisms for dealing with its potential end results through the legal system individualise what are social, political and economic questions. The quick fix mentality assumes that 'fixing' a problem of handicap or disability involves 'repairing' or replacing the 'wrong' gene. Yet this avoids the problem of determining why genetic defects arise in the first place: would it be a better world if factories were allowed to continue to pollute the atmosphere with, say, radiation resulting in genetic abnormality in fetuses, if they paid taxes or made donations to develop gene therapy to correct those abnormalities? Would we want to support a legal system which saw as its aim the 'correcting' of genetic disabilities by providing for suits against doctors failing to utilise gene therapy, or facilitated damages claims by handicapped children against corporations which polluted the atmosphere resulting in genetic defects to the fetuses which later became those children with rights of action? Or would we prefer social responsibility to be lived out earlier, by eliminating the genetically damaging pollutants altogether?

Rothman concludes:

> Retardation and disability are social issues, threatening the stated values of our society: the values of equal opportunity and a fair share for everyone. We treat these social issues as individual troubles, to be individually solved. We treat them *clinically*, not *politically*. It fits in with the private property idea of children: the needs of *your* children are *your* problem.

With gene therapy, the argument collapses into 'the needs of your fetuses are your problem': you have a genetic problem, you seek gene therapy to correct that problem.

Gene therapy and the 'perfect' child

'Better' plants and 'better' animals are commonly developed through plant and animal husbandry. *New Scientist*, in 'Genewatch', a Bulletin of the Committee for Responsible Genetics, reports that agrichemical manufacturers and new biotechnology companies 'are enlisting the powers of bioengineering to enhance and broaden the use of herbicides in agriculture'. They are planning to give crops 'that may be damaged or killed by herbicides the genes that will make them resistant to the chemical's damaging side effects'.[52] The *New Scientist* of 13 March 1986 reported on the efforts of Richard Palmiter of the University of Washington and Ralph Brinster of the University of Pennsylvania who produced 'transgenic' mice. These mice were injected with a fusion gene, consisting of a promoter from a mouse bound to a rat or human gene for growth hormone. Producing the protein hormone at levels three times higher in the blood, these genes meant that the mice grew twice as large.

The history of reproductive technologies involving AID and *in vitro* fertilisation, embryo transfer and other techniques shows that developments amongst animals are eventually transposed into the human sphere of reproduction. There is no reason to believe that genetic engineering to make 'better' plants and 'better' animals will not be replicated with human embryos, to produce 'better' embryos, 'better' babies, 'better' human beings. Warnings about the need for caution are sounded at regular intervals. In 1967 Marshall Nirenberg, one of a number who pioneered the translation of the genetic code, raised the ethical context of genetic engineering:

> The point which deserves special emphasis is that man may be able to program his own cells with synthetic information long before he will be able to assess adequately the long-term consequences of such alterations, long before he will be able to formulate goals, and long before he can resolve the ethical and moral problems which will be raised. When man becomes capable of instructing his own cells, he must refrain from doing so until he has sufficient wisdom to use this knowledge for the benefit of mankind.[53]

But the ethical context is viewed in a limited perspective. It has in fact already been laid down in other fields of medicine and the legal response to them. In the field of plastic surgery, for example, a medical operation carried out on a body which is perfectly healthy is legal, although it involves extensive surgery. The legality is based upon the consent of the party upon whom the operation is carried out, and the necessity of the operation for the well-being of that patient. For example, women wishing to undergo augmentation mammoplasty give as their reason the fact that their breasts are 'too small', interfering with their psychological well-being. Women and men undergo drastic surgery to reduce fatty tissue or fatty deposits. Some plastic surgeons or other specialists accept them on the basis that without the treatment, their well-being will be severely affected due to stress and other psychological problems arising from being 'too fat', or overweight. Face lifts are carried out because the 'patients' are judged as being in psychological danger through looking their chronological age. Yet as Janice Raymond points out, such surgery 'which begins as a consequence of sex role stereotypes often becomes a cause of those very stereotypes or, at least, a contributing cause to their existence':

> ... many [people] go to great lengths to adapt to the culturally prescribed body type ... [undergoing] various forms of plastic surgery

for purposes of conforming to culturally-prescribed images of masculinity or femininity. A woman who feels that her breast size is inadequate and therefore undergoes augmentation mammoplasty is measuring both her prior inadequacy and her post-surgical adequacy by cultural standards which encourage women, in particular, to submit themselves to such intrusive surgery to conform to those measurements . . .[54]

It is therefore not difficult to foresee a time when genetic engineering will be acceptable as a means of manufacturing children who conform to the parents' views of the culturally desirable.

What role will the law play? As the law condones 'beautifying' operations, sometimes of a most intrusive, dangerous, and extreme kind, under the consent and well-being argument, there is no reason to believe that it will not condone operations undergone for the purpose of 'beautifying' the baby to be. Certainly it would be foolish to suggest that such operations will be readily available: face lifts, breast implants, bottom tucks and the like are not. Particularly where done by the 'best' surgeons, they can be expensive.[55] Yet some are available on the National Health in England or Medicare in Australia, and refunds at least in part are available.

Katz Rothman concludes that in the present value system, in the developing ideology:

> . . . we are learning to see our children as products, the products of conception. Even while they still move within us, they are not part of us — we have learned to see them as other, as separate, as products. We work hard, some of us, at making the perfect product, what one of the doctors in the childbirth movement calls a 'blue ribbon baby'. Modern adoption practices have long encouraged us to think of babies as commodities: they are, after all, available for purchase.[56]

In this atmosphere, the development of technologies which could allow parents the 'choice' of characteristics is likely to be seen as positive — or merely eccentric, just as those of us who do not feel any great desire to undergo removal of pouches under the eyes, or have chins nipped and tucked gaze with slightly cynical eye, should we bother to gaze at all, upon those harbouring that desire, and putting it into effect. And where the operation 'goes wrong', the legal system will be there to provide a cause of action, if it can be shown that the medical practitioner was negligent in surgical technique or failed to give the explanation required under informed consent provisions. Yet if 'informed consent' were made meaningful in terms of the social, political and economic conditions of the world in which it is sought, and an obligation were placed on members of the medical profession to talk through these issues with prospective patients, in conjunction with other efforts made to reorientate the world away from a commodity based, commodity biased centering, the law could be used constructively to phase out ideas of 'genetic perfection' through manipulation of genes.

CONCLUSION

The law has generally been seen as lumbering, and failing to facilitate 'great leaps forward' in science (or even to keep abreast of those 'great leaps'), particularly in reproductive technology and genetic engineering. However the reality is that the law has generally been used to smooth rather than hinder these developments, at least in recent times. Moves to prevent experimentation on embryos have not generally been supported by government committees and legislators. In the United Kingdom, the Warnock Committee recommended that such experimentation should be able to go ahead up to fourteen days in the life of an embryo. In Victoria, the Waller Committee recommended likewise. Although in Victoria the legislation as originally framed prevented embryo experimentation, in 1987 an amendment accommodated experimentation in certain circumstances. A governmentally appointed committee monitors the operation of the legislation, particularly in relation to experimentation, and it was this committee which recommended the change.[57] In the United States although federal funding is not now available, private funding goes ahead and science proceeds. In Australia, the National Health and Medical Research Council has prohibited funding to programmes where embryo transfer (ET) is carried out. Funding remains available for various new reproductive technology programmes and experimentation. Indeed, NHMRC funding is skewed toward new reproductive technology.[58] Private funding and commercialisation of the technologies goes on regardless.

Some attempt is made at an ethical stand in terms of monetary gain: generally legislation in Australia and England dealing with new reproductive technologies has recoiled from the idea that people should be allowed to sell their body parts — ova, sperm, embryos. (Although in the USA, the opposite appears to be so.) Under the *Infertility (Medical Procedures) Act* 1984 (Victoria) persons are allowed to be reimbursed for travel expenses only, where they donate sperm or ova to programmes. In parliamentary debates, this provided members with a reason for believing that the human body remains sacrosanct, and human reproduction is not tainted by filthy lucre. Yet in view of other moves on the new reproductive technology front, this seems painfully short sighted and somewhat naïve. Whilst the ordinary participant in the programmes, or donors to others, are prevented from profiting from sale of bits of their bodies, medicos involved in developing the technologies which would not be able to be developed, apart from the ready availability of bodies and parts for experimentation, make efforts to patent the embryo transfer process and other developing technologies. Companies and corporations are established to market the technologies overseas. Even where the technologies or genetic engineering 'go wrong', there will be new techniques, more scientific and medical entrepreneurs ready to apply new miracles of science to repair and improve — until the next round of technological ruin and repair.

Commercial laws, based firmly in the ethic of profit, facilitate this progress even more readily. In a capitalist market place, at least the labourer is deemed to have a right to a partial payment for his labour. In the new reproductive technology market place, the labourer pays for her participation — and the profits are all in the capitalist court.

Endnotes

1. Barbara Burton, "Contentious Issues of Infertility Therapy — A Consumer's View", Paper presented at Australian Federation of Family Planning Associations Conference, Lorne, Victoria, March 1985, p.4. (Unpublished, copy held by present author.) The following quotations come from the same source. See also Barbara Burton, "Counselling — My Needs as a Patient", Paper presented to the Fertility Society of Australia Annual Conference, December 1985, Melbourne, Victoria (unpublished, copy held by present author); Barbara Burton, "The Need for Reproductive Control and Self-Determination for Infertile Women", nd, Infertility Federation of Australia, (unpublished, copy held by present author).

2. Burton, 1985; Burton, 1985; Burton, nd; see also Naomi Pfeffer and Anne Woollett, *The Experience of Infertility*, 1983, Virago, London. The immediately following quotations come from Burton's papers.

3. There are varying degrees of difference between the positions taken by the court systems in the various countries, but the basic premise is accepted. See for example *Sidaway v. Bethlem Royal Hospital and Maudsley Hospital HA and Ors* [1984] 2 *Weekly Law Reports* 778;
   Chatterton v. Gerson [1981] *Queens Bench* 432;
   Reibl v. Hughes [1981] 114 *Dominion Law Reports* (3d) 1;
   Natanson v. Kline 350 *Pacific* 2d 1093 (Kan, 1960);
   F. v. R. (1983) *South Australian State Reports* 189;
   Canterbury v. Spence 464 *Federal* 2d 772 (DC Cir, 1972).
   For an overview, see J.K. Mason, "Informed Consent — Paper presented in Law Reform Commission, Victoria Symposia Series — Informed Consent", Symposium 9, 23 September 1986, Law Reform Commission, Victoria, Melbourne.

4. See generally *Attorney General's Reference (No.6 of 1980)* [1981] *Queens Bench* 715;
   R. v. Donovan [1934] 2 *Kings Bench* 488;
   I. Kennedy, "The Patient on the Clapham Omnibus", *Modern Law Review*, 1984, vol.47, p.454.

5. *Chatterton v. Gerson* (1980) 3 *Weekly Law Reports* 1003.

6. *Smith v. Auckland Hospital Board* (1964) *New Zealand Law Reports* 241.

7. *Bolam v. Friern Hospital Management Committee* [1957] 1 *Weekly Law Reports* 582.

8. *Sidaway v. Board of Governors of the Bethlem Royal Hospital and the Maudsley Hospital* [1985] 2 *Weekly Law Reports* 480.

9. *Natanson v. Kline* 354 *Pacific* 2d 670 (1960).

10. *Canterbury v. Spence* 464 *Federal* 2d 772 (1972).

11. *Cobbs v. Grant* 502 *Pacific* 2d 1 (1972).

12. *Sidaway v. Board of Governors of the Bethlem Royal Hospital and the Maudsley Hospital* [1985] 2 *Weekly Law Reports* 480. The immediately following quotations come from the same source.

13. Burton, 1985. The next immediately following quotation comes from the same source.

14. Gena Corea, "Determining Priorities in Health Resources: The Case of IVF", Paper presented to Law Reform Commission, Victoria, 1986 seminar on priorities in health funding, Reference on Medicine Science and the Law, Law Reform Commission, Melbourne, Victoria, Australia. The next immediately

following quotation comes from the same source. The Corea-Ince study is commented on therein.

15. See Christine Crowe, "Bearing the Consequences — Women Experiencing IVF", this volume;
    Burton, 1985. The next immediately following quotation comes from Burton, 1985.

16. Erica Bates and Helen Lapsley, *The Health Machine*, 1985, Penguin Books Australia Ltd, Ringwood, Victoria, p.25.

17. Corea, 1985. The next immediately following quotation comes from the same source.

18. J. Barker-Benfield, *The Horrors of the Half-Known Life: Male Attitudes Toward Women and Sexuality in C19th America*, 1976, Harper and Row, NY.

19. Deborah Larned, "The Epidemic in Unnecessary Hysterectomy" in *Seizing Our Bodies*, 1978, Claudia Dreifus, editor Vintage Books, NY, pp. 195-208. The next immediately following quotation comes from the same source.

20. Jocelynne A. Scutt, *Even in the Best of Homes — Violence in the Family*, 1983, Pelican Books Australia Ltd, Ringwood, Victoria.

21. Christine Crowe, "The Reproductive Fix", *Australian Left Review*, Autumn, 1985, pp.4–9. The next immediately following quotations come from the same source.

22. See Gena Corea, *The Hidden Malpractice*, 1980, Harper and Row, NY;
    "Wide Variety of Uterine defects Tied to DES Exposure", *Ob/Gyn News*, 15 March 1985, vol.20, no.6;
    "Pregnancy Outcomes in DES-Daughters", *Ob/Gyn News*, 15 December 1985, vol. 20, no. 1.

23. True it is that the government has produced a discussion paper on recovery of maintenance payments, proposing that this be done through the tax system, by an agency acting in concert with the Taxation Department at federal level. However, it is yet to be seen whether any scheme will be implemented. The proposals to date appear to be unnecessarily complex. See Jocelynne A. Scutt, 'Who is Right, Whose Responsibility? Assessment and Payment of Child Maintenance' (1987)vol. 9, no. 1 *Labor Forum* 1–5.

24. Graham Russell, *The Changing Role of Fathers?* 1985, 2nd edition, Queensland University Press, p. 199.

25. David Chambers of the University of Michigan Law School has conducted various surveys confirming this for the United States.

26. Julia Brophy, "Child Care and the Growth of Power" in *Women in Law — Explorations in Law, Family and Sexuality*, Julia Brophy and Carol Smart, editors, 1985, Routledge Kegan Paul, London, p. 110.

27. Senate Standing Committee on Constitutional and Legal Affairs, *Report on National Uniformity in Laws Relating to the Status of Children Born through the use of In Vitro Fertilisation*, 1985, AGPS, Canberra, ACT, p. 17.

28. The Hon. Caroline J. Hogg, M.L.C. (now Minister for Community Services, Victoria), *Hansard of the Legislative Council*, 11 October 1984, p. 754.

29. Law Reform Commission of Canada, *Report on Human Artificial Reproduction and Related Matters*, 1985, Law Reform Commission, Canada, Government Printer, Ontario, Canada.

30. Susan Maidment, 1981, p. 16.

31. Brophy, 1985, p. 102.

32. Polly Toynbee, "Guardian Women", *The Guardian*, 1 July 1985, p. 9.

33. The case in the USA where the child was born with a handicap which the surrogate mother claimed was not a result of any bad faith on her part. The

man arranging the surrogate contract on his and his wife's behalf alleged the surrogate mother had had sexual intercourse with her own husband. There, the implications were that the surrogate mother-to-be had not fulfilled her part of the bargain, and she was entirely responsible for the child resulting from the agreement, both in terms of its handicap and its future well-being. On the position in the USA generally, see

Avi Katz, "Surrogate Motherhood and the Baby-Selling Laws", *Columbia Journal of Law and Social Problems*, 1986, vol. 20, no. 1, p. 1.

34.   See for example *In re Grady* 426 *Atlantic* 2d 467 (1981);

Alan B. Munro, "The Sterilisation Rights of Mental Retardates", *Washington and Lee Law Review*, 1982, vol. 39, p. 207;

Deborah Hardin Ross, "Sterilisation of Developmentally Disabled: Shedding Some Myth-Conceptions", *Florida State University Law Review*, 1981, vol. 9, p. 599;

Robert T. Kourie and Margaret A. Somerville, "Comments on the Sterilisation of Mental Incompetents in Canadian Civil Law", *Review Droit University Scher.*, 1980, vol. 10, p. 599;

and generally Ruth Macklin and Willard Gaylin, *Mental Retardation and Sterilisation — A Problem of Competency and Paternalism*, 1981, Plenum Press, NY.

35.   See generally J. K. Mason and David W. Meyers, "Parental Choice and Selective Non-Treatment of Deformed Newborns: A View from Mid-Atlantic", *Journal of Medical Ethics*, 1986, vol. 12, p. 67;

and E. Schneider, "Rights Discourse and Neonatal Euthenasia, *Law Quadrangle Notes*, 1986, vol. 30, no. 2, p. 33.

The question was raised in a case before Justice Vincent of the Supreme Court of Victoria, in *Re F; F.* v. *F.*, unreported, 2 July 1986.

36.   Bentley Glass, "Science: Endless Horizons or Golden Age?", *Science*, 1971, vol. 171, pp. 23–28.

37.   Ruth Hubbard, "Personal Courage is not Enough: Some Hazards of Childbearing in the 1980s" In: *Test Tube Women*, Rita Arditti, Renate Duelli Klein and Shelley Minden, editors, 1984, Pandora Press, London, pp.331, 341. The next immediately following quotations are from the same source.

38.   See for example Edward Yoxen, *The Gene Business — Who Should Control Biotechnology?* 1983, Harper and Row, NY;

John C. Fletcher, "Moral Problems and Ethical Issues in Prospective Human Gene Therapy", *Virginia Law Review*. 1985, vol. 69, p. 515;

Stuart H. Orkin, "Genetic Diagnosis of the Fetus", *Nature*, 1982, vol. 296, p. 202.

39.   *Watt* v. *Rama* [1972] *Victorian Reports* 353.

On the United States' concept of 'wrongful life', see general discussion Robert H. Blank, *Redefining Human Life — Reproductive Technologies and Social Policy*, 1984, West View Press, Colorado.

40.   *McKay and Another* v. *Essex Area Health Authority* [1982] 1 *Queens Bench* 1166. The immediately following quotations come from that same source, pp. 1180–1181.

41.   *In re D., The Times*, 25 March 1986, Editorial;

"Care Ground and the New Baby", *Justice of the Peace*, 1986, vol. 150, p. 226.

42.   Blank, 1984, quoting J.S. Kashi, "The Case of the Unwanted Blessing: Wrongful Life", *University of Miami Law Review*, 1977, p. 1432. See also M.E. Cohen, *"Park* v. *Cheson*: The Continuing Judicial Development of the Area of 'Wrongful Life'," *American Journal of Law and Medicine*, 1978, vol. 4, p. 217.

43.   Blank, 1984, p. 99; Note, "A Cause of Action for 'Wrongful Life'", *Minnesota Law Review*, 1970, vol. 55, p. 67.

44.   See general discussion Blank, 1984, p. 100ff.

45.   *Cox* v. *Stretton* 352 *New York Supplement* 834 (1974).

46.   Horton Rogers, "Legal Implications of Ineffective Sterilization", *Legal Studies*, vol. 296, p. 307.

47.   *Thake* v. *Maurice* [1986] 2 *Weekly Law Reports* 337;
      see also *Emeh* v. *Kensington and Chelsea and Westminster Area Health Authority* [1985] *Queens Bench* 1012.

48.   Carl Wood and Ann Westmore, *Test-Tube Conception — A Guide for Couples, Doctors and the Community to the Revolutionary Breakthrough in Treating Infertility Including the Ethical, Legal and Social Issues*, 1984, revised edition, Hill of Content, Melbourne, p. 92. The immediately following quotations come from the same source.

49.   Andrew Veitch, "Pre-Natal Tests Urged to Cut Stillborn Birth", *The Guardian*, 11 May 1983.

50.   John A. Robertson, "Procreation, Liberty and Control of Conception, Pregnancy and Childbirth", *Virginia Law Review*, 1983, vol. 69, p. 464.

51.   Barbara Katz Rothman, "The Products of Conception: The Social Context of Reproductive Choices", *Journal of Medical Ethics*, 1985, vol. 11, p. 188;
      see also Barbara Katz Rothman, "The Meaning of Choice in Reproductive Technology" in *Test Tube Women*, 1984, p. 23. The immediately following quotation comes from the same source.

52.   Christopher Joyce, "New Scandal Halts Gene Engineers" (Genewatch), *New Scientist*, 10 April 1986.

53.   Marshall Nirnberg, cited Rothman, 1985.
      Further on the issue of plant and animal reproductive technology and genetic engineering, see Marion Brown, Kay Fielden and Jocelynne A. Scutt, "New Frontiers or Old Frontiers Recycled? this volume.

54.   Janice Raymond, "Images and Models: Informed Consent in Relation to Operations which Change Physical Form to Conformed Stereotypes," Paper presented to Symposium on Informed Consent, Law Reform Commission, Victoria, Melbourne, 13 May 1986.

55.   An article appearing in the *Weekend Magazine*, accompanying the *Sydney Morning Herald* and *The Age* indicated that plastic surgery such as face lifts are sought abroad, at places such as Tahiti and Brazil — transport costs atop surgical and recuperation costs! 14 June 1986.

56.   Rothman, 1985.

57.   Committee to consider the Social, Ethical and Legal Issues Arising from In Vitro Fertilisation (Professor P.L. Waller, chairperson);
      see *Report on the Disposition of Embryos Produced in In Vitro Fertilisation*, Department of Attorney-General, Melbourne, August 1984;
      also *Report on Donor Gametes in In Vitro Fertilisation*, August 1983.
      The committee also produced an *Interim Report* in 1982.

58.   See Ramona Koval, "The Commercialisation of Reproductive Technology", this volume.

11 Genetic & reproductive engineering – *The global view*

Renate D. Klein

It would have been better for men to have gotten children in some other way, and women not to have existed. Then life would have been good. *

Genetics and reproductive engineering are rapidly becoming the weapons for what their creators see as the 'ultimate conquest': control and power over the production of the human species as well as control and power over the production of plants and animals. An international multi-billion dollar competitive rat race has developed among scientists, pharmaceutical companies, medics and politicians. The prize they are clamouring for is to be leaders in conquering this latest 'frontier' of human domination of nature. The race has led to an explosion of new methods, the application and products of which could well mean the total destruction of life on earth. Before that destruction, however, there will almost certainly be domination, appropriation and exploitation of women to a yet unprecedented degree, unless women organise to fight back against this new form of exploitation.

Before the advent of these latest technological 'successes', women's whole bodies could be forced into, or out of, having children. The new aspect of the new reproductive technologies is that now, parts of women are used, and abused, to control reproduction of the human species. 'Technodocs' have embarked on dissecting and marketing parts of women's bodies — eggs, wombs, embryos.

---

*Euripides' *Medea*.

Women are being dismembered — split into separate parts which can be reassembled, perhaps in a different order, perhaps using parts from different women. Woman has become, as Gena Corea so aptly terms it, the 'mother machine' — an incubator, a vessel, a reproductive body; or to use Robyn Rowland's expression — a 'living laboratory'.[1]

If women are to organise on a global scale to launch a coordinated plan of action to stop this technology craze, first it is necessary to learn of what the technology consists, its underlying philosophy and reality, and the way that those peddling the technology have coordinated their experimentation and transmitted their knowledge internationally. Scientists and doctors are linked with drug companies, and politicians' desires for re-election are used to support programmes devised to gain monetary support of taxpayers, clients, and future clients. Women must ask: who makes the rules? whose needs and interests are catered for? who profits from this power? who benefits? — and who pays the price?

PATRIARCHAL ENQUIRIES INTO REPRODUCTIVE TECHNOLOGIES

Since the advent of the British *Warnock Report*[2] in 1984 on the medical, scientific, ethical and socio-legal implications of the new reproductive technologies (NRTs) on human beings, an increasing number of governmentally instigated committees, medical associations and research councils, local and national ethics advisory boards, church and right-wing groups and concerned individuals, and special interest campaigns such as *Progress* in England, are publicly voicing their views on the new reproductive technologies. They have prepared, or are preparing, recommendations for ethical guidelines and legal changes. Sweden, Denmark, the Netherlands, Norway and Australia are among those with governmentally appointed committees. Reports have already been published in Australia — the Waller Committee and the Asche Committee;[3] France — the Comité Consultatif National d'Èthique pour les Sciences de la Vie et de la Santé; the Ontario Law Reform Commission in Canada;[4] and the Benda Commission in West Germany.[5]

Many local ethics commissions and professional associations have given their opinion on the new reproductive technologies and genetic engineering (although the latter has only more recently been placed on the agenda). Although the United States of America's Ethics Advisory Board (EAB) noticeably became defunct in 1980, in January of 1984 the American Fertility Society issued a report entitled *Minimal Standards for Programs of In Vitro Fertilisation*.

The Medical Associations of Britain, West Germany, Switzerland, Australia, Japan and others have issued guidelines, and the European Society of Ethics (Societas Ethica) held their 1985 congress on the topic 'Problems in Bioethics: The Paradigm of *in vitro* fertilisation'. Their conclusion was simple:

> Infertility means suffering.
> IVF eliminates infertility, ergo suffering.
> Consequently IVF is good.[6]

The various committees, boards and other bodies vary in their assessment of the potential dangers and mismanagement of 'high' new reproductive technologies, such as *in vitro* fertilisation (IVF) and embryo transfer (ET) and associated embryo research, sex selection and fetal therapy. They also include — without discussion — such 'low' technologies as artificial insemination by husband/partner (AIH) and by donor (AID) and the problem of 'surrogate motherhood', and their views are remarkably similar:

- they mirror a fetus-centred analysis (whether or not they see the embryo/fetus as an unborn child) and seek provisions for the legal protection and well-being of the prospective child
- they are concerned with ensuring as much 'academic freedom' as possible (for example many propose a 14 day limit for embryo research) to enable science and medicine to continue their purportedly beneficial embryo research which will, they claim, fight infertility, prevent miscarriage, develop new contraceptives and develop fetal gene therapy to 'cure' genetic disorders or, even, to fight cancer
- they advocate the establishment of a regulatory body, called a 'licensing authority' in England or 'ethical committee' or 'advisory committee' in other countries, to monitor the development and oversee the application of the NRTs so that they will not fall into the 'wrong hands'.

Biotechnology, especially genetic engineering using the recombinant DNA technique, *needs* some spectacular successes to justify continuation of these programmes. Successes create a climate of acceptance and (importantly for those working in and running the programmes) attract funding for continuation of the programmes, and for their expansion. So far, biotechnology has succeeded only in artificially producing insulin (for which there was no real need as the animal supply seems adequate), human growth hormone (which has already been put to unethical use in experiments on children in the United States),[7] and some preliminary stages of Factor VIII (to treat haemophilia). The long-heralded *interferon*, a drug to cure everything from the common cold to cancer, is still not on the general market, although human trials have been conducted. One suspects the problem is that different people react differently. Also, considerable side effects from taking interferon have been confirmed such as fever, muscular pains, stomach upsets, tiredness and loss of appetite.[8]

According to Robert Winston, IVF specialist at Hammersmith Hospital in London, NRTs may fall into 'wrong hands', including private practices and university units who may open IVF clinics without sufficient knowledge of all its implications.[9] Winston thus wants IVF to remain 'safely' in the hands of a few 'experts' which would provide them with even greater control and power. The 'wrong hands', where artificial insemination is concerned, might also mean women's groups who have been using self-insemination for many years. By proposing to regulate artificial insemination through 'licensing authority' the present unofficial practice of artificial insemination in women's own hands would become a criminal offence. Indeed, past experience in the medical field suggests it is almost inevitable that regulation will remove the possibility of self-insemination by 'low' technology being used by women's groups.[10]

Regulatory bodies are also designed to ensure that the application of the NRTs remains 'ethically acceptable', that is, that no cloning and no production of human and animal hybrids, for example, takes place. This is stated explicitly in a recent joint recommendation of nine European medical research councils:

> The nine research councils (Denmark, Finland, West Germany, Italy, Sweden, the Netherlands, United Kingdom, Austria and Belgium) agree that IVF should be restricted to the 'pre-embryo', the collection of dividing cells before the appearance of the primitive streak, and should have the aims only of reducing infertility, of reducing congenital and hereditary disorders, and of the development of safer contraceptive methods. Cloning of pre-embryos, manipulation of the genome to alter characteristics, growing pre-embryos beyond 14 days and the production of hybrids are all banned. Each country is urged to set up an ethical committee 'to advise doctors and scientists and to inform and reassure the public'. The committee should also contain 'substantial lay membership'.[11]

Analysing the statements of the various bodies shows evidence of a 'softening up' phase in which the possible abuses of the NRTs are discussed whilst the principles on which these technologies are based are ignored.

First, nowhere do the recommendations suggest that the NRTs — specifically, the core techniques of IVF and embryo transfer (ET) — might be both undesirable and irresponsible because they are based on the idea of the 'technological fix'. They rest on the proposition that complex socio-economic/medically induced/ psychological and biological problems (such as the need for a biological child of one's own and the production of children to exact specification) can, and should, rightly be met by technological 'solutions', rather than looking more deeply into the underlying structures producing those problems. The NRTs are never exposed as an obsession with conquering what is possibly the last frontier — controlling the production of the human species (and finally all life on earth) — by means of utilising women's bodies, or parts of them. Women may be alienated from children, just as men have been.

Men have never been 'sure' they are the fathers of 'their' children, in the sense of knowing irrefutably that the sperm which fertilised the ovum came from their body and not from that of another man. A woman has always, until now, been in a position of knowing that a child produced from her womb is her biological child. Now that ova can be removed from one woman's body and implanted in another, or fertilised outside the uterus, a woman will not know for certain if the child to which she gave birth is biologically hers.[12]

Nor are the NRTs discussed for their wildly overstated and unfounded claims that fetal screening, based on recombinant DNA techniques, will prove helpful in diagnosing disease on a large scale. Many of these diseases consist of substantially more variables than can be detected with genetic screening. Also, as new diseases, caused by environmental factors such as nutrition, pollution and stress, are appearing almost daily, it is unlikely that the 'technological fixes' would be able to catch up with reality. According to US gynaecologist Dr S. Fabro, in the majority of birth defects in humans, the cause is unknown. About two per cent of birth defects are related to chromosomal abnormalities; five per cent are attributed to mutant (changed) genes; and approximately 20 per cent are multifactoral, which is another way of saying the cause is unknown.[13]

Secondly, it is never openly stated that IVF is the whole reason for embryo research. On the one hand, the media image of the few happy 'test tube mothers' serves to sway public opinion in favour of the NRTs — 'infertile people want it'; on the other hand (and this is far more important), the IVF procedure provides the 'technodocs' (doctors and scientists) with access to the 'raw material' for their research — women's eggs and the use of a woman's body as a 'living laboratory'. Yet embryo research is most prestigious, promising academic fame and glory for the technodocs and money for the pharmaceutical companies involved. There is also a lot of money in IVF treatments, especially in private clinics where prices are exorbitant.[14]

Finally, these committees do not recognise that the NRTs and, in particular, IVF/ET, are a further crucial step towards the medicalization of women's bodies and minds. Indeed, the NRTs, physiologically, psychologically and materially harm women, as individual IVF 'patients' as well as women as a group. These 'ethics' committees fail to expose the technologies as an example of violence against women in both a direct way (by experimenting on women's bodies or parts of them) and an indirect way (by de-stabilising a woman's sense of bodily integrity, autonomy and self-worth). Thus, women will become the perfect potential buyers of tomorrow's wider range of IVF applications such as routine sterilization in puberty (by removing the ovaries) when egg cells will be frozen and stored, ready to be thawed, matured and fertilised at a convenient time for the woman to bear a child (or rent another woman to carry her embryo to term).

The freezing of egg cells is reported to have been achieved for the first time by Alan Trounson at the Queen Victoria Medical Centre, Melbourne, Australia in March 1985. The technique is far from being perfect as the high percentage of water contained in egg cells tends to crystallise when frozen, causing the eggs to break. Egg freezing is one of the research priorities in Australia. Linda Mohr in Western Australia is developing a technique of 'vitrification' which uses a special cryoprotectant and freezes the egg very quickly to –148°C. Once the technique is perfected IVF and embryo research can be conducted at much greater distance from a woman's body. Put differently, a live woman will not be necessary at all as long as her eggs have been frozen, stored in a laboratory, and thawed, matured and fertilised at a convenient time. If by that time the artificial womb has been developed, women will have ceased to be necessary for procreation.

As John C. Fletcher and Joseph Schulman point out:

> *Research with fetuses ex utero including non viable fetuses*:
> *A pressing long-range problem in fetal research* is the development of methods to sustain the pre-viable fetus (the spontaneous abortus less than twenty-four weeks) *ex utero* until it develops to the point of sufficient maturity for independent survival.[15]

Omar Sattaur's research report confirms the belief that research to discover how to replace the living 'maternal environment' with a better machine is proceeding. Describing the culture fluid in which IVF embryos grow, Sattaur says:

> The various recipes for growing embryos and other tissues have all been developed by trial and error for particular animals. What is good for the mouse embryo is not necessarily good for the human embryo. For example, mouse embryos do not need the proteins contained in maternal serum in order to grow. Human embryos do get those proteins but *biologists are not certain that human embryos need serum.*[16]

Confronting the difficulties of creating an artificial womb, some technodocs have taken a different approach, but one which would equally exclude women from the traditional conception and pregnancy role. The journal *Omni* of December 1985 featured, among other exaggeratedly pro-technology articles, an article by Teresi and McAuliffe on 'Male Pregnancy', the subheading reading: 'Can men have babies? Research indicates they can, and volunteers are lining up.' The article discussed the desperate need of transsexuals to become 'real women' by bearing their own child, but mentioned 'ordinary' men too for whom such a possibility seems desirable.

Since the event of a woman from New Zealand giving birth (by caesarean section) to a child *after* a hysterectomy, everything seems possible. The fertilised egg attached itself to her bowel in the abdomen, where it received sufficient nutrients to develop a placenta and mature. With IVF technology a fertilised egg could easily be inserted into a man's abdominal cavity. Teresi and McAuliffe assert that the 'omentum: a fatty tissue loaded with blood vessels that hang down in front of the intestines . . .' could provide adequate blood supply and nourishment. Hormone treatment would sustain the pregnancy.

In addition to these possibilities, widespread 'embryo flushing' for genetic screening of chromosomal abnormalities could become a reality. *Progress*, the newly formed British campaign for research into reproduction, stated in 1986:

> Some inherited diseases are not fatal but cause terrible handicap. Many couples who learn that their foetus is affected will seek abortion. How much better to be sure from the outset that the pregnancy does not carry a genetic abnormality. *This may become possible through development of IVF* . . . There are at least 50 types of severe congenital disease which may one day be detectable by pre-embryo screening.[17]

And, as with other technical developments in the area of female reproduction, such as ultrasound monitoring and amniocentesis which were initially reserved for 'high risk' women, this procedure would become routine even for 'low risk' women as time went by, despite side effects remaining unexplored. Wendy Farrant provides an excellent overview of the development and application of amniocentesis in Britain:

> Amniocentesis was first used for prenatal diagnosis of chromosome disorders in 1967, and extended to the prenatal detection of neural tube defects in 1973. Since then there has been a rapid increase in the number of women undergoing diagnostic amniocentesis in early pregnancy . . . Initially prenatal diagnosis was confined mainly to a select group of high risk women who had themselves often initiated the referral because of concern about their increased chance of producing a baby with a severe abnormality. As the service has expanded, there has been an increasing trend for referrals for amniocentesis to be doctor—rather than patient—initiated. A particularly important development has been the introduction of *routine* maternal serum AFP screening for neural tube defects.[18]

As to the constantly increasing use of ultrasound monitoring in normal pregnancies, Fletcher and Schulman write:

> In one of the ultrasound studies, the technique is being evaluated as a predictive test for respiratory distress syndrome (RDS) following delivery. In the second, it is used to study fetal heart, lung, and other functions as responses to hypoxia and the effects of smoking in pregnancy. In 1984 an NIH consensus development panel on diagnostic ultrasound imaging concluded that because some biological effects had been observed after ultrasound exposure in various experimental systems, the question of risks deserved more study and that 'data on clinical efficiency and safety do not allow a recommendation for routine screening at this time.' . . . Thus, some issues of minimal risks from questionable routine tests can only be settled by long-term studies of children who did and did not have such examinations.[19]

Research on embryos opens the door for the development of more tests which every pregnant woman will be urged to undergo. A first step in this direction has been taken in California, USA where the alpha feto-protein test (to detect neural tube defects) is soon to be offered to all women seeking ante-natal care. If a woman does not want the test, this requires signing a form stating that the test is refused. If a woman wants the test, this requires signing a form consenting to the test. If a woman refuses the test yet bears a child with some 'defect', she lays herself open to feelings of guilt that the child need not have been born 'defective' had she undergone the test. Could she be sued by the child for 'wrongful life'? In having the woman sign the necessary forms, the clinic or hospital is clearly engaged in ensuring that any responsibility for the birth of a 'defective' child will not fall upon it.

It is possible for women to have the last vestige of control over their procreative capabilities removed. If an amniocentesis or the new chorionic villi test (which can be performed in the eighth or tenth week of a pregnancy) could test for, say, 300 chromosome irregularities and a woman undergoing the test scores, say, 120 out of these 300 irregularities with the particular embryo, the mother is faced with deciding whether she has the courage to carry the embryo to term, or decide upon an abortion. Again, the woman is faced with having to cope with guilt if the child is born with a defect detected by the testing. But if she chooses the abortion, she may never know whether or not the test was 'true' as mistakes in testing are inevitable. The important question is whether in a particular case a test result was wrong, or test results were mixed up in the laboratory (a not unfamiliar occurrence).

Furthermore, what kind of 'defects' and 'deficiencies' are sufficiently serious to warrant abortion? The wrong sex? wrong colour? social background and sexual orientation of the mother? The more these issues are considered, the more dangerous selection practices, based on pre-natal testing, appear. Who is to decide? There is also talk about 'genetic therapy' (a less threatening term than 'genetic engineering', though it covers the same process) which means surgical replacement of a defective gene either on body cells (somatic cell therapy) or on egg cells or sperm cells (germ line therapy). With germ line therapy the genetic change becomes hereditary, and would be passed on to children.

We may have to face a future when embryo flushing or perhaps egg donation from a 'better' woman has become the norm. In response we should ask 'the norm for what kind of women, and in which countries?' Such ideas do not belong to the realm of science fiction, as evidenced by the following news item appearing in the Johannesburg, South Africa newspaper, *The Citizen*, on 6 December 1985:

Donor Egg Plan for Motherhood
Cape Town, South Africa — Investigation into the use of donor eggs in test-tube baby programmes has been launched by the Department of Health and Population Development.

A similar appeal was launched in Britain by Edwards and Steptoe in 1984, as announced in the British newspaper, *The Guardian*, of 20 July. Alternatively, surrogacy using IVF is already practised, according to a report in the *Detroit Free Press* in Michigan, USA, of 27 August 1985:

> At Mount Sinai Medical Center in Cleveland, Ohio, Dr. James Goldfarb of the Life Program Laboratory reports that a woman's egg was fertilized by her husband's sperm in a test tube and placed in another woman to be carried to term. According to Dr. Goldfarb, if the procedure works, this will be the first surrogate birth to produce a baby that is genetically related to both parents.

In this, the 'softening up phase', the world is confronted by messages contending that all new reproductive and gene technologies are produced to ease pain and human suffering

- of involuntary childless couples,
- of people with genetic diseases, and
- of the world's population, 'which is dying of famine'.

The message is that these technologies are developed out of the goodness of heart of all involved parties, their love for humanity. The picture is that of the bountiful patriarch, the altruistic surgeon, the scientist who invents for world good.

From England come pictures of Robert Edwards and Patrick Steptoe, the 'fathers of the century', laboratory parents of Louise Brown — the world's first test-tube baby. Steptoe sits at the piano, in the press photographs, with a benevolent smile on his face. Edwards is a serious looking scientist in his white laboratory coat. Both personify well meaning benefactors. From Australia comes the saga of the 'lonely lifestyle of the test-tube hero': Carl Wood, photographed next to 'his' first deep frozen and thawed test tube baby, Zoe. He has especially good news for us. Test tube kids, he believes, are brighter and better than 'ordinary' ones. The 'softening up phase', aimed at making reproductive and genetic engineering acceptable, and even in chronic demand, is already working. Increasingly (and internationally), a low sperm count is accepted as a reason for IVF. In other words, women subject themselves to extensive (and expensive) hospital and surgical procedures — because *their partners* are infertile! Perfectly fertile women are undergoing the trauma of IVF because of their partner's low fertility.

None of these chilling possibilities (and the equally chilling realities) is discussed in the various committees' reports. On the contrary, engaging in the softening up phase themselves, committee reports depict IVF as beneficial. The 'regulators' agree with the scientists and doctors whom they set out to monitor. In biotechnical language, they become their true 'clones'. In the words of the *Warnock Report*, the new reproductive technologies have 'opened up new horizons in the alleviation of infertility and in the science of embryology'.[20]

INVASIVE AND DESTRUCTIVE NATURE OF REPRODUCTIVE TECHNOLOGIES

The issue is not only who controls the new reproductive technologies, but that the technologies in themselves are invasive and destructive. Some (including some feminists) believe this reproductive technology should not be rejected out of hand. On the contrary, we should try to appropriate it. But where else are women in control of technology? And secondly, and more importantly, these technologies are not neutral. The 'happiness from the test-tube' ideology has a bitter ring to it. It is associated with even more loss of freedom for women, and with more bodily and spiritual damage.

Women opposing the NRTs and, specifically, IVF are faced with two camps of 'experts', both of whom operate from within a patriarchal model which, despite women being indispensable to IVF and embryo research, denies women visibility. On the one hand are the medico-scientific practitioners whose 'treatments' have already been experienced by women in the form of dangerous contraceptives, thalidomide for nausea in pregnancy, DES (diethylstilboestrol) to prevent miscarriage, and invasive high tech pregnancy and birth techniques. On the other are the ethical and legal 'experts' already well known for their moral and legal control of women's sexual and reproductive behaviour, including abortion. Neither camp acknowledges that the very principles of the NRTs are detrimental to women.

Usually the IVF technique is described as 'fertilising a woman's egg cells with male sperm *in vitro*'. However, for the woman undergoing the procedure, it starts with long-term fertility monitoring and administering fertility drugs. Nothing is known about the long-term effects of these drugs, about the increased risk of ovarian cysts,[21] or breast cancer, or whether menstrual cycles will ever return to normal. Once the eggs have ripened, egg removal takes place with the help of a laparoscope through one incision in the woman's abdomen, forceps to grab the ovary through the second, and the instrument to remove ovarian follicles with eggs through a third. This operation takes place under general anaesthesia, after distending the woman's belly with carbon dioxide (CO_2). The average death rate is one in 100 000 laparoscopies although, within an IVF context, two women — one in Brazil and one in Israel — are the first casualties of the procedure.[22] The long-term effects of twisting and turning the ovaries in order to get to the ripe egg follicles should not be overlooked. If a fertile woman is undergoing IVF because of her partner's low fertility, she could be rendered sub-fertile or infertile. Moreover, when no ripe eggs can be found, laparoscopies must be repeated.[23]

Next comes the transfer of the fertilised egg — the embryo — in its four to eight cell stadium, to the woman's womb. The fertilised egg grows more slowly in the culture medium than it would in the woman's fallopian tube, so she is usually given supplementary hormone treatment for the first 10 weeks to ensure her womb remains ready for implantation and sustains the pregnancy. If she is one of the lucky few, and the embryo does implant and grow, frequent ultrasound monitoring and amniocentesis (or the more recent method of chorionic villus sampling) will survey the development of the precious product. Finally, delivery will probably be by caesarian section.

Yet the technodocs describe IVF as 'simple' and 'under control'. 'It's quite easy', they say, 'all you need is an egg and some sperm. You place these in a glass dish in the laboratory. If all works well, fertilisation takes place within minutes. You then have a cluster of two cells, four cells, eight cells, at which stage you transfer the embryo, as it is now called, into the woman's womb. No operation is needed, it's easy . . . almost natural . . .'

What they do not mention is that in order to produce ripe egg cells that can be 'harvested' (in the language of the technodocs) the 'egg donor' (that is, the woman) is subjected to hormonal stimulation, or hormonal bombardment, that goes on over weeks and of which no one knows, cannot know, long-term side effects because there are no long term data to consider. Later, in order to prepare 'the maternal environment' (the technical term for a woman's uterus) for the embryo transfer, another hormonal treatment is needed.

On top of all this is the trauma and anxiety caused by all the visits to, and the time spent in, hospital. As well, there is the very real possibility that the woman will be forced to give up her paid job due to the disruption of the treatment cycle, thus becoming financially dependent on her partner (that is, in most cases, her husband). There is also her abysmal distress and extreme sense of failure when it hasn't worked, when her period begins, and when she has to begin all over again.

And this outlines a straightforward version of IVF with no accounting for complications such as using donor eggs, which means that not one but two women have to undergo hormonal treatment.[24] It is difficult to understand how anyone can recommend such a procedure in good faith to an infertile woman, even if her wish for a biological child is causing her great distress. It is even more difficult to understand if it is her partner who wishes for his own biologically produced child, and his infertility prevents this from occurring naturally, so that the woman must undergo the procedure for him.

It might be argued that new and improved IVF methods will be developed. Indeed, new developments are underway, but these seem no less invasive or dangerous for women. The new method for egg collection known as TUDOR (Trans-vaginal Ultrasound Directed Oocyte Recovery), developed in Sweden, Denmark and Australia and to date used in the United States and West Germany, is hailed in some circles as 'progress'. TUDOR can be used without general anaesthesia and it was introduced as a cheaper and safer method than laparoscopy. However it appears to be equally cruel.

The woman's bladder is emptied with a catheter before being refilled with a sterile saline solution. Next, a needle is introduced through the vagina, a hole is made in the bladder and the needle guided in the direction of the ovary. Its direction is followed via ultrasound on a television screen. Once it arrives at the ovary, the egg follicles with (it is hoped) mature egg cells are torn out. Here, the problems arise, as one of the experts, Dr. Grier, Director of Genetic Consultants in Bethesda, Maryland, in the United States says:

> The problem is that sometimes the ovary moves when you try to press against it. When we do laparoscopy, the ovary also moves but we are able to use instruments to hold on to the ovary. But so far there are no instruments you can use in ultrasound other than the needle.[25]

Far from the alleged ease and painlessness of TUDOR, women report experiencing pain and, when the ovary is touched, feeling a sort of 'ramping sensation'. Many doctors return to general anaesthesia or try out 'various medications' to numb this pain. Furthermore, TUDOR produces fewer eggs than laparoscopy. The method hailed as a major technological advance does not seem to be too promising, after all.

GIFT (Gamete IntraFallopian Transfer) appears no better. Euphemistically claimed to be a 'back to nature cure for infertile women'[26] GIFT was originally developed by an Argentinian in Texas, Ricardo Asch, and is now being tested in 20 countries, among them Australia and the USA. After hormonal pre-treatment, superovulation and egg collection (by laparoscopy or TUDOR), two collected eggs and approximately 10 000 sperm are injected into each fallopian tube where (if it works) fertilisation takes place. While this method makes the embryo inaccessible for manipulation — (of course, it could always be flushed out once it arrives in the womb) — it does *not* make things better for the woman. She still has to undergo superovulation and hormonal treatment. It does make clear, however, that more than ever women are being used as guinea pigs for medical experimentation. Asch recently achieved a pregnancy with GIFT in a woman without ovaries, using donor eggs and hormone treatments.

On 18 April *The Guardian*, a British newspaper, reported upon the expected births of 'frozen egg twins'. Six of the eggs of the woman concerned were frozen and stored at minus 196 degrees centigrade. They were later thawed in a warm water bath, three being fertilised and then grown in the laboratory for nearly two days before implantation in the mother's uterus. The pregnancy was said to be 'progressing satisfactorily at 26 weeks' gestation' by the head of the 'frozen egg programme' at Flinders University in Adelaide, South Australia, where the hoped for birth was to take place. However it was also reported that all was not necessarily well:

> Doctors here and in Australia are concerned that freezing might damage human eggs — they are much more delicate than embryos — and lead to abnormal babies. No one has yet examined the chromosomes of a frozen egg to see if the process causes genetic damage.

Yet the 'chopping up' and combining of various parts from various women continues. Whilst various groups in various countries continue to try to grasp the complexity of the NRTs and propose ethical committees or law changes,[27] experimentation on women's bodies has already moved outside the realm of science fiction and it is the bodies and minds of real, live women which are being abused.

Despite all these new trial and error methods, the success rate of IVF is not rising. On the contrary, it is stagnating or even decreasing to a mere five to seven per cent. Or, to put it differently, the percentage which the technodocs offer today — five to seven per cent — is different from that which they offered earlier which was 10 to 15 per cent or higher. In the softening up phase the tactics have changed: whilst in the early days it was important to convince the public that the test-tube miracle would indeed work, today it is necessary to convince the public that more embryo research is needed.

This ability to turn the argument to advantage, to keep in touch with community perceptions and possible demands for integrity in the programs and the research is also evident in the increasing tendency in the medical and medical lay literature dealing with the new reproductive technologies to use the term 'pre-embryo' or 'conceptus' instead of embryo. This is clearly done to keep public opinion in favour of (pre-)embryo research and counteract the right wing/anti-abortionist tactics (which attack embryo research by depicting a four to eight cell mass as an 'unborn child'). This was exemplified by the British Powell *Unborn Child (Protection) Bill*, introduced in 1985 and seeking to prevent experimentation with embryos. The right wing notion that a (pre-) embryo is an 'unborn child' to be protected is one with which I profoundly disagree. Strictly speaking, the differentiation into embryo cells and placenta has not taken place at such an early stage. However this subtle name change is illuminating. It again depicts the technodocs' power to change the terms when it is in their perceived interest. In 1986 *Progress* reported:

> What has popularly been called 'embryo' research is not really that at all. It is research using 'pre embryos' (conceptuses) well before the fourteenth to sixteenth day after fertilisation when the embryo itself begins to form.

Such a subtle change of emphasis can be found in yet another aspect of the IVF debate. Twenty to 30 years ago (particularly during the period of the so-called sexual liberation movement in the 1960s) women's fertility was highlighted by exaggerated talk that 'simply looking at a man would make one pregnant', and women produced babies like rabbits (a metaphor still used for women in developing countries). Today, IVF specialists point out how very *difficult* it is for a woman to become pregnant. Robert Winston in Britain emphasises that without contraception, within one cycle a woman has only a 12 per cent chance of getting pregnant.[28] Howard Jones, one of the United States' most successful IVF specialists concurs:

> Medically, human reproduction is surprisingy inefficient. With normal and regular sexual intercourse the average woman can expect to become pregnant only one month of every three. Of all women who ever become pregnant in any given year, only 50 per cent will become pregnant after three months of trying.[29]

The intent seems clear: in the 1960s it was the recently introduced Pill that required a rationale for its existence; in the 1980s it is IVF, or rather embryo research, that needs to be protected and promoted. Of course the very real possibility exists that in the last twenty years fertility has indeed decreased, and infertility increased. But even if this is the case, it does not figure in the IVF specialists' arguments. They claim that the low fertility rate is due to 'human nature' — specifically women's nature — and that therefore IVF with a now admitted low success rate of five to seven per cent is already quite an adequate procedure.

The flexibility of the arguments sustains the technologies which constitute an invasion of and a violence against all women's bodily autonomy and integrity, both now and in the future, in the Western and Third Worlds. Gena Corea has already found evidence that United States entrepreneurs are looking to the Third World for 'cheap' surrogate mothers.[30] In addition, with embryo freezing becoming more and more common, the possibility arises of international temporary surrogates. Women could be artificially inseminated, their fertilised eggs flushed out and flown back to the sperm donor's country, and implanted in his partner's womb. Corea called this 'reproductive prostitution'. These technologies, and the techno-patriarchal mindset promoting them, are nothing less than a violation of the human dignity of women.

THE LONG FIGHT BACK

Feminists who are opposed to the NRTs should take the discussion back to its roots. We need to contest the basic techniques of IVF which enable an outsider to have access to the ripe egg cells necessary for the manufacturing and freezing of and experimenting on embryos. By opposing the roots of the NRTs, comes the best chance of voicing a women-centred resistance. By insisting that women ARE our bodies, not that we 'own' them,[31] we can deny access to outsiders who want to remove, experiment on and replace a part of our bodies. Using the same argument, we can re-assert that we alone are the lawful judges to decide whether or not to use pre-natal tests and whether or not to terminate our own pregnancies.

To do this, we must expose what the technologies are doing to women's — and indeed to all people's — identity. But in addition to 're-acting', we must also act. By 'acting' I mean

- that we actively fight back by publicly exposing and resisting the very basis of the NRTs;
- that we expose and accuse techno-patriarchy for the damage it is doing to women now and in the future;

- that we demand proofs that the experimentation on women will have no detrimental effects; and
- that we promote a philosophy which looks positively at reproduction, taking into account the wholeness of women's bodies.

We must also promote

- infertility research and the eradication of technologies and environmental hazards which have caused, and continue to cause, infertility;
- the notion that women and men can lead full lives without producing 'their own' biological children;
- that children are not for owning, and
- that caring for children and about children is not located in the fact that one has simply happened to have given birth to, or fertilised, a particular child.

Women are already fighting back in each of these ways, collectively and individually. Both individual and collective efforts must be acknowledged and publicised, for they add to the momentum, like the stand of Dr. Robyn Rowland of Deakin University, Victoria, Australia, who in protest to Carl Wood's team at the Queen Victoria Medical Centre in Melbourne resigned in 1984 from chairing the committee to co-ordinate social and psychological research in the area of the NRTs. The Queen Victoria Medical Centre team had announced its intention to introduce the 'flushing' technique for obtaining human embryos from women's bodies. By going public, Robyn Rowland marked the beginning of a women-centred resistance to the NRTs which was taken up by the press. This public resignation sparked an enquiry by the National Health and Medical Research Council (NHMRC) of Australia into 'embryo flushing', and a moratorium on any funds from the NHMRC going to programmes using this method of embryo harvesting.

Fighting back has initially been limited to acquiring knowledge and getting that knowledge to women: collecting information from around the world about the various technologies and their use in diverse countries, and the experimentation occurring in those countries, and distributing that information to all women and to those men who are willing to attempt to reject their patriarchal heritage and act on behalf of women. Feminist writings on the NRTs are reaching the international scene through feminist journals and pamphlets and through books published by feminist and commercial presses. In 1981 Helen (Becky) Holmes, Betty Hoskins and

Michael Gross edited *The Custom Made Child* and *Birth Control and Controlling Birth. Test-Tube Women: What Future for Motherhood?* edited by Rita Arditti, Renate Duelli Klein and Shelley Minden appeared in 1984, together with *Reproductive Wrongs — Male Power and the New Reproductive Technologies* by Debbie Cameron, Elizabeth Agnes, Kathryn Eldith and Maree Gladwin. Gena Corea's *The Mother Machine*, and *Man Made Women* by Corea, Duelli Klein, Jalna Hanmer, Holmes, Hoskins, Madhu Kishwar, Janice Raymond, Robyn Rowland and Roberta Steinbacher were published in 1985. *The Baby Machine* continues the tradition, and other works are also in the planning or writing.[32]

In many countries conferences, public debates and discussions, and 'speak outs' have been held to exchange information and alert women to the invasive nature of the technologies, and to plan for further action. In the United States, Becky Holmes and Janice Raymond organised the first conference on human reproductive technologies that had a decidedly feminist participation and analysis in Amherst, Massachusetts in 1980. In England, the first conference took place in March 1984 at Leeds where about 150 women met to discuss the NRTs. It was followed by a second meeting in London, in November of that year.[33] In April 1984 a panel discussion on the NRTs was convened by Robyn Rowland and Becky Holmes at the 2nd Interdisciplinary Congress on Women, held in Groningen, the Netherlands. In April 1985 more than 2000 women met in Bonn, West Germany at the Congress Frauen gegen Gentechnik and Reproduktionstechnik (Congress of Women Against Genetic Engineering and Reproductive Technologies). Organised by the Women's Section of the Green Party and the Feminist Social Science Association (Sozialwissenschaftliche Forschung und Praxis für Frauen), women from all parts of West Germany as well as other European countries and India gathered together to learn about the state of the art of the new technologies, to discuss their impact on women, and to start campaigning against them. It was the first time that anywhere in the world such a large group of feminists officially recognised the threat of the technologies to women's present and future lives. As the organisers stated, it was a 'meeting *against* the technologies, not a pluralistic discussion on its supposed advantages and disadvantages for women'. It was also the first time that gene *and* reproductive technologies were jointly discussed from a feminist viewpoint and their many technical, ideological and financial interconnections exposed.[34]

At the conclusion of the Bonn conference the organisers told the press:

This first historic conference may be happening in Germany because German women are so clear on where all this leads. We German women have a special responsibility to stop this.

West Germany is of course a fitting place for such a strong first national reaction. It cannot be without significance that the recent past in Germany has an important bearing on the fierce opposition expressed to these technologies. There is no doubt that if Hitler lived today his 'deadly science' and his eugenics could be practised with much more sophistication. However eugenics is not dead nor was it ever limited to Germany. The concept was developed by Francis Galton, an Englishman and Charles Darwin's cousin, in 1883. He was anxious about Jews immigrating to Britain. Eugenics had its first heyday in the United States in the 1920s when people were worried about the immigration of workers from Southern and Eastern Europe.[35] Then as early as 1926 in Germany guidelines for 'race hygiene' were published, indicating who came into the category of social/moral/physical 'deviant' and therefore who should be sterilised.

The tragedy of this history is that limitations on reproductive rights and freedoms hold true not only for the Nazi period but even today. As bacteriologist Bernard Davies of Harvard Medical School states, it is advisable to reduce 'the production of those individuals whose genetic make-up limits their capabilities to survive in a technologically complex environment.'[36]

The design today may at first glance be apparently different — the seeking of scientists and medicos to enable 'genetically defective' individuals to produce children without passing on the 'defective' genes, through genetic engineering and the NRTs. However, the underlying philosophy is the same. Who of you has thalassemia or haemophilia? changes quickly to who of you has an allergy? who is short-sighted? who has asthma? Not to speak of who doesn't want to be a 'proper' unpaid home-maker — which has in the past and even today been attributed to defective psychological makeup, or to chromosomal deficiencies.[37] And who is lesbian? — a 'condition' which has only recently been taken off some of the classified lists of 'diseases' with psychological or genetic origins. (Although the World Health Organisation's listing of homosexuality as a mental illness will not be changed before 1990 at the earliest, said *CREW Report* in April 1986.)

In the past, eugenicists would have demanded the listing of such persons for sterilisation. Today, they may be listed as requiring the 'help' of the NRTs to produce non-genetically related children, or genetic engineering to replace the 'defective' genes with 'perfect' genes. It is this increasing loss of control and self-determination over women's lives (*our* bodies, *our* lives) that the West German women recognised so clearly and began to fight at the Bonn conference.

As the Congress proceeded and more information became available on what is technologically feasible and the socio-political potential of such technological 'advancements' to control women to a yet unprecedented degree, the growing concern and anger among the conference participants was palpable, together with their determination to fight against the technologies. When, in a plenary session at the close of the Congress, the draft of a resolution containing total condemnation of gene and reproductive technologies was read, it was applauded with a long standing ovation. Proposals from the floor for amendments made it even stronger. They included the rejection of prenatal testing and genetic counselling in its present form. There could be no doubt that the great majority of women attending the Bonn conference were strongly opposed to the ideology underlying the new gene and reproductive technology. They did not believe there are any good parts that women might use. They identified themselves as being ready to fight. Statements of participants included:

> We didn't ask for the technologies.
> We don't need the technologies.
> The technologies are made at our expense.

A session at the United States National Women's Studies Conference in Seattle in June 1985; a half-day debate at the Australian and New Zealand Association for the Advancement of Science (ANZAAS) in Melbourne in August 1985; and a session at the eighth annual conference of the Women's Studies Association of New Zealand in August 1985, continued the process of informing and building strength internationally within the Women's Movement to gain some control in the burgeoning field of reproductive and genetic engineering. The aim of that control is not to 'join in with the boys' in their misappropriation and mutilation of women's bodies and birthright, but to exert power to reject these technologies.

As well, in April 1984 the Feminist International Network on the New Reproductive Technologies (FINNRET) was established, following the Interdisciplinary Congress on Women in Groningen, to monitor international developments, share information among women, and devise strategies and actions for how to stop these technologies. FINNRET called an 'Emergency Conference' in July

1985 in Sweden attended by some 80 women already involved in debating the issues, from 16 countries. Five days of discussions and presentations shared information on the state of the technologies in the various countries; legislation or moves toward drafting special laws; and feminist resistance. Several of the women attending travelled directly to Nairobi in Kenya afterwards, to present the results of the conference at Forum '85, the alternative conference organised to coincide with the official United Nations 'End of the Decade for Women' conference. These women also took part in two workshops on reproductive technologies and their development in relationship to international population policy.

Doctors, scientists and the mass media present developments in reproductive technologies as new hope for the childless and a way to overcome nature's 'imperfections'. During the Emergency Conference, however, it became clear that these technologies are in fact powerful tools for social control, which will have far-reaching consequences for women's lives and health. The development of technology surrounding IVF has been rapid. The first test-tube baby, Louise Brown, was born in 1978 in England. Today, several hundred IVF clinics are spread all over the world. In 1983, only five years after Louise Brown's birth, researchers for the first time succeeded in using an egg that did not come from the woman who later went through the pregnancy. In November of that same year, the first baby without genetic material from the birthing mother was born. The next step was embryo transfer, with the egg fertilised in the donor woman's body and after a few days flushed out of the uterus, to be implanted into another woman who then bears the child, or frozen to be used at a later date. The first embryo transfer baby was born in early 1984 in the United States, followed in July of that same year by the birth of another embryo baby in Holland. Also in 1984 the first child who had been frozen as an embryo was born in Melbourne, Australia.

The national updates at the conference showed that these 'firsts' have been followed by commercial exploitation and application of the technologies to larger and larger groups of women. In addition to commercial potential encouraging the rapid development of the technologies, comes the researcher's wish to be 'first' to succeed with a new technique and the excitement among scientists in controlling life. Participants from all countries represented at the conference testified to the inordinate amount of attention the press and other media give to 'test tube' births and the so called miracles of man over nature. 'We're fighting a scientific rat race,' one woman at the conference said.[38]

Sharing of information revealed the facts about the thriving industry now existing throughout the world, and growing rapidly. Although the United Kingdom led the way with the first 'test tube' birth in 1978, in 1985 by comparison with programmes in other countries, its industry pales. There are eight clinics operating in Britain, two of them private, with over 200 children whose births are attributed to the NRTs. Australian figures are greater than those in the United Kingdom. The first birth attributed to the NRTs took place in 1979 in Australia, with over 200 births designated 'test tube' babies. Ten clinics were operating in 1985, three of them on a private basis. It was reported that West Germany runs 21 clinics, two operating on a private basis, the first birth attributed to the NRTs occurring in 1982 and around 130 births designated 'test tube' by 1985. In that same year, East Germany had one clinic operating, with around three births; Switzerland seven, with two births; the USA 108 clinics, at least 26 private, with around 180 births attributed to the NRTs. In France over 60 clinics were reported to be operating in 1985, with over 150 births; Israel had its first 'test tube' birth in 1983, with six clinics operating in 1985 and the number shortly to be increased to eight. Sweden had seven clinics in 1985, three of them operating on a private basis; Japan had 27 clinics, nine operating privately, with some 20 to 30 births designated 'test tube'. At the conference, the Netherlands was reported to have eight clinics, with private clinics being prohibited, and around 20 'test tube' births; Denmark and Norway had four (two private) and two clinics respectively, with four to five births labelled 'NRTs' in Norway, two in Denmark.

The conference discussed the various techniques used, the experimental nature of the programmes, and the position of Third World women in the developing trade — the use of Third World women for experimental purposes, or the developing traffic in women as surrogate mothers between developed and Third World countries. Ana Regina Gomes dos Reis, a doctor from Brazil, documented the development of IVF in her country. Her story revealed the international links between the 'test tube kings', the technodocs involved in developing and exploiting the NRTs. She told the conference of the huge sums invested in Brazil by European pharmaceutical companies, with the main focus of research being gene technology. There was also a recounting of the often months long 'working' visits of the *crème de la crème* of the international 'test tube kings'. The local operator is Milton Nakamura, a Japanese doctor operating in Sao Paulo, with a Brazilian IVF project under his control. Simultaneously he is involved at top level in population growth control projects. Since 1979 he has played host to the international test tube jet set: in 1979 the American Sherman, who in 1963 succeeded for the first time in freezing human sperm, visited the Sao Paulo project; in 1980 it was the Englishmen Robert Edwards and Patrick Steptoe. (For the latter it was announced in the press in 1979 that 'ten volunteers' would be 'placed available for their initial experiments'.)[39] In 1982, financed by a television station, Alan Trounson, a leading light in the Queen Victoria/Epworth Hospital programme in Victoria, Australia (who succeeded in 1985 for the first time in freezing unfertilized human egg cells) visited the Nakamura NRTs project in Sao Paulo. In 1982 the American Howard Jones from Norfolk, Virginia, USA who with his wife Georgeanna Jones is responsible for over 100 American children attributed to the NRTs, arrived in Brazil to visit Nakamura's project.

Dr Ana Regina Gomes dos Reis reported that the death of one of Nakamura's IVF patients, Zenaide, was embarrassing, but apparently did not halt the programme. During ovum extraction by laparoscopy the patient suffered, as it was described, a 'respiratory collapse' and died. The exact circumstances have never been explained.[40] Nakamura continues his research, and it is certain that the procession of his illustrious guests will continue. Since the successful birth of Anna Palua Caldeira in 1984, Gomes dos Rios reported, Nakamura has been 'fully rehabilitated'.

In 1982, after Zenaide's death, the Brazilian Society for the Advancement of Science spoke of an 'Obstetrics Carnevale'. Unfortunately such accusations belong to the past. The expensive research goes on relentlessly, the number of exploited women growing larger. Gomes dos Rios forecast that as the poor in Brazil are getting poorer and poorer, accordingly more women will become available to reproductive technology as guinea pigs, in order to earn a little money.

Money is closely connected with developments in the NRT field, particularly in Third World countries where poverty amongst the greater populations is a fact of life (and too often of death). Farida Akhtar and Sultana Kamal from Bangladesh told the Sweden conference of sterilization campaigns in Bangladesh, Pakistan and India, often accompanied by coercion or economic rewards. They also spoke of how hormonal birth control methods such as Depo-Provera and Norplant (a hormone preparation implanted under the skin, which makes a woman infertile for at least five years) are distributed without any restrictions and without any follow-up of side effects.

In these countries, women are often made sterile against their will. But with more and more biotechnical multinationals working feverishly on developing new diagnostic kits to be used in pre-natal tests, large numbers of women will increasingly be needed for experimental purposes. Farida Akhtar pointed out how Western pharmaceutical companies, in violation of the Helsinki Convention, are carrying out their tests for a new cholera vaccine using mainly women who are undergoing sterilisation operations as guinea pigs.

There is also a technological argument that development of the NRTs will make sterilization programmes operate more effectively and efficiently, without the great need to resort to coercion. If it can be demonstrated to women that sterilisation does not mean an end to their becoming biological mothers, then their acquiescence may be more easily secured. This does not, of course, mean that women sterilised in Bangladeshi 'family planning' programmes will gain access to the NRTs for themselves.

The unanimous resolution passed at the close of the Emergency Conference in Sweden emphasised not only the necessity to develop a critique of the NRTs, but also to place that critique within a broader context of analysis of the patriarchal nature of science and technology. Sociologist Maria Mies from West Germany warned the Emergency Conference that the model of 'the machine' is inherent in the logic of technology, and it is 'this logic we see when a woman's body is turned into a machine and a child becomes a commodity'. Women at the conference also emphasised the need to support women who are infertile and demand that governments and corporations take action to eliminate the environmental and industrial conditions which lead to so much infertility. Without these conditions genetic and reproductive engineering would be shown up for what it is — unconcerned, in reality, with the real distress of those who are infertile, and designed to bring glory to the technodocs and money to commercial concerns.

The Emergency Conference concluded by declaring that the name FINNRET should be changed more specifically to describe the nature of the organisation and its purpose, to the Feminist International Network of Resistance to Reproductive and Genetic Engineering (FINRRAGE). It endorsed unanimously a final resolution:

We, women of Australia, Bangladesh, Brazil, Canada, Denmark, England, France, Ireland, Israel, Japan, Netherlands, Norway, Sweden, Switzerland, United States of America and West Germany, declare that the female body, with its unique capacity for creating human life, is being expropriated and dissected as raw material for the technological production of human beings. For us women, for nature, and for the exploited peoples of the world, this development is a declaration of war. Genetic and reproductive engineering is another attempt to end self-determination over our bodies.

We know that technology cannot solve problems created by exploitative conditions. We do not need to transform our biology, we need to abolish patriarchal social, political, and economic conditions.

We shall resist the development and application of genetic and reproductive engineering. We want to maintain the integrity and embodiment of women's procreativity. Externalization of conception and gestation facilitates manipulation and eugenic control. The division, fragmentation and separation of the female body into distinct parts for its scientific recombination disrupts historical continuity and identity. The individual becomes the dividual, the divided one.

There is no right to a child as property. Neither infertile nor fertile women, neither lesbian nor heterosexual women require permission to have a child from authorities like the state or the medical profession.

We call on women to resist the take-over of our bodies for male use, for profit-making, population control, medical experimentation, and misogynist science.

Life for us always means risk. It cannot be programmed or perfected. Living demands courage. We shall not surrender ourselves to the technocrats. We shall hold fast to the collective responsibility for ourselves and our lives.

We resolutely oppose all attempts through genetic and reproductive engineering, to bring about a racist and fascist division of women into 'valuable' women in the industrial world, who should have children, and 'inferior' women in exploited countries, who are forbidden to have children. In our own countries, we opposed differential treatment of poor, disabled, lesbian, black, and foreign women by patriarchal medicine. We resolutely oppose eugenic population policies, in particular the fabrication of 'perfect' babies. We condemn all governments that allow genetic and reproductive engineering.

We condemn the international traffic in women, specifically for purposes of reproductive prostitution. We condemn the use of women from exploited countries and poor women by men and international conglomerates in the interests of global capital and patriarchy.

We condemn men and their institutions that inflict infertility on women by violence, forced sterilisation, medical maltreatment, and industrial pollution and repeat the damage through violent 'repair' technologies. We oppose coercive prenatal diagnosis.

We support the exclusive rights of all women to decide whether or not to bear children, without coercion from any man, medical practitioner, government or religion.

Recognizing that infertility is often determined by political, social and economic conditions, we support compassionate treatment of infertile women and intensive study into the prevention of infertility.

We support the recovery by women of knowledge, skill, and power that gives childbirth, fertility and all women's health care back into the hands of women.

We seek a different kind of science and technology that respects the dignity of womankind and of all life on earth. We call upon women and men to break the fatal link between mechanistic science and vested industrial interests and to take part with us in the development of a new unity of knowledge and life.

Following the Emergency Conference the Feminist Hearings on Genetic Engineering and Reproductive Technologies were held at the European Parliament in Brussels, Belgium from 6–7 March 1986. Out of that conference arose plans to hold a European follow-up conference against the NRTs in 1986; and to stage an International Tribunal on Scientific and Medical Crimes Against Women in 1988. Women in Australia organised their first congress on the NRTs in May 1986 and women in Spain in September that same year.

In Australia, Robyn Rowland's initial consciousness-raising effect of going public in 1984 was steadily enhanced through the action of other women, including Ramona Koval, science writer and lecturer, writing news and feature stories in *The Age* and *Australian Society*, and the Australian FINNRET national co-ordinator Lariane Fonseca's almost one-woman effort of producing five newsletters on the NRTs. In May 1986 the work of Janet Ramsey and others of the Centre for Continuing Education at the Australian National University, Canberra, in conjunction with a national organising committee comprising members of FINNRET, came to fruition with the *Liberation or Loss? Women Act on the New Reproductive Technologies* conference. Funding was secured from the federal Office of the Status of Women; the Law Reform Commission, Victoria; and the New South Wales Law Foundation, with support from TAA (Trans Australian Airlines). Three days of exchange of information, discussion and debate of the issues, and plans for fighting against exploitative technologies which deny women autonomy and reproductive freedom led to a national awareness amongst women on a scale not previously achieved in Australia.

And many other countries have begun to organise resistance to the NRTs. Antigen is a particularly active feminist group in Zurich, Switzerland, which has produced a series of slide talks and tours the country to raise people's consciousness and involve them in active resistance to gene and reproductive technologies. This is only one of a number of such groups. Meanwhile on an international level the Feminist International Network of Resistance to Reproductive and Genetic Engineering (FINRRAGE), with contact women in 21 countries continues to monitor the NRTs and to distribute information and notes for resistance the world over.[41]

Spectacular actions have been taken by women, as happened in Basle, Switzerland, on 28 August 1985, where women disrupted the participants in an advanced training course on IVF, for practising physicians and gynaecologists, with 'stink, noise and smoke'. They let fly with a stink bomb thrown with rage for the lives and bodies of all women. During the action they distributed among the physicians the "Gencredo" published in *Emma* in October 1985, parodying the technodocs:

> I believe in gene technology and the researchers, the almighty creators of poison gas clouds and atomic explosions. And in the superbaby, the *in vitro*-son, conceived by expensive tortures, born of the birth machine woman, examined, gene-manipulated, stuffed full of medicines on the third day, raised above all deformity, incorporated again, sitting on the right hand of the industrial magnate whence it shall come to judge those who want to live and those who have already perished from hectic living and over-consumption. I believe in economic growth, in a generally militarized daily life, the community of white oppressors, forgiveness of sinful resistance, resurrection of the omnipotent robot and the legend of eternal life. Amen.

These women, too, are building on the fine tradition of women fighting back, just as the suffragettes in England chained themselves to railings; underwent hunger strikes, and dug holes in golf-courses; swung from ceilings in halls to disrupt patriarchal political rallies which denied votes to women; flew over Whitehall in a balloon, distributing leaflets shouting 'Votes for Women'; and in the United States, Canada and Australia marched into male only bars and clubs demanding a drink; and in Australia chained themselves to the precincts of the Australian Conciliation and Arbitration Commission demanding equal pay, and swarmed onto trams demanding the right to pay 65 per cent only of the adult fare, a rate more commensurate with their discriminatory rates of pay.[42]

On a deliberately direct level, there are no better spokeswomen against these technologies than the women who have actually gone through IVF programmes whether they are without or with a child. At first this may seem an horrendous idea — haven't these women suffered enough? Why put more pressure on them? But 50 years ago, if someone had suggested that women raped or sexually harassed, whether within the family or without it, speak out against rape (or even more so against rape in marriage), sexual harassment and incest, she would have been told this was unwise and in fact would jeopardise the women. She would also have been lectured that it was 'selfish' or too demanding to expect these women to speak out, that such a proposal failed to understand the position of the exploited and abused women. And yet it is only thanks to the courageous women who disregard advice to 'suffer and be still', coming out strongly and publicly, first producing shock but gradually a greater recognition of male violence against women, that some changes in attitudes and laws have occurred.

The actions of women who have been and are intimately involved with the new reproductive technologies could help to make this problem of infertility visible. Public platforms can be used, such as television and radio appearances, a tribunal of medical crimes against women, and even taking legal action by suing public patriarchy (that is, the technodocs) for violence against a woman's basic human right to bodily autonomy and integrity.

Patricia Hynes, a United States' environmental engineer, deserves full credit for being the first to discuss the possible uses of the legal system in the regulation of the NRTs. In "The Road Not Taken. Environmental Protection in the USA: A Paradigm for Regulation of the Biomedical Industry" in 1985,[43] Hynes describes the development of US environmental protection — for which Rachel Carson's work, *Silent Spring*,[44] was the catalyst. Hynes maintains that Carson's ethical and political work 'holds paradigmatic value for the international feminist movement against the NRTs'. Looking at the example of the creation of the Environmental Protection Agency (EPA) in the United States in 1970, she enumerates similarities and differences between the principles of environmental protection and the protection of the rights of women with respect to the NRTs. Dr. Hynes suggests 'the materialization of principles into law and regulation is crucial for the translation of the reality of ideals into the reality of daily life'. She urges feminists:

- to ask for representation on the ethics committees and policy making bodies to regulate the NRTs, or form their own
- to scrutinise the concept of acceptable or "0" risks

- to consider risk-benefit analyses with regard to NRTs (including the category of 'existential' risk) and research into industrial, medical, and medically induced causes of infertility
- to consider legislation for regulation and banning.

Although the law generally is unsympathetic to women's (and feminists') interests, it may be possible to devise new laws for prevention rather than using those of protection or prohibition. A law suit by IVF patients against their doctors for failing to give them adequate information about the technologies and the long term effects might create a great public fuss over how women's bodies are being used as living laboratories and how medical procedures are declared 'safe' on the basis of a lack of information. Public favour (including monetary sources) might be turned against the technodocs and eventually force them to close their clinics and stop embryo research. Such a suit could perhaps be filed at the European Court at Strasbourg on the grounds that the NRTs purposefully — through lack of knowledge of medium or long term effects — violate the human dignity of a woman; that it is her 'basic right' to bodily integrity and autonomy. Clearly, such an approach requires no less than the application of a woman-centred code of ethics to the existing legal system which is based on the premise that women *are* our bodies in our own right. This would shift the terms of the debate: from us having to prove to them (that is, the doctors/scientists) that the NRTs are harmful, to them having to prove to us that they are not. How many more dead women do we need? Two are obviously not sufficient. Will only defective children be 'proof' enough that the NRTs are dangerous? As Anita Direcks, herself a DES daughter, said at the Feminist Hearings on Reproductive and Genetic Engineering in March 1986, at Brussels: how many more catastrophes do we need before the craze will stop?

Women involved in the NRTs programmes or who have been involved, or who are, simply, infertile, could become a strong lobby themselves. They could:

- openly voice the pain and the contradictory feelings inherent in wanting a biological child of one's own; and voice their anger if the infertility was medically caused
- discuss the problem of 'choice' in a society where a 'real' woman is still seen as a woman with child and the economic and psychological power differences between the sexes remain unchanged
- expose the distress and discomfort they experienced on the

program, including lack of information, the problem with 'informed consent', and possibly malpractice — for example, whilst at the hospital or clinic and/or in experiencing middle and long-term effects of the IVF procedure

- make public the strain that IVF produces on their personal relationships and their whole life, and possibly expose also problems that IVF children experience
- make demands for an alternative science to investigate the nature of infertility by taking a person's whole life-context into consideration rather than trying to 'fix up' some 'defective' part
- establish support groups for women who consider IVF as a possibility, and those who were not successful, to discuss alternatives such as coming to terms with one's infertility; pursuing (and pushing for easier) adoption which takes into account the need to create loving relationships with children, without a need for 'owning' children; recognising the positive sides of being without children.

The current low 'success' rates of five to seven per cent cannot be ignored. Globally, approximately 2000 babies have been born through the NRTs. This leaves at least 20 000 women without a child but with real and potential damage to their bodies and minds. The number is probably much higher, as only the women who have had some kind of 'success' (for example, successful egg collection; embryo implantation) figure in the IVF statistics.[45] Hopefully, some of these women will speak out against the new 'compulsory techno-motherhood ideology' and the detrimental effects it has had on their lives. Indeed, some women are already speaking out in this way. These women, together with those of us who may not be infertile but who oppose the technologies for their misogynist, inherently eugenic, fame and profit-seeking ideology, could join forces to become a powerful and supportive group which — and one needs to have faith in utopias! — would contribute to the demise of techno-patriarchy.

CONCLUSION

By fighting genetic engineering and the new reproductive technologies, rather than trying to live with them, we may avoid our own collusion with the softening-up rhetoric of both the IVF promoters and the IVF regulators. Women will have to think very carefully whether or not to try to join *their* committees and influence the nature of *their* regulations, and whether or not to endorse proposed

legislative changes. As in many areas of women's fight for autonomy, the specific circumstances of a situation need to be taken into
account before deciding on a particular strategy.[46]

But we should acknowledge that neither the 'technodocs' nor
their 'clones' (the professional surveillance committees) base their
theory and practice on feminist principles. They will not speak up
for women from a woman-centred perspective which respects
women as autonomous beings with bodily integrity. Technology
promoters and self-controlled regulators alike are bound to simply
reshuffle the cards and continue to play their game of
'dissection-science' on women's bodies. We are also faced with collaboration between some women and the technocrats and
technodocs. After the 'test tube kings' and the 'clone kings' — the
men producing the NRTs, and the men giving these developments
ethical credibility through their commissions, committees and
reports, come the 'test tube princesses'.

Some women unfortunately have been socialised into imagining
that if they revere the kings and the clone kings, demand 'control'
and hope in this way to prevent the worst effects of the technologies
for women, they will one day perhaps even become the queens
accompanying the kings. Maria Mies has called this pre-
adaptation. In fact they should know that in the Realpolitik of kings
there is no right of succession to the throne for princesses. Other
test tube princesses hope that they will at least keep their 'princess'
status. And it is princesses like this who in several countries, but
particularly England on the occasion of the debate of the Bill by the
right wing Conservative Member of Parliament, Enoch Powell, *For
the Protection of the Unborn Child*, made common cause with the
pharmacrats. They feared that the adoption of Powell's Bill would
be a prelude to an anti-abortion campaign. But first, kings in some
countries — particularly and most profoundly in West Germany
— have always been in favour of tightening up abortion legislation.
Women's desire for autonomy must be stamped out, according to
this lobby, independently of attempts at assimilation and a willing-
ness for compromise on the part of women in other fields — for
example in reproductive technology.[47] Secondly, the princesses do
not acknowledge that the necessary and energetic women's resistance to Powell's Bill and legislation like it should fight the intensified control over women he advocates, *not* just form temporary
alliance with the pharmacrats, by supporting their claim to keep on
with embryo research. Thirdly, and this is the most serious point,
the pharmacrats abuse these princesses as alibi women, though the
princesses do not realise it. Ultimately in this they drag in not only

themselves as accomplices in the crime of the physical and mental dissection of the IVF candidates, but they also bear co-responsibility for the nipping of women's resistance in the bud, by the kings Realpolitik. That the princesses themselves are women is particularly convenient for the kings: 'divide and rule' is an old established kingly tactic.

However, there are also some 'princesses' who are women-centred feminists. For them, self-determined autonomy and the claim to the integrity of woman represent the main pillars of the ideology of freedom. For them, forward flight is the only solution: ruthless exposure of the alliances and machinations of the Realpoliticans and a total rejection of the proposals from the 'experts'. If we lend ourselves to even discuss proposals on regulations elaborated from the viewpoint of the kings, we embark on collusion and collaboration with their profoundly anti-woman ideology.

But fighting back with information is not easy. Information will inevitably be kept from those who are opposed to genetic engineering and the new reproductive technologies. Indeed, information is assiduously kept from us all, until the time is judged 'right' by the controllers of the technologies. For example, since 1981 not one article on the subject of artificial wombs or experimentation in this field has been published in the specialist journals. Industry, for reasons of competition, demands secrecy over research projects, at least until a process or product is ready for patenting. I am convinced that work is being done in several locations on the development of artificial wombs, financed by pharmaceutical and chemical concerns and industrial interests.

It is also difficult to obtain information about the funding of genetic engineering and reproductive technological projects through the military. The financing of gene and test tube technology by military institutions must be named. A large number of gene-technological laboratories are known in the USA, in which (with the aid of recombinant technology, which permits a deliberate alteration of the (human) genotype DNA) possibilities for the field of chemical and biological warfare are being investigated. Nothing has yet come to light of research projects on female reproductive biology, but it would be naïve to imagine that financing in this area is not being pursued — not least through experiments on embryos.

In *For The Record* Dale Spender points out that none of us 'is free from the disposition to assume that our experience is *the* experience, and that what we know represents the limits of the knowable'. She continues:

None of us has a true analysis, a correct line, a monopoly on the right meanings. And if we want to see the end of one group defining the world of another group, on the grounds that this constitutes oppression, then all of us have a reponsibility to strive to extend our horizons, to encompass and validate women's experience that is different from our own. All of us have to be vigilant about what we are leaving out of our explanations — and why![48]

But Spender goes on to emphasise that feminism is not value-free liberalism 'which "tolerates" each and every view':

Feminism is based on values, on values of self-identity, responsibility, autonomy, equality and the absence of dominance, coercion and oppression. Understandings which do not respect these values, no matter from whom they emanate, are not tolerated.

Without doubt, where the new reproductive technologies are in question it is time to put aside that sort of liberalism which says 'anything goes'. It is time to take on responsibility. By rejecting these technologies women are *not* insensitive or paranoid or anti-technology grouches. We are not conjuring up a conspiracy theory. Reality is bad enough. By rejecting these technologies, we take a women-centred stand; we are with infertile women and *not* against them. We are supporting values of self-identity, responsibility, autonomy, equality and the absence of dominance, coercion and oppression. We deny the technocrats and the pharmacrats our bodies. We speak out angrily against them in public. We do this in the belief that, eventually, those exploiters of women's biology and women's lives, those who dominate, coerce and oppress us, will be forced to stop.

Our resistance makes *them* angry. The anger is expressed in intemperate words which reveal all too well the hatred the technodocs, the pharmacrats, the medical specialists have for women. The mysogyny, accompanied by a real fear that we are making headway against their dreams of controlling the world through women, is apparent in an item titled "Organ Technology" appearing in *Deutsches Arzteblatt* (Newsletter of the German Medical Doctors) of 14 February 1986:

It is rather amusing to see women in politics who have no understanding about their own bodies — this, in fact, from women in two different political parties. According to newspaper reports it seems as if a number of leading ladies from the AsF (the Working Party of Social Democrat Women) have spoken out against *in vitro* fertilisation. Of course, everyone has the right to oppose IVF, but the reasons for doing so should at least be partially correct. But one of them — a medical doctor! — complained that in the IVF procedure, it is the doctor who assumes an 'absolutely domineering position', and what's more, that he is the only person who decides whether a couple is suited for this procedure. But who else, I ask you, should be making this decision since the procedure is indicated according to whether a fallopian tube is irreversibly blocked or doesn't exist at all?

Another woman (the Vice Chairperson of the AsF), lamented the high failure rate which causes women a lot of psychic distress. As a matter of fact, the failure rate of the IVF procedure and the ensuing embryo transfer to the womb is smaller than in the case of an embryo which is produced through fertilization in the fallopian tube of a healthy mother and then tries to implant itself in the womb.

But it gets downright odd when we hear the demand of the same lady (the Vice Chairperson of AsF), that we should stop IVF and instead establish psychological/medical counselling units for couples who remain involuntarily childless. She claims that the IVF procedure reduces sterility to a purely organic problem and is incompatible with holistic medicine. This brings us back to square one; blocked or missing fallopian tubes are, indeed, an organo-technical problem which can be solved only by organo-technical methods. Anyone who could unblock a tube with psychological methods would be a miracle man. It should, of course, be well known that if the sterility has a different cause, other treatment methods must be applied.

Not surprisingly, 'Green Women' do not want to be left behind; and indeed, we hear a Green Member of Parliament say that she believes that the IVF procedure reduces human bodies to a 'storehouse of raw materials' [Rohstofflager]. Well, if we look at the word in a value-free (unbiased) manner, what else should human bodies be considered to be in the context of human reproduction? Nevertheless, there is one grain of truth to it in the case of surrogate motherhood. There, one could even use the term "Rohstofflager" [storehouse of raw materials] in a perjorative sense.[49]

It is clear that women opposing IVF and embryo research as violence against women's human dignity will have to continue to speak up for themselves, for ourselves. We should offer energetic resistance, prepare our own laws, determine to file legal actions against the technodocs and the pharmacrats, and against the hospitals, clinics, or other institutions in which these experiments and surgical operations are carried out on our bodies. And, who knows, perhaps we should even throw a few more stink-bombs. The least we can do is to expose the techno-patriarchal bias of the new reproductive technologies and genetic engineering, and refuse to enter the dialogue on the terms of the technodocs and the clones. We should not forget that women hold one enormous power: techno-patriarchy still needs access to our bodies in order to pursue IVF and embryo research. We can capitalise on this power, refuse them access, and organise — infertile and fertile women together or sep-arate — to fight back and resist becoming test tube women.

*   For the information in this article I am greatly indebted to the participants at the FINNRET (Feminist International Network on New Reproductive Technologies) Emergency Conference on the new reproductive technologies (NRTs) in Sweden in 1985 and the 21 national FINRRAGE (Feminist Inter-national Network of Resistance to Reproductive and Genetic Engineering) contact women who keep sending news to the network. Above all, my deep gratitude goes to Gena Corea, Jalna Hanmer, Janice Raymond and Robyn Rowland without whose constant feedback, comments and generous sharing of their work and friendship the fight against the NRTs would be unbearable and even more depressing than it already is. Finally, my special thanks go to Jocelynne Scutt, without whose efficient and skilful editing and the willing-ness to work with fragments rather than a completed manuscript, there would be no chapter in this book.

Endnotes

1.   Quoted Gena Corea, *The Mother Machine*, 1985, Harper and Row, NY. See also Robyn Rowland, "A Child at any Price?" *Women's Studies Inter-national Forum*, 1985, vol. 8, no. 6, pp. 539–346.

2.   *Report of the Committee of Inquiry Into Human Fertilization and Embry-ology* ("Warnock Committee Report"), 1984, Department of Health and Social Security, London.

3.   Family Law Council (Australia), *Creating Children*, 1985, Attorney Generals Department, Canberra, ACT; Committee to Consider the Social, Ethical and Legal Issues Arising From In Vitro Fertilization, *Report on the Dispositon of Embryos Produced by In Vitro Fertilization* ("Waller Committee Report"), August 1984, Attorney-Generals Department, Melbourne, Victoria.

4.   Ontario Law Reform Commission, *Report on In Vitro Fertilisation*, 1985, Government Printer, Ontario, Canada.

5.   These reports are discussed further in Patricia Spallone, "The Politics of Reproductive Technology: Government Sponsored Committees Reviewing Reproductive Technology and Genetic Engineering" in: *Made to Order: The Myth of Reproductive and Genetic Engineering*, Patricia Spallone and Deborah Lynn Steinberg, editors, forthcoming, Athene Press, England.

6.   Ina Praetorius, "Den Ethickern fällt nichts ein", in *Dokumnetation zum Kongress Frauen gegen Gentechnik und Reproduktionstechnik*, Die Grünen und Sozialwissenschaftliche Forschung und Pracis für Frauen, editors, 1986, Cologne, West Germany, pp. 196–197.

7.   Ruth Hubbard, "Personal Courage is Not Enough" in *Test-Tube Women*, Rita Arditti, Renate Duelli Klein and Shelley Minden, editors, 1984, Pandora Press, London, p. 331.

8.   Agathe Bieri, "Die Forschung ist gut, die Zukunft fantastisch", *Wochenzeitung*, 27 September 1985, no. 39, Zürich, Switzerland, p. 4.

9.   Personal communications; public lecture, King's College, London, 17 February 1986.

10. Renate Duelli Klein, "Doing it Ourselves: Self Insemination" in *Test-Tube Women*, 1984, pp. 382–390.

11. Maxine Clarke, "News", *Nature*, 30 January 1986, vol. 319, p. 349.

12. Mary O'Brien, *The Politics of Reproduction*, 1981, Routledge Kegan Paul, London and Boston.

13. *Ob/Gyn News*, "Information Centre on Substances Harmful to Fetus", 15–31 August 1985, p. 4.

14. Increasingly companies are also being set up to market IVF technology: Fertility and Genetics Research, Inc. 1981 (owned by the Seed Bros. USA — see further Gena Corea, "Women, Class and Reproductive and Genetic Engineering" this volume); and IVF Australia (owned by Monash University — see further Ramona Koval, "The Commercialisation of Reproductive Technology", this volume); also an advertisement published in the *Journal of In Vitro Fertilisation and Embryo Research* in 1985 reads:

Please send curriculum vitae to

IN VITRO CARE, INC.

Attn. Donald P. Jacobs, President
50 Church Street, c/o P.O. Box 267
Cambridge, Massachusetts 02238

15. John C. Fletcher and Joseph Schulman, "Fetal Research: The State of the Question" in *The Hasting Center Report*, April 1985, p. 10.

16. Omar Sattaur, "New Conception Threatened by Old Morality", *New Scientist*, 27 September 1984, pp. 13–14.

17. See generally Helen Roberts, editor, *Women, Health and Reproduction*. 1981. Routledge & Kegan Paul, London.

18. Wendy Farrant, "Who's for Amniocentesis? The Politics of Prenatal Screening" in *The Sexual Politics of Reproduction*, Hilary Homans, editor, 1985, Gower Publishing Company, Aldershot, England, pp. 96–122.

19. Fletcher and Schulman, 1985, p. 8.

20. Warnock Report, 1984, p. 4.

21. John C. Fanta, "Legal Issues Raised by In Vitro Fertilization and Embryo Transfer in the United States", *Journal of In Vitro Fertilization and Embryo Transfer*, 1985, vol. 2, no. 2, pp. 65–86.

22. See Myra Noveck, "Health Ministry inquiry into Eisenberg Death", newspaper report, Israel, August 1985: 'The Health Ministry decided this week to conduct an investigation into the death of Aliza Eisenberg, as a result of the coroner's report. Eisenberg, 37, died two weeks ago at Hadassah Hospital in Ein Kerem after undergoing a procedure that is part of *in vitro* fertilization . . . She had lost consciousness following the procedure and died a few hours later. Aliza's husband Emmanuel has charged gross negligence on the part of the hospital staff for leaving her without treatment until it was too late. A Health Ministry spokeswoman refused to give details of the coroner's report, saying only that Eisenberg's death 'was not by natural causes'. The spokeswoman was also unable to say how long it would take the investigating committee to issue a report.'

23. Even when ripe eggs are found, laparoscopies may be repeated: ripe eggs may be found, but not fertilized; or fertilized, but the pregnancy does not take — so they go back in for more eggs.

24. For an interesting 'fictional case' of egg donation and responses from two experts, see "When Baby's Mother is also Grandma — and Sister" in *The Hastings Center Report*, October 1985, pp. 29–31.

25. Quoted in Gena Corea and Susan Ince, "Report on a Survey of IVF Clinics in the US", 1985, Paper presented at the *Women's Emergency Conference on the New Reproductive Technologies*, Vallinge, Sweden, 3–8 July 1985; pp. 24–25.

26. Andrew Veitch, "Back to Nature Cure for Infertile Women", *The Guardian*, 24 November 1985, London.

27. The state of Victoria, Australia (September 1984) and the United Kingdom (July 1985) are the first to legislate against commercial surrogate motherhood.

28. Robert Winston, Public lecture, see note 9 above.

29. Howard Jones, "First Word", *Omni*, December 1985, Special Issue on new birth technologies, USA, p. 6.

30. See Gena Corea, "How the New Reproductive Technologies Could be Used to Apply the Brothel Model of Social Control over Women", *Women's Studies*

International Forum, 1985, vol. 8, no.4, pp. 299–306; Corea, 1985.

31.   Maria Mies and the editorial board of the *Beitrage zur feministischen Theorie und Praxis* make a very useful clear distinction between a woman's 'right' to her body and a woman's concept of herself as *being* her body. See *Dokumentation zum Kongress Frauen gegen Gentechnik und Reproduktionstechnik*, 1985, p. 7.

32.   For example, Spallone and Steinberg, editors, *Made to Order: The Myth of Reproductive and Genetic Engineering*, forthcoming, Athene Press, England;
a book of papers from the *Liberation or Loss? Women Act on the New Reproductive Technologies* Conference, held in Canberra, ACT, Australia in May 1986 is to be edited and published by Heather Dietrich, Janet Ramsey and Robyn Rowland.

33.   Although these meetings were well attended, enthusiastic and valuable learning processes (at least for the women involved) those working with a traditional perspective on the new reproductive technologies failed to make themselves knowledgable about these important initiatives. In a radio discussion on *Tuesday Despatch*, ABC second network in 1985 the issue of women's activism in England arose in the context of the Warnock Report. Mary Warnock, chairperson of the committee which wrote this report was asked whether there had been feminist input or outspokenness in the way it had been manifested in Australia by Robyn Rowland, in particular. The response was that there was nothing of that sort in England, and indeed all women's responses had been favourable — through the columns of women's magazines.

34.   See report, *Dokumentation zum Kongress Frauen . . .* , 1986.

35.   See Germaine Greer, *Sex and Destiny*, 1985.

36.   In September 1986 the American Fertility Society, a professional association of about 10 000 medical practitioners etc. produced an 'ethics report' on the work being done by its members, concluding it is ethical. The report argues that the United States' Supreme Court would most likely recognize a right to reproduce, at least for married people — a right which would include the human right to use egg and sperm donors and surrogate mothers and, just generally, practice 'medically-assisted reproduction'. But, it adds, some ethical constraints on the right to reproduce do exist. There are a number of grounds, alleges the report, on the basis of which one might have a moral duty not to reproduce. They include: 1. transmission of disease to children (in other words, people have a moral duty not to bring severely handicapped children into the world); 2. unwillingness to provide proper prenatal care; 3. inability to rear children; 4. overpopulation. Personal communication 5 December 1986, Gena Corea. This report appears to fit well with Bernard Davies' statement.

37.   See for example Phyllis Chesler, *Women and Madness*, 1974, Allen Lane, London. Jill Julius Mathews, *Good and Mad Women*, 1985, George Allen and Unwin, Sydney, NSW.

38.   I am grateful to Annika Nilsson of Sweden for her report, "FINNRET/ FINRRAGE Emergency Conference on the New Reproductive Technologies, Vällinge, Sweden, 3–8 July 1985", Translation by Cindy de Wit, *Feminist Forum*, newsletter supplied to regular subscribers of *Women's Studies International Forum*, accompanying that journal, vol. 8, no. 6, pp. i–v, for some of the content in this and immediately following paragraphs.

39. Ana Regina Gomes dos Reis, "IVF in Brazil: The Story as Told by the Newspapers", Paper presented at *FINNRET Emergency Conference* in Sweden, July 1985, unpublished.

40. Gena Corea, "Determining Priorities in Health Resources: The Case of IVF", presented to Law Reform Commission, Victoria, Seminar on Priorities in Health Funding, May 1986, Melbourne, Victoria, Australia.

41. FINRRAGE was formed out of FINNRET at the Emergency Women's Conference in Sweden in July 1985. A central coordinating office, presently located in London, exchanges a vast amount of information on the legal, scientific, feminist and ethical aspects of the debate with women in 21 countries who serve as national contacts. The address is PO Box 583, London NW3 1RQ. A proposal is being circulated for funding an International Feminist Resource and Research Center on Reproductive and Genetic Engineering to take over this (currently unfunded) role.

42. See Zelda d'Aprano, *The Coming of a Woman*, 1977, Sun Books, Melbourne.

43. To be published in Spallone and Steinberg, *Made to Order*, forthcoming; paper presented to the FINNRET Emergency Conference in Sweden, July 1985.

44. Rachel Carson, *Silent Spring*, 1962, Houghton Mifflin, Boston.

45. I am grateful to Francoise Laborie of France for pointing this out to me.

46. Also, there are examples in recent history — for example, the rise of "liberated sexuality" around the turn of the century — in which some feminists associated with so-called progressive male sexologists contributed to the promotion of a sexual ideology which turned out to be detrimental to women's independence: see Sheila Jeffreys, *The Spinster and Her Enemies*, 1985, Pandora Press, London/Boston;
see also Jocelynne A. Scutt, "Confronting Precedent and Prejudice: Child Sexual Abuse and the Courts", Paper presented to the *International Congress on Child Abuse*, Sydney, Australia, 11–14 August 1986.

47. See further, Gena Corea, "What the King Cannot See", Paper presented to conference in Saarbrücken, West Germany, 10 October 1985. (Title in German — 'Was der König Nicht Sehen Kann".)

48. Dale Spender, *For The Record*, 1985, Women's Press, London. The immediately following quotation comes from the same source.

49. Translation by the present author.

12 Epilogue

Jocelynne A. Scutt

[The] *in vitro* fertilisation program is like any other program of medical treatment or health care. It involves a contract based on informed consent between the couple or the patient and the treating doctor or specialist. It is not a contract between a doctor and an embryo . . .

Senator Rosemary Crowley*

. . . we strongly support the understanding that medical and scientific research should be 'of service' to the people, not vice versa . . .

Senator Crowley and Senator Olive Zakharov*

At the close of the 1980s the voices clamouring for more 'progress' through new reproductive technologies and genetic engineering were no less pronounced. Despite continuing funding cutbacks in health and a lack of resources for preventative health programmes and programmes for the disadvantaged, those working in new reproductive technologies and genetic engineering continued even more strongly to demand that government recognise their value and support them directly by way of more and more funds. Threats of a 'brain drain' of scientists and specialists to overseas climes continue.

Senate Hansard, Debate on Human Embryo Experimentation, 8 October 1986, p. 980

**Dissenting Report in *Report of Senate Select Committee on the Human Embryo Experimentation Bill 1985*, 1986, AGPS, Canberra, ACT, p. 91

Calls for a national body to be established by the federal government to oversee or advise on bio-ethical issues surrounding developments in the field, though more muted and less likely to be reported by the media than the voices for 'progress' were acknowledged in 1987 with a government proposal to set up the body. In 1988 the national council came into being. Yet federal and state government ministers continue to cite biotechnology as the prime example of innovative research and development, and the premier drive for exporting Australian produce and expertise. Monash Medical Centre IVF Australia has been matched by a similar initiative by a Western Australian company.

Opposition to these 'advances,' or even requests that there be fully open debate, continues to be portrayed often by those in favour of the technologies and by some sections of the media as antedeluvian, scare-mongering or 'mad Right'/'mad Left'; or simply not heard at all. Yet simultaneously there appears to have been a growth (albeit small) of more balanced coverage, with media articles and programmes more often pointing out the pitfalls of IVF, or the 'downside' of genetic engineering and other biotechnologies. Less often are these isolated instances of a lone journalist developing a perception about the area or exercising a critical faculty. At the same time, developments have continued to leap forward.

Two themes, whether or not explicit, underlie the continuing debate on new reproductive technologies and genetic engineering where led by those 'for' such progress. One is that the technologies are for the benefit of those entering programmes as recipients (or 'patients'), and thereby to the benefit of society as a whole. The second is that as the days, months and years are chalked up in the hospitals, clinics and medical laboratories, 'success' rates will improve, techniques will become (even!) more proficient, the laboratory process will show itself to be far superior to the old fashioned, natural way of reproducing children. But even were all this true, reservations demand a voice. Even more disturbing, the evidence is that both themes are false: benefits to recipients and society remain questionable; improvement with time is not the reality of the programmes.

LATEST MEASURES OF 'SUCCESS'

The statistics of 'success'

In a study reported in the December 1987 issue of the *Australian Medical Journal* Dr. Ditta Bartels of the University of New South

Wales analyses the most recent statistics available from the National Perinatal Statistics Unit at Sydney University, finding the 'success' rate on IVF programmes as measuring 7.9 per cent only.[1] This is far *less* than the 15 to 20 per cent cited so frequently for Australian IVF programmes. Time has not increased the measurement of success; even if 7.9 per cent is simply a more accurate measurement, if it continues to be argued that time has led to improved success rates, then what was the true measure in past years?

In the April 1987 issue of the *Medical Journal of Australia* R.P. Jansen found that a monthly probability of pregnancy of 25% to 30% appeared to be achievable in the 'best' units, including Monash University, Bourn Hall in Cambridge, England, and the University of Eastern Virginia in Norfolk, Virginia, in the USA.[2] As Dr. Bartels observes, this 'fits in with the prevalent perception among medical practitioners and the general public that in-vitro fertilization programmes constitute a most effective way to ensure that infertile women give birth to healthy babies.'

Yet in addition to biochemical pregnancies being classified so as to be included in the 'success' category of 'pregnancy', as Bartels writes:

> . . . in-vitro fertilization pregnancies can also result in spontaneous abortions, when products of conception are passed, which occur between six and 19 weeks after the last menstrual period. [Also], ectopic pregnancies are recorded separately, and finally, pregnancies which proceed beyond 20 weeks are termed to be viable.
>
> The Perinatal Statistics Unit [in Sydney] recorded a total of 1510 in-vitro fertilization pregnancies for the period 1979 to 1985. Of these pregnancies, 251 pregnancies terminated in a preclinical abortion [biochemical pregnancy], 292 pregnancies terminated in a spontaneous abortion and 65 pregnancies were ectopic. Taking these outcomes into account, the original figure of 1510 pregnancies is reduced to 902 viable pregnancies.

The number of children born on in-vitro programmes is itself not a measure of how many infertile women (or women with infertile husbands) bore children whilst on IVF: of the 902 viable pregnancies, 22.2% were multiple, with 169 of them twin and 32 triplet pregnancies.

Analysing statistics of 'success' based on in-vitro fertilisation pregnancies against her success measure of births of live, healthy babies, Dr. Bartels concludes:

During [1980 to 1984], 885 women underwent a total of 1775 treatment cycles; about half the women received two treatments and four women received as many as eight treatments each. The interesting conclusion . . . reached was that the chance that a woman would achieve an in-vitro fertilisation pregnancy was not diminished by her previous number of failures. Over the five-year period, the Monash group's pregnancy rates per treatment cycle fluctuated somewhat, with the highest rate of 15.7% being achieved in 1984.

The Monash group is, of course, the most successful in-vitro fertilization group in Australia, and possibly world-wide. Even so, according to [an analysis of live, healthy births in contradistinction to 'pregnancy rates'], *a woman who undergoes an in-vitro fertilization treatment cycle has only a 7.9% chance of giving birth to a live and healthy baby.* (Emphasis added.)

This is for the 'most successful in-vitro fertilization group in Australia, and possibly world-wide'. At other IVF centres, Bartels adds, this chance 'decreases considerably':

> . . . so much so that it comes into the range of failure rates for contraception with an intrauterine device! In other words, *a fertile woman who is fitted with an intrauterine contraceptive device has almost as much chance of becoming pregnant as does an infertile woman of having a healthy baby after an in-vitro fertilization treatment cycle.* (Emphasis added.)

Can the expenditure of funds continue to be justified against such a low 'return', even apart from women's (and children's) health and other ethical (and practical) issues?

'Success', women's health and wellbeing

And not only are the so-called success rates of today evidence of a singular lack of success. Evidence that women's health and wellbeing are not enhanced by new reproductive technologies was growing rather than lessening in the late 1980s. The practice in the international IVF professional community is to describe women in programmes as 'patients'. Certainly use of this terminology for women who are or are trying to become pregnant automatically classes well women together with the sick. Studies of the women tend to find they exhibit ill health in many instances — but through participation in the programmes themselves! As Klein says: '. . . in many instances it is only whilst on the IVF programme that women get physically or mentally sick.' She has also pointed out that despite the publicly voiced sympathy with involuntarily child-less people:

> . . . women who decide to try IVF are depicted as oddities or even deviants or in the words of a German psychiatrist, Peter Petersen, an opponent of IVF, as displaying 'emotional passivity, a dearth of feelings', 'pathological' and with a psyche . . . structured in a way which would make their becoming mothers and rearing a child of their own problematic.[3]

In *Tages Anzeiger Magazin*, published in Zurich, Switzerland on 28 February 1987, Christian Bachmann predicted problems for IVF children, because of their 'emotionally insecure mothers who needed a child for their "narcissistic equilibrium"'.

Klein's survey of women in IVF programmes found them to be 'ordinary' women 'whose determination in life to have a (or an-other) child does not make them more or less 'neurotic' than others who would try everything to win a medal in a sporting event'. Yet, as she says of the Petersen and Bachmann analyses:

> Such male interpretations do not acknowledge the societal pressures on women to become mothers. They conveniently blame women for 'wanting it'. They thus create a paradoxical mixture of contempt and pity for women on IVF programmes and also bestow upon themselves the right to use 'these women' as experimental fodder.

The latest response to such criticisms of IVF programmes appears to be to acknowledge a need for counselling for IVF 'patients'. Thus following the delivery by Dr. Renate Klein of a speech at the conference of the Federation of Australian University Women Graduates where she raised these issues, *The West Australian* of 11 January 1988 reported 'New IVF back-ups planned':

> Australia's 15 in-vitro fertilisation clinics planned to put a heavy emphasis on the personal and social effects on couples involved in IVF programmes, the president of the Fertility Society of Australia, Dr. John Yovich, said in Perth yesterday.
> He said that for the first 10 years of IVF the emphasis was on technology but counselling was now recognised as one of its most important components . . .

Yet is the counselling for problems women bring with them to the programmes — or for problems created by, and on, those pro-grammes? Why not counsel women *out* of even entering into pro-grammes? Avenues can be opened that do not trap women on the reproductive roller coaster. Women need to see themselves as, and know themselves to be, human beings of importance and relevance whether or not they biologically reproduce. Women need to have opportunities made and presented which create fulfilled and ful-filling lives, not just further indoctrination of 'persuasion' into seeing themselves as invalid, as 'nothing' without a baby (or a 'viable pregnancy').

And IVF 'counselling' cannot 'correct' other detriments to women's health. Long term effects of hormonal stimulation of women undergoing treatment remain unknown at the end of the 1980s, but information is now becoming available which shows the underlying danger of the new reproductive technologies. Carter and Joyce report an instance seeming to support the view that superovulation may promote cancerous cell growth. In the *Journal of In Vitro Fertilisation* they write of a 25 year old woman undergo-ing hyperstimulation on an IVF programme in Bristol in the United Kingdom, which led to rapidly developing cancer covering both ovaries, appendix, uterus and bladder.[4]

Other dangers for women are apparent. On 5 August 1987 *The West Australian* reported the death of a woman on an IVF pro-gramme. On Saturday 23 April 1988 a second woman died on a Western Australian IVF programme, *The Age* of 25 April 1988 reporting she 'went into a coma during an IVF operation 12 days earlier'. The woman, in her 30s, had a laparoscopy operation to collect eggs at the King Edward Memorial Hospital IVF clinic. A coroner's inquest will be held into her death. *The Age* reported that a clinic spokesperson said the woman 'had been transferred to the Sir Charles Gairdner Hospital after the resuscitation at the clinic. Dr. Bellinge said it was an unfortunate coincidence that the woman had died during an IVF procedure. "Of course, IVF is bearing the brunt of that," he said.' These deaths are to be added to other reported deaths, one in Israel and one in Brazil.[5] In February 1988 in Melbourne, Australia the bodies of a woman, her husband, and seriously wounded mother were discovered in their home in what is classed an 'elite' suburb, Toorak. The morn-ing after the discovery *The Sun*, a Melbourne newspaper, reported the event under the heading 'Bizarre Suicide'. (It seemed the ap-parent killing of the woman by her husband, and shooting of his mother-in-law, were insufficiently important to make the headline — unless the epithet 'bizarre' was intended to include the loss of the one life, serious damage to the other. It was the husband who suicided.) One of the reasons for the killing, suicide, and wounding was, surmised *The Sun*, that the woman/wife had been an IVF participant who had undergone several treatments without being 'successful'. Another Melbourne paper, *The Herald*, in the afternoon carried a detailed account from the woman's doctor about her participation in the IVF programme.

On a broader scale, 'success' in programmes involving women and reproduction must be questioned. In 1987 the 'frozen sister' advance found its way into media headlines: a test-tube sister of an English IVF child (who in 1985 had been 'harvested' from the same egg-crop — a phrase coined by an Australian IVF practitioner) was born; the second child was, as an egg, frozen then thawed and implanted in her mother's womb some 18 months later — 'twins' born some two years apart.[6] In that same year the world learned of the 47 year old South African woman who gave birth to triplets developed from her own daughter's fertilized eggs which were implanted in her (the daughter's) mother's (the triplets' grandmother/mother) uterus. At the Forum International Sur les Nouvelles Technologies de la Reproduction Humaine organised by the Office of the Status of Women, held at the Université Concordia in Montreal, Canada from 29-31 October 1987, the Swiss biologist Dr. Renate Klein reported further on the wide spectrum of successes claimed in the reproductive field, raising the question of what qualifies as 'success':

> . . . the 'reproductive supermarket' . . . has also given us a pool of human eggs to choose from at the Cleveland Clinic in Ohio, USA, and a host of new IVF techniques: PROST — putting the fertilised egg back at the end of the fallopian tubes — or a recent 'success' from London: a pregnancy achieved through the replacement of a donated frozen embryo in the fallopian tube. And we have Michele, the child born seven weeks after her mother was declared dead from a brain tumor but kept alive on a life-support until the birth, and the baby girl without a brain . . . carried to term by her mother, artificially kept alive and flown from Canada to California to have her heart donated to a new born boy with a heart problem.
>
> All these events are hailed as 'successes' by those who seem to perceive women as birth machines whose parts can be combined at will and whose mental state whilst being used as temporary breeders or anxiously waiting to find out whether the embryos are inserted in their wombs would 'take' are of no importance whatsoever.[7]

Klein comments that in contrast to those seeing these events as successes, she views them as 'dehumanising experimentation: as treating women's bodies and minds as matter that is not part of a living being'. The dehumanising aspect becomes most obvious, she writes, in a new method termed 'Intravaginal Culture and Embryo Transfer' which is described as providing 'a simple, fast, and inexpensive approach to fertilisation and culture of human oocytes'. Once the oocytes have been extracted and fertilized, the resultant embryos are put into an hermetically sealed tube and 'placed in the mother's vagina, held in place by a diaphragm, for an incubation period of 44 to 50 hours'. This new technique was promoted by its inventor, Dr. Ranoux of the University Clinic in Paris (who earned a prize for the technique), as superior to other methods:

> Intravaginal culture simplifies the laboratory manipulations needed for *in vitro* fertilization, since no incubator or carbon dioxide is needed.

Dr. Klein responds:

> 'No incubator is needed . . .'!? — or should one say that, as the technodocs see it, the new technology helps a woman to assume her proper role? As Ireland's leading IVF specialist, Roby Harrison, puts it: 'The best incubator is the one God provided.' I can hardly envisage a more reductionist picture of a woman than a body whose vagina incubates her own future child in a test-tube.

'Success' for babies and children?

What of the (few though they are) 'end results' of the programmes — the longed-for babies? Evidence is growing of harm on this side of the equation, too. Of the 902 viable pregnancies recorded by the National Perinatal Statistics Unit at the University of New South Wales (out of a total of 1510 in-vitro fertilization pregnancies for the period 1979 to 1980 in Australia and New Zealand), Bartels reports that in 47 the babies were dead at birth or died soon thereafter.[8] She continues:

> In 25 pregnancies, the babies had major congenital defects, and in 112 pregnancies, the babies were severely premature, and weighed less than 2000 g.
>
> Since there is some overlap among the pregnancies that led to dead, defective and seriously underweight babies, and disaggregated figures are not provided [in the 1987 National Perinatal Statistics Unit] report, we cannot be entirely specific as to the total number of problematical pregnancies. However, on the basis of Tables 35, 37, 41 and 42 in the report, we can estimate that there were at least 140 such pregnancies . . .

Dr. Paul Lancaster, Director of the National Perinatal Statistics Unit, examined 1700 live IVF births in Australia and New Zealand between 1979 and 1986, comparing this group with the general population of new born children. He found IVF babies had five times the expected rate of spina bifida and 6.7 times the expected rate of a major heart defect ('transposition of the great vessels' or 'transposition'). The numbers in the study were small (because of the low number of children born from new reproductive technology): there were six IVF infants with spina bifeda, four with transposition. The six children born with spina bifida came from three of the large IVF units; the four others came from different units. It is ironic that those units having the greatest injection of funds and other resources should be those producing babies having birth defects. And although Lancaster concluded, in an article published in the British medical journal *The Lancet*, in December 1987:

> . . . further data from other IVF groups are needed to determine whether spina bifida, transposition, and possibly other malformations occur more often than usual . . .

as he also acknowledges, the numbers are statistically significant.

This scientific news is additionally important as it runs in direct opposition to earlier tales of children born through IVF being 'more perfect than perfect', 'geniuses' and 'of superior quality'. Yet the way in which this tragic reality is sought to be countered is either by casting responsibility for the defect upon the child's mother, or continuing to promote the idea that children born through IVF and other reproductive technologies are generally 'better' than those born by ordinary biological means.

Thus in *The Age* of 8 January 1988, Philip McIntosh reported upon Dr. Lancaster's birth defect findings in an article titled: 'Birth defects raise new questions about IVF.' In response to the statistics, Dr. John Yovich, president of the Fertility Society of Australia and head of the Perth IVF programme is reported as saying that if IVF did cause an increased rate of birth abnormalities, 'the problem would relate to either the patients or the techniques'. McIntosh reports Yovich's views:

> The problem could arise from laboratory techniques, including the manipulation of sperm and eggs, and the use of drugs to stimulate ovulation. But Dr. Yovich argued that *it was more likely to be a factor in women themselves.*
>
> 'We've got to appreciate that there's an age factor. The woman having an IVF pregnancy is generally older than the average woman

having a natural pregnancy in Australia. It could explain the higher incidence of birth defects.

'Another aspect of the patients that has not yet been answered is whether women who are infertile are more likely to generate problems of pregnancy than a woman who conceives easily.' For example, it was often reported that sub-fertile women had a miscarriage rate of about 30 per cent, which might be 10 per cent higher than for women not sub-fertile. (Emphasis added.)

Dr. John McBain, a gynaecologist in the reproductive biology unit at the Royal Women's Hospital in Melbourne told McIntosh it was 'widely held by teratologists' (doctors specialising in the study of birth defects) that 'some environmental factor is creeping in after conception and implantation'. McIntosh goes on:

Dr. Yovich said spina bifida and transposition 'are not the kind of abnormalities we would have expected to see if we had some defects in laboratory techniques'.

Dr. Robyn Rowland of Deakin University strongly criticises the idea that birth defects in children born on IVF programmes is the 'fault' of their mothers. She believes it is 'peculiar' to promote the view that embryos, in the whole process of manipulation involved in new reproductive technology programmes, 'would remain undamaged':

'Any part of the problem could be the answer. The first thing I would look at is the chemical cocktail used to superovulate the women,' she said. 'What you are asking the body to do is to produce at the wrong time, and in inordinately large numbers compared to the normal situation, a huge harvest of eggs.'

Philip McIntosh continues:

Dr. Rowland said we needed to know which women gave birth to these babies. 'Were these women on programs because their husbands were infertile? Was it donor sperm? Was it a woman who merely had a tubal blockage?'

She said the only problem in many of the women in IVF programs was tubal. If this was the case with the reported abnormalities — and there was nothing wrong with the eggs, the ovaries or anything else — she said that she could not see how that could cause a birth abnormality.

The idea that 'defects in laboratory techniques' are not responsible for producing spina bifida babies through IVF, or babies suffering from transposition of the great vessels (of the heart), and that 'some environmental factor is creeping in after conception and implantation' is reported by McIntosh as being a view 'strongly rejected by one of Australia's leading experts in birth defects, Professor David Danks':

> 'I think it's quite ridiculous to say that if something like IVF is going to increase the frequency of an abnormality, then you could predict what sort of abnormality it would be.
>
> 'I think one ought to have a totally open mind about (a) whether it does or does not cause abnormalities, and (b) if it is capable of interfering with development, what sort of errors could occur.'
>
> Professor Danks said he was not sure what the gynaecologists meant when they talked about environmental effects: whether they meant something in the woman's environment rather than the embryo's environment.
>
> 'I would regard as an environmental effect anything other than the genes in the cells. Spending part of their career in the laboratory and part being implanted in the uterus is clearly an alteration of the normal environment of the cells that are going to become an embryo.'

But whatever the cause of birth defects in these cases, the result is that women are being subjected more frequently to pre-natal tests, and with increased publicity about the defects that battery of tests is bound to increase. Thus infertility specialists emphasise to all doctors having the care of women on IVF programmes that these pregnancies 'may have special problems and may need special vigilence'. Dr. McBain says:

> Our advice to doctors *looking after IVF pregnancies* is to do an ultrasound scan at 18 weeks. This will pick up 95 per cent of spina bifidas and, under optimal conditions, it will also pick up transposition. (Emphasis added.)

The other method of discounting the risks of reproductive technology is to promote with even greater vigour the 'beautiful/clever/super baby' image. Articles in this vein continue to abound. Thus on 12 December 1987 *The Age* published a (somewhat tongue in cheek) feature story by Katharine Lowry in Los Angeles, 'Survival of the cleverest'. Three children — 'Ashley Bradley', Leanndra Ramm, and Doron Blake — are described by their parents and the founder of the spermbank from whose repository the children were fertilized, by the epithets 'amazing', 'genius', 'highly gifted' . . . Ashley's father 'Jeff' 'tells stories illustrating Ashley's amazing sense of direction, her long-term memory and her powers of association'. Doron Blake's mother Afton says that although barely five, Doron's 'grasp of mathematics is that of a second or third-grader. Just for fun, he likes to multiply in his head, and the abstract paintings along one wall fuel his mother's hope that, like his namesake, her son may grow up to be a visionary poet and artist'.

Lowry reports that according to the founder of the spermbank, Robert Klark Graham ('a slender, handsome 81-year-old with close-cropped hair') these children:

> . . . are hardly exceptions. Almost all the repository's babies reach developmental milestones much earlier than most toddlers. Their dexterity, he adds, is such that many of them walk before the age of one; they also talk and utter complete sentences long before Dr. Spock says they should . . .
>
> Graham concedes that environment does play a part but only a small one. 'The comforts of modern civilisation have thwarted natural selection, allowing the less fit to survive, even thrive,' he says . . .

The idea that if a couple has sufficient money, they have a right to 'the best' of everything — including 'the best' child — and *that money can in fact buy this* (and *buy it from a reproductive technology programme*) permeates the thinking:

> Speaking about the generally negative reaction people have about tampering with reproductive fate, Anne's husband Jeff [Bradley] is genuinely bewildered. 'Why is it all right for people to choose the best house, the best school, the best surgeon, the best car, but not try to have the best baby possible?'

If 'best' is measured in the terms Jeff Bradley attributes to it, then going on an IVF programme is no assurance that this will be the end result.

But the potential damage to children born through new reproductive technology programmes does not show up necessarily at birth. The now traditional technique of Artificial Insemination by Donor (AID) has been regarded, generally, as straight forward, simple, and lacking in any or most of the ethical and health-orientated complexities that may surround IVF, Embryo Transfer (ET) and other surgically intrusive methods. Yet children born by AID are now expressing reservations, and indeed distress, about their mode of coming into being. Ivor Davis reports in *The Weekend Australian* of 16-17 January 1988 of the case of Suzanne Rubin, a Los Angeles teacher who when she was 32 years of age discovered that the man she had 'called father all her life was not and that, on one side, she was descended from a frozen file in a nitrogen tank'. Davis continues:

> It produced in her a rage which sent her on a campaign to find the anonymous medical student who had given her life. By a tortuous process of elimination she found out that her father was one of fifty-five Jewish medical students at the University of Southern California in the 1950s. Geneticists at the university told her he would have had blue eyes and either red hair or relatives with red hair. That narrowed it down to 10. She doesn't expect to like him much if she finds him.
> 'What kind of man drops off his sperm, collects $25 for it and then walks off with no thought of responsibility?' she says bitterly. 'I don't hate him but I have a tough time saying my father sold me for that amount.'

With the evidence of the unhappiness and perennial searching for their biological parents on the part of many children who were adopted in past years, it is no surprise that new reproductive technologies should be sparking new waves of children, now grown, or growing up, to follow in a like pattern.

Sadly, it can also be of little surprise that these new methods were plunged into, and continue to proliferate, without solid and sustained consideration being given by community, government, and those most intimately connected with the programmes (whether as 'team' members running them, or recipients of, or participants in, them), to the consequences to be served upon the children thus conceived and born (however few in number). Of course, it might be argued that because so few children are in fact born through IVF, and comparatively few AID children, and not all have concerns about origins and biological parentage, in global terms the sum of unhappiness and distress thereby caused will be negligible. Yet can this seriously be taken as an answer? Individual participants in new reproductive technology programmes may protest: 'I have thought about it.' 'I intend to tell my child everything and assist her/him to find the biological father/mother.' Or: 'I can make sure, and will be sure, that she/he never finds out about her/his origins, so the problem just won't arise.' But individual concern is not enough.

GENETIC ENGINEERING

Problems experienced by those born through AID (and other methods) and concerned to establish their biological roots could be labelled a 'technologically induced "identity crisis"'. One way of addressing the issue is to advocate more, rather than less (or no), artificially induced pregnancies; more, rather than less (or no), AID/IVF/ET . . . children. If those having queries about their biological origins number into thousands, and grow more common sooner, rather than later, then another sort of 'naturalness' will attach to artificial conception and birth. That very 'naturalness' will render of less and less concern the question of origins. Or at least, making the search for biological origins more common by the very reason of numbers, artificially conceived children need no longer for that reason believe themselves to be 'different', 'odd', or 'peculiar', nor think of their sperm-parent (or ova-parent) as an unfeeling oddity who exchanged a portion of what became the child's chromosomal or genetic make-up for a dollar fee, or (where legislation prohibits payment, apart from travel expenses) for the price of the bus fare!

Another way to answer the issue is by directing attention at short-term rather than long-term problems: if we can expediently deal with current crises of identity, what care we for future crises developed out of the answers devised for the problems of the present? That is, if infertility causes distress and unhappiness today, which (though it is begging the question) can be 'solved' by IVF, AID and other reproductive technologies, let's hasten with that 'cure'. Who knows what may happen down the track? No doubt someone will 'invent' a 'cure' for our now technologically induced identity crises?

For the immediate problems confronting IVF programmes, in the revelation of spina bifida and transposition as affecting statistically significant numbers of children (or indeed *any* IVF children), the 'answer' can be genetic engineering for the one, surgery for the other; or simply more experimentation on ova, sperm, and embryos until these 'flaws' in the technology (or the women's bodies!) can be overcome (or so say the technocrats).

Politics of genetic engineering

Within the new reproductive technology and genetic engineering community there appears to be some ambivalence, at least on the part of some practitioners. Often the approach differs as to what the public 'should know'. Where protests are made by laypersons, or even by scientists or other professionals, about perceived dangers of genetic engineering and experimentation, the response is frequently that of declaring that the protestors are 'exaggerating' the possibilities of genetic engineering or, more bluntly, simply don't know what they are talking about; that they are making claims for genetic engineering ('gene therapy') and genetic engineers ('gene therapists') which are outside contemplation or even if within contemplation could never come to pass. On the other hand, where practitioners seek support and funding from government for genetic engineering programmes and genetic experimentation, and support from the community, they do so by promoting the 'wonders' of genetic engineering and the 'immeasurable benefits' genetic engineering and experimentation will bring.

Some of the most outlandish sounding tales of genetic engineering possibilities are actually with us, but when women activists in the 1970s and 1980s predicted their coming, or highlighted in public forums research studies ordinarily available only to the scientific community, those activists were sought to be ridiculed by that very community.[9] In the early and mid-1980s the Australian science writer, broadcaster and lecturer Ramona Koval raised in her public lectures the fact that geneticists were searching for a way to strip fleece from sheep in one piece, through genetic means, without the need for traditional shearing. She was often met with disbelief or an initial lack of comprehension. Some professionals attempted to convey the idea that this was just one more example of 'tall tale telling'. Because the case of genetic 'shearing' was difficult to believe for those who knew nothing of genetic engineering and its possibilities, there was a tendency on the part of some of the public, at least, to discount this along with other aims of genetic engineers and experimenters.

Yet in the late 1980s, the tune has changed. As John I'ons reported in *The Weekend Australian* of 23-24 January 1988, Coopers Animal Health Australia Limited in collaboration with Wellcome Biotechnology has developed the production of epidermal growth factor ('EGF') through biotechnology as a step along the way to the ideal: having sheep shed fleece 'all in one go'. I'ons writes:

> Since the only source of EGF was the salivary glands of mice, getting enough for laboratory testing was bad enough, let alone producing sufficient for large-scale field trials or commercial use.
> Then, a development in fundamental science came to the rescue. The increased sophistication of genetic engineering ushered in a means of manufacturing EGF in relatively large amounts. All that was needed was to insert EGF genes into common bacteria which then became a sort of biological factory for the compound.

As he points out, there remains the problem of taking the loosened fleece from the sheep without any loss or damage. Dr. Trevor Scott, who heads the CSIRO (Commonwealth Scientific and Industrial Research Organisation):

> . . . says the initial aim was to administer just enough EGF to weaken the fleece to the point where it could be pulled off easily without falling off of its own accord. 'Inject too much and the wool would fall off in the paddock, too little and it would stubbornly resist being plucked by hand,' he says . . .
>
> A local partnership, Nimmity Coats, engaged in the manufacture of protective coverings for sheep, suggested netting as a simple solution. Wrapped in a jacket of this material, the fleece can be kept in place on the animal until it is time to remove it in the shed. 'The fleece retains its integrity and can be thrown on to a table and skirted,' says Dr. Scott.

There remain problems — such as the expense of producing EGF, 'despite the wonders of genetically-engineered biological mass production'; checks on whether EGF has deleterious effects upon rams' fertility (checks have been made which, so far, report no deleterious effects upon ewes' fertility); checks upon whether there is any impairment of textile properties of biologically shorn wool (such as weakening of the fibres induced by EGF carrying over to quality of garments produced from the wool); and developing and marketing 'the package' to farmers. Yet now it is clearly being acknowledged, publicly, that genetic shearing of sheep is not a 'gleam in a mad scientist's eye' — nor an 'exaggeration' on the part of those seeking to bring to public attention the experimentation and plans of workers in the field of genetic engineering.

Similarly in *The Weekend Australian* of 16-17 January 1988 Julian Cribb reported, under the heading 'Monster Magic . . . And animals tailored to order': 'The creation of a race of man-made super-animals is no longer simply a gleam in a mad scientist's eye, given the dramatic progress taking place in livestock genetics around the world.' He goes on:

> A motley assortment of strangely harlequin beasts, creatures with four parents or more, animals that produce young utterly different to themselves, and long lines of eerily identical clones are starting to populate the world's live-stock laboratories.
>
> The genetic revolution, until recently a thing of science fiction, is fast becoming a fact.
>
> In Australia and overseas, the race is on to create the super livestock of the 21st century as the frontiers of genetics are rolled back.

The griffin may remain a creature of heraldry and mythology — but the chimera no longer is . . .

Again, CSIRO is reported as being involved in 'making several breakthroughs . . . [which] may well launch Australia's beef industry on its next big phase of genetic gain and financial prosperity . . .' One example of how this might be done is to produce a chimera 'consisting of a normal bull equipped with genetically outstanding testes — in other words, a plain bull that would throw champion offspring'. Another 'prime target for the geneticists' is gene transfer, or the production of transgenic animals 'carrying new and enhanced genes for particular purposes such as increased growth, improved wool, better disease resistance and so on . . .'

Thus, at the close of the 1980s it is apparent that a significant change has taken place. Rather than keep these 'wonders' back from public view (through isolating discussion in scientific and agricultural journals, and in academic circles, only), there is an increasing tendency to publicise genetic engineering and experimentation as being commercially significant, or having commercial potential. It can be no coincidence that this occurs at a time when government agencies are under pressure to perform in accordance with rigorous management standards, to produce value for the public purse and, in sum, to embrace economic rationalism. Nor can it be coincidence that the publicity runs hand in hand with increasing praise on the part of government ministers, state and federal, for biotechnology and its perceived value to Australia in economic terms. Now that the 'money spinning' aspect of genetic engineering and experimentation has gained such a dominant role in the economic debate, little wonder that earlier attempts to keep the field out of the sight of all apart from those working in genetics and reproductive technologies are being replaced with a new, public, entrepreneurial fervour.

Human genetic engineering and experimentation

A similar politic appears to be driving genetic engineering and experimentation in the human field into broad public view, where it is invariably combined with a 'human face' rationale: so many people *will* (less often 'may') be helped by the wonders of biotechnology, who otherwise would live short lives of torment, or not live at all. Popular magazines and newspapers now carry stories of developments and benefits, present and proposed, in genetic technology. The *Good Weekend* of 19 September 1987 carried a

five-page feature article by Bob Beale titled 'Designer Genes —
Fashioning the future or shrinking rights?' It concentrated upon
defects identifiable as genetic in origin, and about which most
public discussion has taken place during the late 1980s — thalassemia and haemophilia. But additionally Beale raised the identification of genes by researchers as increasing an individual's
susceptibility to heart attacks, juvenile diabetes, multiple sclerosis,
some (rare) forms of cancer, and some forms of emphysema. Some
evidence shows genes playing a part in alcoholism, schizophrenia,
Alzheimer's disease, cleft palate, manic depression in some forms,
and a rare intestinal cancer, he reports. Professor David Danks,
director of Murdoch Institute for Research into Birth Defects,
located in Melbourne, is reported as saying that over the past
decade it has become possible for up to 200 genetic disorders to
be diagnosed with high levels of accuracy.

In the Fifth Keith Roby Lecture in Community Science, presented at Murdoch University in Western Australia on 14 October
1987, Dr. Ditta Bartels of the School of Science and Technology
Studies in the University of New South Wales spoke of 'The Engineering of Reproduction: Is it heading off the rails?' Amongst
other matters she raised the issue of recombinant DNA technology:

> . . . the geneticists have come up with [a] . . . spectacular break-
> through based on genetic engineering or recombinant DNA tech-
> nology. This is the development of so-called gene probes which are
> purified and radioactively labelled stretches of DNA. Depending
> on the conditions that are investigated the gene probes are either
> whole genes or fractions of genes. Their main property is that they
> bind to DNA in a highly specific way, and so a gene probe for sickle
> cell disease, for example, binds to the DNA of a person or foetus
> with the disease, but not to the DNA of a normal individual. There
> are now over 3 000 genetic diseases known [according to the ex-
> perts], and in principle the new technology of gene probes should
> permit the detection of all of them.[10]

Bartels went on to point out that commercial interests assert that
if diagnostic kits could be produced containing gene probes for
'a whole range of genetic defects', then it (so they say) becomes
worthwhile for large numbers of pregnant women to seek gene
diagnosis of their fetuses:

> It is obvious that as genetic technology becomes more powerful,
> and many of the 3 000 genetic conditions can be detected by means
> of gene probes, more and more women will opt for the genetic
> diagnosis of their foetuses. In turn, this will increase the market for
> the production and distribution of gene diagnosis test kits.

On the basis of such expectations, she reported, 'the production of gene probes has become big business in the United States'. An estimate has been made of the market being over three million pregnancies annually in the USA. The Congressional Office of Technology Assessment reports in a 1987 survey that over 50 companies are involved in research and development on gene probes. These companies will be striving to market their technology as widely as possible, not only in the United States' market, but worldwide, in order not only to survive, but to expand.

Bartels notes that if prenatal testing for genetic defects is relevant to women participating in new reproductive technology programmes, then it is relevant to all those women 'who would like to feel assured right from the start of their pregnancy that they are not carrying a genetically defective offspring' (that is, women outside IVF programmes as well). These women therefore 'become potential clients of IVF', because an early embryo produced by IVF is the target of testing for the whole range of genetic conditions. If an embryo is found to be defective during such a test, then it will not be inserted into the woman's uterus:

> Undoubtedly this will appeal to a large number of women, particularly to those who have left reproduction for late in life. This is in fact the market that the commercial companies involved in the development of gene probes are interested in. With around 50 companies in this business, we can be sure that the new conjunction of the field of IVF with that of gene diagnosis will be pushed ahead at an accelerating rate.

Of course, an alternative is that the panoply of tests is relevant neither to women in IVF programmes, nor to pregnant women achieving this state outside IVF. How accurate are the tests? What are the conditions that are being 'detected'? Is it in fact necessary to eliminate all embryos which are ruled 'defective' by gene probes? This opens up a whole new area: can these 'genetic conditions' really be located on the genes by the technology? And what of the socio-economic and environmental components of so-called genetic defects? Because embryos produced through IVF are more likely to harbour conditions that may make life intolerable or impossible, the result seems to be the generation of new commercial interests and initiatives: the money machine rolls on (catching up natural conceptions in its forward movement); the real value of this mode of production or reproduction, its fixation on the technological 'fix', is never questioned or, if questioned, in the name of economic expansion and scientific progress the questioners are overridden.

What if genetic defects are detected whilst the embryo is in the womb — say by chorionic villus biopsy or amniocentesis; or if detected outside the womb in an IVF programme, whilst in the petri dish, but the woman (or couple, or husband) does not want the embryo destroyed, deciding to go ahead with the pregnancy despite any perceived genetic deficiency? The next step is to eliminate the 'bad' genes or work on 'correcting' any 'deficiencies' of those to be retained.

Experiments are continuing in the animal world of agriculture. In his *Weekend Australian* article Julian Cribb reports:

> Dr. Murray and Dr. Ward [in Sydney, Australia] achieved their supersheep by directly injecting into the fertilised egg the DNA containing the growth hormone gene and the switching gene.
>
> Scientists around the world are experimenting with more precise methods of injecting new genes into embryos.
>
> One method, explains Dr. Pashen [an Australian scientist working at the United States university, Davis, in California], is the use of embryonic stem cells, which can be grown in a culture, equipped with the desired gene, and then introduced into a growing embryo.

The aim is also to ensure that cells ultimately carrying the desired gene are present in the animal gonads so that the animal is able to produce offspring having the same characteristics. For humans, it would be important to ensure not only that a particular embryo had a deficiency 'corrected', but that the 'good' gene was implanted in such a way that the child then born was not at risk of producing a child or children bearing the 'bad' gene rather than its 'good' replacement.

Yet according to some medical experts only three per cent of all present birth 'defects' are caused by genetic disorders.[11] The public is led by other medical experts to believe that proven genetic disorders are much more frequent. This 'justifies' expenditure in the area of genetic technology, and experimentation in this field, using human beings as a fertile field. In her Montreal lecture Dr. Renate Klein alluded to this aspect of the new reproductive technologies and genetic engineering at the close of the 1980s decade:

> . . . there remains a lot of work to do on refining this technology. And as it needs to be done on humans the only way to develop more pre-implantation tests is via embryos obtained through IVF. *It is here that the compulsory link between IVF and embryo research becomes evident: a link that so few people want to acknowledge, or even see.*[12]

The second report of the British Voluntary Licensing Authority (VLA), in April 1987, does acknowledge this:

> There are important research projects both to improve the present success rate for IVF and to develop techniques such as the freezing of eggs and pre-embryos that may be used with safety. Recently some projects have started that are related to the diagnosis of defects in the pre-embryo. *The aim is to avoid replacing pre-embryos with chromosomal or other abnormalities in the uterus; a vital concern for couples who are at risk of giving birth to children with severe inherited genetic disorders.*[13]

And, asks Dr. Klein, 'Where do these embryos come from?' They come from women who have been superovulated to produce eggs (and who are possibly harmed greatly, both physiologically and psychologically). Until these tests are fully developed it is imperative for the experimenters in IVF programmes to have a 'constant supply of women's bodies'.

Klein cites an article published in 1987 and titled 'The Next Stage: Gene Therapy', where scientist Robert Desnick from Mount Sinai Medical Research Center in the United States is quoted as saying:

> Ultimately, genetic cures would mean 'correcting all sperm and eggs as well, so you could never pass it on'.

Thus are the ideas of the scientists working in agriculture echoed. But statements such as this, in addition to raising questions of eugenicist notions, are profoundly misleading. Klein comments:

> . . . one needs to be very clear about how unspecific gene therapy using the recombinant DNA technique really is: whilst it may be possible to substitute a specific gene, it is not possible to know (or even to test for) the effects the exchange gene will have on other parts of the body.

This, she says, is where the real danger of the technology lies:

> . . . in a way similar to using hormones in IVF technology and disrupting hormone cycles, pre-implantation technology is playing around with disrupting peoples' genes without knowing any of the 'side effects'. In addition, the idea of gene therapy reveals a bio-logically determinist belief: surfacing once more is the old belief that 'biology is destiny' — this time it is our genes which are wrong and should be changed.

LAW UPDATE

Multiple embryos and 'fetal reduction'

The late 1980s also saw further developments in the legal field, both legislatively and through court decisions, as well as non-legislative regulation being called into question. In 1987 Margaret Harris reported in an article titled 'Test-tube doctors facing flak in foetus furore', appearing under the heading 'Britain's fertility fraternity blasted over multiple pregnancy procedure', in the Sydney newspaper *The Sun-Herald* of 8 November, that Professor Ian Craft of the Humana Hospital Wellington, a private London hospital, was being criticised for using a 'controversial technique' — 'foetal destruction' — to 'prevent risky multiple pregnancies'. She said Craft's technique is to place a large number of fertilised eggs in the wombs of women on his IVF programme 'to increase their chances of becoming pregnant'. Because it is 'usual' for only one or two of the fertilised eggs to survive and go on to develop into babies (although in terms of 'success' it must be relatively rare for even this to occur!), where a woman finds herself expecting 'as many as four babies', Craft 'offers his patients the option of having some of the foetuses "reduced"'. Harris continues:

> The procedure, which has been used in many countries including Australia in cases where one foetus is severely handicapped or malformed, involves inserting a needle into the amniotic sac surrounding the selected foetus and injecting it with a drug.
> In some cases the doctors insert the needle into the amniotic sac and destroy it rather than injecting a drug.
> The technique can be used as early as nine weeks when the developing foetus can be seen clearly using an ultra-sound scanner.
> It is used in cases of severe malformation because the affected foetus is likely to die later in pregnancy and may cause the other foetus to die or be miscarried along with it.

But, says Harris, Craft and other doctors at the Humana Hospital Wellington are not using 'fetal reduction' on severely malformed fetuses — 'they are using it to eliminate healthy foetuses they themselves implanted.'

In the November 1987 issue of *New Scientist* Ian Craft gives his own explanation for the adoption of the technique. An analyst might not be blamed for taking the approach as one dependent upon seeing the female body as causing difficulty — a difficulty to which the practitioner addresses his efforts in multiple implantation. For a pregnancy, fertilization of the ovum is not enough. The fertilized ovum has to adhere to the wall of the uterus if the embryo is to develop into a fetus ripe for delivery. Women's wombs are 'roomy' and therefore a single fertilized ovum has lots of space in which to move without necessarily adhering to the uterine wall. With many embryos placed into the womb, filling the available space, there is less room to move and the chances of an embryo attaching itself to the wall of the womb are markedly increased. For Craft the method of inserting multiple fertilized eggs makes it more likely that a viable pregnancy will be the outcome of his IVF programme. The 'problem' is thus seen to be the size of women's wombs, the means for overcoming this 'bodily defect' being a multiple pregnancy technique followed by a further technocratic solution — fetal reduction.

Approximately 10 'fetal reduction' operations have been performed at the hospital, according to reports. The hospital lost its IVF licence, issued by the Voluntary Licensing Authority, as a result of this and the policy of placing a high number of fertilized eggs in participants in the programme. The hospital is not thereby precluded from continuing with IVF, however: being a non-statutory body with regulatory duties but no legal powers, the Voluntary Licensing Authority's decision has moral suasion only.

For Australia, in *The Sun-Herald* of 8 November 1987 Michael Perry reported that fetal reduction does not occur. Dr. Robert Jansen, head of the Royal Prince Alfred Hospital Fertility Services, was reported as saying the hospital had considered the practice but decided it was unethical. He knew of no hospital in Australia which performed fetal reduction. Monash Medical Centre and the Royal North Shore IVF clinic were noted as adopting a practice of limiting the number of fertilised eggs being implanted into each woman on IVF.

The practice of inserting multiple embryos raises a number of legal issues: if once inserted, all the embryos are left in the uterus, and as a result some or all are lost because the pregnancy is unable thereby to continue to full term, is there any liability in hospital or doctor for failure of the IVF procedure? Does removing some of the embryos have legal implications? Is the situation different if the embryos removed from the womb have been pretested and the embryos removed are understood thereby to be sound/defective? Is there any legal 'flow on' if all the embryos are born as healthy quads, or quintuplets, or sextuplets . . .? Are there any further legal developments as to the status and 'ownership' or 'custody' of multiple embryos not implanted as a result of the practice of limiting the number of eggs placed in each IVF patient's uterus at any time?

Dr. Jansen of Royal Prince Alfred Hospital was reported by Perry in his *Sun-Herald* article as saying that doctors performing the multiple implant, then fetal reduction, procedures 'faced the legal danger of being held responsible for any remaining embryo being born defective':

> 'It's a real dilemma,' he said. 'And the horns of the dilemma are that whether you have quintuplets or sextuplets, if you leave the pregnancy alone then it will almost certainly terminate itself before the foetus is viable, which means all the foetus die.'

The doctor's liability in each situation would depend upon the standard of care required to be exercised by a medical practitioner in IVF surgery and treatment. What is the general standard accepted by the medical profession to be appropriate? (In Canada and the United States the standard would be in accordance with those principles determined upon in cases decided by their respective Supreme Courts.)[14]

If a woman on IVF believes she is being implanted with one embryo only, but unbeknownst to her and without her consent multiple embryos are inserted so that she gives birth to, say, triplets, it is arguable that some liability may lie against the doctor. That is, if she is not forewarned of the possibility of a multiple birth although the medical practitioner superovulates her, then places three embryos in her uterus, all of which go to full term and safe birth, she may sue the doctor for negligence. An analogy may lie with those cases where a woman finds herself pregnant having earlier undergone a tubal ligation (or her husband a vasectomy) without being warned of the possibility that the tubes may grow back, where a doctor might be seen to have been negligent and therefore liable to be sued. Damages could be calculated in accordance with trauma suffered at the shock of giving multiple rather than single birth, and expenses involved in caring for and bringing up two extra children.[15] The Royal North Shore IVF clinic reportedly seeks to protect itself against liability by requesting patients to sign a consent form stipulating the number of fertilized eggs they wish to have implanted. Perry in *The Sun-Herald* comments:

> [The form] goes on to warn the patient . . .: 'The chances of pregnancy increase quite a bit the more embryos are transferred, but this risks the chance of a multiple birth and therefore we implant no more than four embryos.'

Legal consequences flow for the parents of multiple birth children: they have the ordinary legal responsibilities for each of the children, just as they would have had, had one child only been born, and the additional financial responsibilities large families entail. Taking into account the current rate of marital breakdown — being in the vicinity of one in three marriages — and problems with custody and child support arising out of divorce,[16] women entering IVF programmes should consider their legal position carefully.

What of the euphemistically named 'fetal reduction' procedure — which by another name is effectively abortion? Had the Enoch Powell Bill of 1986 (the *Unborn Child (Protection) Bill*) become law in the United Kingdom,[17] or the Harradine Bill (the *Human Embryo Experimentation Bill*) entered the statute books in Australia,[18] legal implications for fetal reduction are clearly present: the procedure would be illegal where those laws applied; alternatively there would be a legal 'battle' between the idea of protecting the putative mother's health, or her optimum health, and the right of the embryo to 'reach its full human potential' (in accordance with the terms of the Harradine Bill). The *Human Embryo Experimentation Bill* contemplated that any embryo created on an IVF programme should be protected in law, by granting to the embryo a right to develop to its 'full human potential'. The implication is that an IVF embryo *must* be implanted in a womb to develop to full term and birth and that under no circumstances — inside or outside the womb — can it be destroyed.

If a woman IVF patient found she was pregnant with, say, quads as a result of having four embryos implanted and all 'taking', she would not only have no right to an abortion unless she could (in accordance with the law) have a doctor accept that her health was reasonably at risk; but also, that the existence of a law stating that the IVF embryos each had a right to develop to their 'full potential' did not preclude the doctor from acting in accordance with the assessment that the putative mother's health was at risk. That is, abortion law and IVF law would be in direct conflict. Indeed, aborting one or two fetuses, or all but one, may well place the remaining fetus or fetuses at risk: the operation could well damage the fetus or fetuses left behind, so that their right to develop to their 'full human potential' is thereby endangered.

Passage of a law such as that embodied in the proposed *Human Embryo Experimentation Bill* also places at risk the right of a woman to abortion where she is on an IVF programme and discovers that the potential child is suffering from, say, spina bifida or a major heart defect, such as transposition of the great vessels.

The legislation would arguably force her to continue with the pregnancy, so that the spina bifida child would be born, to reach its 'full human potential' for as long as the child survived. Similarly with the child suffering from a major heart defect: the legislation would arguably force the putative mother to continue with the pregnancy and give birth, so that the child could reach full human potential, although this may mean death shortly after birth (unless surgery was available to intervene to correct the heart defect).

The status and storage of surplus embryos

As for the status of embryos 'left behind' where the policy of a hospital (or IVF doctor) is not to implant all embryos produced, but to limit the number implanted at any one time, or the patient chooses not to have all embryos implanted together, in the late 1980s questions continue to arise in many jurisdictions. Those with frozen embryos have a legal liability for 'storage fees' in some IVF programmes, at least. This was revealed in an interview conducted by Dr. Renate Klein in her research on infertility and women undergoing IVF. One woman after talking to Klein 'with great anger about how abysmally badly she had felt when treated by Professor X ('he is a real pig' — 'he is absolutely star-struck with himself', 'he isn't interested in people, only in science') and how deeply she resented being dismissed from the programme because of the presence of sperm antibodies and being told that there was no hope for her and her husband — they 'were and would always be infertile' — told her that only four weeks after leaving the programme she became pregnant. The pregnancy was achieved without drugs, and she was at the time of interview mother of an eight month old baby. 'But then', writes Klein, 'she proceeded to say "I suppose, however, that one day I will have to go back." "I don't understand",' replied [Klein]. 'Go back? What do you mean?' 'Well,' she continued:

> You see it's these frozen embryos. I've got frozen embryos from all three attempts. Now, I don't want them to be flushed down the sink, I don't want to give them for research and I don't want to give them to another woman (I couldn't bear the thought that my child was running around without me knowing it). So what other option is there than go back.
>
> I know it sounds sick. Here I am feeling so angry about the programme, being totally sick of it, even having my own child . . . and yet, you know . . . you just plug on, on and on . . .
>
> Also, I must admit I feel quite maternal towards my embryos in the fridge — I used to tell my friends and they used to laugh — and

I'm actually worried: *I don't think we had a bill for a while for storage fees* . . . I'd be really p. . . off if something had happened to them . . .[19] (Emphasis added.)

Klein comments:

The mention of storage fees made us both burst into laughter. Mrs. X couldn't remember the ongoing storage fee but said that initially it had cost $160 to have the embryos frozen. She also remembered when she got the following receipt in the mail: 'It has been received from "X" six frozen embryos, three of which were destroyed', and commented: 'It was just a receipt for paying a bill, it was just so totally weird.'

In late 1987 the Victorian government at last made a decision about the fate of two frozen embryos which had been in storage for some years, following the death of the 'parents' in a 'plane crash three kilometres north of Santiago, Chile. Sarah Harris in the *Sunday Telegraph* of 29 November 1987 reported that Chilean authorities and the couple's surviving 24 year old son 'did not discover for some months that Elsa and Mario Rios had left two potential heirs orphaned in the Melbourne IVF clinic'. Following the discovery, Harris reports:

Top Australian lawyers were flown to California, the couple's last home, to consult with Los Angeles county officials on the future of the embryos . . .
  Administrators of the estate quickly dispelled lawyers' fears, saying they had no plans to claim the embryos as part of the estate, even if it were possible. This relieved the lawyers' concerns that the tiny specks of human life might be sold to the highest bidder if they became part of the estate.

As a result, a report was prepared for the government by the Victorian Crown Solicitors office. Ultimately, the government determined that the embryos should take their place in the queue, for implantation into the uterus of another woman on the IVF programme, should the fertilised eggs survive the thawing process. Where there is no legislation, similar questions of 'ownership' and responsibility arise — of donors; if dead, of the administrator of an estate of donors; of doctors in IVF programmes; of hospitals running IVF programmes.

The legalities of human experimentation

But the problem posed by frozen embryos in Victoria went beyond 'what to do with the "pre-baby Rios" in the fridge'. In 1987 the question of embryo experimentation came to a head. The Victorian Standing Review and Advisory Committee on Infertility proposed an amendment to the *Infertility (Medical Procedures) Act* 1984 which, if made, would give to the Committee a power, in exercising its functions under the Act, to approve the conduct of certain experiments involving the fertilization of human embryos (or 'gametes') for research purposes. At that time, Section 6 of the *Infertility (Medical Procedures) Act* provided:

(1) A person shall not carry out a prohibited procedure.
Penalty: 100 penalty units or imprisonment for four years.
(2) In sub-section (1), 'prohibited procedure' means —
(a) cloning; or
(b) a procedure under which the gametes of a man or a woman are fertilized by the gametes of an animal.
(3) A person shall not carry out an experimental procedure other than an experimental procedure approved by the Standing Review and Advisory Committee.
Penalty: 100 penalty units or imprisonment for four years.
(4) In sub-section (3), 'experimental procedure' means a procedure that involves carrying out research on an embryo of a kind that would cause damage to the embryo, would make the embryo unfit for implantation or would reduce the prospects of a pregnancy resulting from the implantation of the embryo.
(5) Where ova are removed from the body of a woman, a person shall not cause or permit those ova to be fertilized outside the body of the woman except for the purposes of the implantation of embryos derived from those ova in the womb of that woman or another woman in a relevant procedure in accordance with this Act.
Penalty: 100 penalty units or imprisonment for four years.
(6) A person shall not carry out a procedure that involves freezing an embryo.
Penalty: 100 penalty units or imprisonment for four years.
(7) Sub-section (6) does not apply to a procedure carried out in an approved hospital that involves freezing an embryo if that procedure is carried out for the purposes of enabling the embryo to be implanted in the womb of a woman at a later date.
(8) Nothing in this Act prevents or inhibits the carrying out in an approved hospital of research on, and the development of techniques for, freezing or otherwise storing ova removed from the body of a woman.

All of these provisions were proclaimed to commence on 10 August 1986, except that sub-section (5) was not. At the time the Standing

Review and Advisory Committee approached the Minister for Health requesting an amendment to the Act, there was no operation of sub-section (5) — that the removal of ova from a woman's body could not be done, for fertilization (as in IVF), except for the purpose of implanting embryos thus derived into the uterus of the woman from whom the ova were taken, or into another woman's uterus *in an IVF procedure only*.

There were reportedly differing views of committee members as to the status of this provision, and as to the meaning of the whole section, and whether or nor experimentation on embryos could or could not be authorised by the committee whether sub-section (5) was proclaimed (that is, brought into effect) or not. Time was also reportedly expended on the question 'where does life begin'. The Solicitor-General's opinion was sought which stated, unsurprisingly, that as long as the provision was not proclaimed, the committee should have regard to the whole of section 6, minus sub-section (5). Thus, they would have a right under the Act to authorise experimentation on embryos, because there was no effective requirement under the operative legislation for embryos created on an IVF programme *only* to be implanted into a womb. If the committee approved such requests, then experimentation could be done which resulted in damage to the embryo, or made it unfit for implantation, or would reduce the prospects of pregnancy resulting from the embryo were it implanted into a woman's uterus. However, apparently some members of the committee did not accept the legal interpretation, choosing to believe they were bound by sub-section (5) of the Act, despite its inoperativeness due to lack of proclamation.[20]

The problem for the committee was that some members reportedly believed research proposals could be approved although they resulted in destruction of embryos. Others believed they ought not to approve of procedures which would end in the destruction of embryos. However, a way of 'getting around' this problem was put forward: that the legislation be amended to introduce a new 'stage' of embryo development, where experimentation would be approved by the committee, as opposed to experimentation on 'embryos as such'. The proposal for an experiment which caused the committee such angst was one that nominated a stage called 'pre-syngamy', up to 22 hours after fertilization has occurred. The view promulgated was that an embryo at 'pre-syngamy' stage was not really 'an embryo' at all; rather it was (or could be termed) a 'pre-embryo'. This apparently satisfies some people concerned about experiments on 'human life': a 'pre-embryo' (runs the argument) is not a 'human life'. Where does life begin? is the monumental question attempted to be answered. If a 'thing' (a 'pre-embryo') can be defined as 'not human life' or 'not *yet* human life' then the worries are over; experimentation can legitimately go ahead. (Yet the fallacy of this position is clear: either it is accepted that 'life' begins at the time an ova and sperm join together, from that first instant of contact and envelopment of sperm by ova the organism being 'alive' with human being potential; or the debate is endless and unanswerable, being in the philosophical realm of 'what is truth' and its analogues.)

'Spare' embryos could already be used under the Act for experimentation of a destructive or damaging (to the embryo) nature, if those embryos had been created for the purpose of implantation, but for some reason the couple from whom they derived did not wish to have them implanted and determined to hand them over to their 'team' for experimentation. But it was the issue of *creating embryos specifically for the purpose of destructive or damaging experimentation* that exercised the committee.

It was therefore proposed to government that the Act be amended to provide that embryos in the 'pre-syngamy' stage could be used for destructive experimentation and that ova and sperm could be used for fertilization *specifically for this purpose*, but that the only persons able to donate embryos for such experimental purposes, or have their ova and sperm taken for the purpose of fertilization for 'pre-syngamy' experimentation, should be those on an IVF programme. Sub-section (5) of the Act therefore had to be amended to accommodate this, then brought into effect.

Ultimately, the goverment accepted the committee's view, amending the Act (with approval of the Liberal opposition, holding a majority (with the National Party) in the upper house, the Legislative Council, and without whose votes the Bill could not have been passed to amend the Act). Now experimentation can take place on embryos up to 22 hours into their existence (that is, at the pre-syngamy stage), as a result of which they are destroyed or damaged, and ova can be fertilised solely for this experimentation. But the creation of such embryos for experimentation is limited to the bodies of participants in IVF.

This approach raises problems. First, it is notable that the committee entangled itself in (almost) endless discussions about whether or not embryos should be experimented upon, and futile debates about when 'life' begins. Meanwhile, women's bodies are (and have been since they came into existence) being experimented upon in new reproductive technology programmes. It seems that concern is greater, or appears to be greater, in the case of live ameboid material with the potential to develop into a human being, than in the case of real human beings in the here and now — female human beings. Secondly, in proposing the amendment the committee may have allowed itself to be tangled up in semantics, rather than concentrating upon the matters under the Act to which it is to direct its attention. Introducing 'syngamy' into the Act as a 'different' or 'pre-embryo' stage, takes the debate about reproductive technologies and experimentation out of the social realm, where it should be, and into debates about the medical naming of parts. The debate on IVF, ET and like procedures, and about experimentation in IVF, *is not* about when or how or whether medical experts determine 'when life begins', or what medical experts term 'life' or 'union' or sperm and ova. The embryo issue is about what representatives of the community decide, as a matter of social values or conscience, should be acceptable in experimenting (or not) on combined ova and sperm — commonly known as embryos, whatever the stage of development (once fertilization has taken place by sperm meeting with and being enclosed by ova). But the real issue goes way beyond this, to what society sees as acceptable 'use' or 'treatment' of actual, live, presently existing human bodies.

If the great concern is about embryos, using the term 'syngamy' in effect is a semantic way of overcoming the recognition that what is being destroyed or damaged in experiments is an embryo. Because there are objections from some quarters about embryo experimentation, the introduction of a 'new' term — 'syngamy' — is designed to overcome the problem. Those objecting to embryo experimentation can be told: 'There's no problem. It's not experimentation on embryos. It's experimentation on 'pre-embryos' or embryos at the 'pre-syngamy' stage, which means they're not 'real' embryos at all'!

But 'pre-syngamy' is a medical term. Ordinary, everyday people call embryos 'embryos', and understand that that is what is being destroyed or dealt with in an experiment using fertilized ova. That is (presumably) what the Victorian parliament understood, as representatives of the citizens of Victoria, when the *Infertility (Medical Procedures) Act* 1984 was originally subjected to debate during its passage. Notably, the committee did not (and nor did those applying for agreement that the research should go ahead) choose the so-called primitive streak stage as the appropriate stage for experimentation. Some writers in the field (and this was debated in the United Kingdom report by the committee chaired by Mary

Warnock)[21] have suggested that experimentation should be allowed in embryos until the 'primitive streak' develops (about 14-17 days after fertilization), and then should be 'outlawed' because it is at this stage that the neurological system has begun to develop in the organism and arguably the embryo may feel pain. However, this stage is way beyond the 22 hour limit attached to syngamy, and may have been perceived to be more difficult for members of the committee or of parliament to embrace because of sensitivities to the strict view of some that no embryo should be subjected to experimentation.

The committee by its debate, no doubt inadvertently, served only to deflect the community and parliamentary discussion about reproductive technologies and experimentation from one level to another. The question in issue as seen by the committee was that medical terminology should be introduced into the Act to overcome the problems of those who did not want to approve of, or be seen to be approving of, experimentation on embryos. One level of objection to this is that the real debate should focus on whether it is acceptable *in society's terms* (supposedly represented through the Victorian committee) for experiments, or particular experiments, to be carried out on a combined egg and sperm — an embryo in common parlance, rather than being concerned about what the medical fraternity chooses to call the object of experimentation. But even this level of debate misses the point. A debate about what is or what is not 'syngamy', or whether there is any such thing as a 'pre-embryo' (or whether the term has been conveniently manufactured or relied upon, by medicos and scientists, to overcome resistance against embryo experimentation by groups such as the Right to Life and other religious bodies) by slight of hand deflects attention from the most important question, the issue at base in reproductive technology and experimentation: its effect upon women's bodies and wellbeing. The fundamental question is whether it is positive for the physical and mental health of women (and thence whether it is beneficial for society as a whole) for the hyperstimulation of women's ovaries so that more eggs can be retrieved for experimentation; and simply for women's bodies to be surgically intruded into for the purpose of retrieving ova so that medicos and scientists can experiment further on the 'harvest'.[22] It is academic — and indeed irrelevant — whether the final object of experimentation is called an embryo, a 'pre-embryo', a group of cells at 'syngamy' stage, or is an ovum. The real object of experimentation in reproductive technologies, and thence in genetic engineering, is not the embryo produced from the ova taken from the woman's body. *It is actually the woman's body itself.*

As Klein comments on the Victorian approach, that the Act specifies that embryo research up to 22 hours may be conducted on embryos from women on IVF programmes only:

> . . . may afford some protection to other women from being super-ovulated to donate or sell their eggs (as happens in Vienna, Austria, with medical students . . .), it opens all doors to more experimentation on those who are already most vulnerable. Since they are now — officially at least — [in Victoria] the only legal gamete donors, there will be even more pressure on them to comply with the IVF practitioners' research demands. The price they have to pay gets higher and higher and reinforces the belief that these women are obsessive and neurotic and 'ask for it'. Within a feminist theory of solidarity with the ultimate goal to free *all* women from the tyranny of patriarchal control which coerces them into using the [new reproductive technologies], such a division of women is highly questionable and must be resisted.[23]

By institutionalising medical definitions in the Victorian legislation, the Act now becomes a tool for those in the medical fraternity who wish to impose their views of what is right and proper in the field of the new reproductive technologies, rather than the law remaining to be effected in accordance with community values, standards and views as was presumably intended at the outset. Arguably, the committee should be able to concentrate upon its very large role as defined in section 29 of the Act, sub-section (6):

> The functions of the Committee are —
> (a) to advise the Minister [of Health] in relation to infertility and procedures for alleviating infertility;
> (b) to consider requests for approval of, and if it sees fit, to approve, experimental procedures for the purpose of section 6 (3); and
> (c) to advise and report to the Minister of any matters relating to infertility and procedures for alleviating infertility and any other associated matters referred to it by the Minister.

Why isn't the committee spending most of its time — at least two-thirds — on infertility issues? Clearly, parliament intended the committee to concentrate its attention upon the problem of infertility as such — both subsection 6 (a) and 6 (c) refer to this task. The provision does not talk about infertility as limited to issues of new reproductive technologies; indeed, in the context of infertility in relation to the functions of the committee new reproductive technologies *are mentioned not at all*! And approval of experimentation is mentioned once only, then not as the primary issue. Yet the committee has apparently been given minimal resources with which to do its tasks — and those resources appear to be taken up in deliberating upon 'when does life begin', medical terminology and embryo experimentation. These matters are no doubt of interest and concern to (respectively) philosophers, and those in the field of new reproductive technologies and genetic engineering as professionals. But their value to others, and to the community as a whole, may well be questioned. As Klein points out, eggs for experimentation come from women: it is women's bodies which are being used, and superovulated to produce eggs. This can now legitimately be done solely for the purpose of experimentation. More than ever, now, she says, 'women are "living laboratories" in the hands of the triumvirate scientists, doctors and pharmaceutical companies'.

Dr. Klein observes that Patrick Steptoe, one of the 'fathers' of the first test-tube baby, in his private clinic Bourn Hall in England:

> . . . is following cattle breeders such as Ian Gordon at the University College of Dublin, Ireland. Gordon, according to Vines [in an article published in *New Scientist* on 13 August 1987]:
> '. . . harvests immature eggs from the ovaries of cattle carcasses in slaughterhouses and matures the eggs in the laboratory. He has fertilised the eggs and matured them in the laboratory to the morula stage, when the embryo is a solid mass of cells.

Christopher Polge of Animal Biotechnology in Cambridge, England (and one of Gordon's colleagues) explains the aim:

> We are looking for a cheap and more reliable source of embryos in cattle . . . Then breeders wouldn't need to keep animals just to produce embryos . . .

Klein concludes:

> Once the development of immature egg cells *in vitro* is possible, any slice from *any* woman's ovary — young or old, fertile or infertile — will do. Women could still be used as cheap labour, especially those of the 'wrong' colour from the 'wrong' class and the 'wrong' culture . . . and women would still have to carry the embryos to term, unless, of course, the artificial uterus, as again developed in cattle breeding, were to be perfected soon.

This, says Klein, means that individual women are no longer wholly essential to the reproductive process.

Legal developments in surrogacy

In February 1988 another area of legal dispute came into focus, and was clarified — at least for one American jurisdiction, New Jersey. A year earlier, under the heading 'The Court battle for "Baby M"', Leonard Doyle of *The Independent* (a New York newspaper) reported in an article syndicated in *The Age* on 6 January that year:

> The emotive issue of surrogate parenting — a beacon of hope for thousands of childless American couples — was brought before a New Jersey court yesterday when a natural mother was sued for failing to give up the child born to her after artificial insemination.

The fee to be paid to Ms. Mary Beth Whitehead, married with two children aged 10 and 12, was $AUS 14,992 (the 'going rate' in the United States at the time was said by Doyle to be about $AUS 15,000). She gave birth to the child, a girl, then changed her mind. She had signed a surrogate agreement through the Infertility Centre of New York, the contracting party being a 40 year old biochemist, Mr. William Stern. Ms. Whitehead 'maintained close relations with Mr. Stern and his wife while she [Ms. Whitehead] was pregnant':

> A month before 'Baby M' was born, [Ms. Whitehead] told the counsellor that she had 'no ambivalence' about following the agreement. But after the birth, she told the court, she became anguished and determined to keep the child. She fled to her mother's house in Florida where she was tracked down by detectives who took the baby from her. Since . . . July [1986] the Stern family has had temporary custody of the child.

Doyle commented that the case was complicated because Mr. and Ms. Stern, seeking the custody of the 'contracted for' child, 'may be able to have children themselves although [Ms. Stern] was deemed 'infertile' in the surrogate contract'.

The case was fought by lawyers for Ms. Whitehead arguing that the 1985 contract was invalid as being in violation of a New Jersey law against baby-selling. Lawyers for the Sterns contended in opposition that Ms. Whitehead, 'a housewife', was an 'unfit mother who threatened to kill herself and the baby unless she got custody'. They contended principles and laws covering adoption had no effect where surrogate motherhood arrangements were in question, and that new legal principles should be established by the New Jersey court. According to Doyle:

Mr. Stern told a packed courtroom: 'She (Ms. Whitehead) said she didn't want to live if she couldn't keep the baby. She was acting suicidal. We were afraid of what she might do.'

The Sterns say they chose to delay having a family until Mrs. Stern finished her medical training in 1981. She was then 36 and they thought a pregnancy might pose a 'significant risk to her health'. But in the surrogate agreement she is said to be 'infertile', and Mrs. Whitehead's lawyers say they will argue fraud in the contract.

In the upshot, although the contract was reportedly between Ms. Whitehead and Mr. Stern, the courtroom battle in the first instance, before Judge Harvey Sorkow of the New Jersey Superior Court, concentrated almost solely on the women in the case, and their respective abilities — or lack of them — for motherhood.

Merle Hoffman in *On the Issues — The Journal of Substance for Progressive Women* reports on the respective qualifications of the two women, as seen by the court:

> Possessed of two graduate degrees, MD and PhD, Stern is the quintessential feminist paragon. Married to a 'supportive professional husband' who did not by all reports force her into childbearing, she is successful in her field — so much so that she even diagnoses herself and decides that she has multiple sclerosis and is unwilling to take the risk of biological childbearing. Therefore, she enters into a commercial arrangement with Whitehead, or more specifically with Whitehead's womb. [Although the contract was really between Mr. Stern and Ms. Whitehead's womb.]
>
> Whitehead, highschool graduate, ex barroom dancer, mother of three, wife to a Vietnam Vet with drinking problems. A woman who takes pride in her role as mother . . .[24]

'Expert witnesses' — psychiatrists — were called to give evidence. Hoffman comments that the case 'brought into the harsh daylight' continuing discussion and debate on the many theories of mothers and mothering:

> Leaning heavily on traditional stereotypic definitions of the 'good mother' all differences of class, personality and style were psychologized and manipulated into medical models so that there was no room for rational effective disagreement — there was in fact no room for dissent. How complicated these competing definitions of mother had become.

She adds:

> It was the pots and pans that finally activated me. I had followed the case for days in the media with a somewhat distant intellectual

curiosity, but then I read that a psychiatrist had testified that Mary Beth Whitehead was an unfit mother because she gave her child stuffed pandas to play with instead of pots and pans. Stuffed pandas? How extraordinary that our psychiatric system regarded the image of an animal so loved and rare as a panda as subverting the normal growth and development of a 20th century female child. The implied sexism of giving a little one-year-old the tools of the kitchen was certainly not lost on me either

Another psychiatrist then testified that Mary Beth was a bad mother because she was 'overmeshed' with her kids and still another testified that Mary Beth was 'narcissistic' because she dyed her hair, that in fact her hair was all white, creating a true 'white-head'. Having turned grey at the age of 24, I could definitely empathize with the desire to change her hair color to meet the societal demands of what it means to be attractive.

What message was this bastion of the psychiatric establishment trying to relay? asks Hoffman:

> That women who love their children too much are immoral and evil — that stuffed animals are subversive, that normal American consumer vanity is somehow pathological? . . .
> Whitehead's passion, her [alleged] lack of social controls, her use of any manipulative tool to fight her battles, the infamous tapes on which she threatens to kill herself and her child, her seeming lack of deference for the system make her somewhat of an uncomfortable spectacle for many feminists and an unacceptable role model for anyone's definition of a good mother. Any wonder that public sentiment rides with Elizabeth Stern, the woman whose love is limited by the desire for genetic perfection, whose motherhood is not dependent upon sexual intercourse — whose body is somehow removed from the act that so traditionally defines woman?

'Baby M' *had* to be the 'perfect product', the 'perfect child', race congruent, colour congruent. Under the contract Mary Beth Whitehead was required to have an amniocentesis in the fourth month of the pregnancy. If the test proved positive for any fetal abnormality (evidence of a 'defective product') the contract with Mr. Stern was rendered null and void. As Merle Hoffman points out, Whitehead's remaining options included abortion or assuming sole responsibility for the 'imperfect' child.

'How could any one of us withstand the scrutiny that Mary Beth had to go through,' asked one woman outside the New Jersey courtroom. 'My God, if they were to have put me on the stand, I would have lost my child 10 times over,' commented another. As Phyllis Chesler writes in *Mothers on Trial*, her book on child custody battles following divorce, many mothers are scrutinised in this way, losing custody of their biological (and social) children as a result, as did Mary Beth Whitehead.[25]

Hoffman's assessment of Whitehead was that she was 'first and foremost a dissident, a radical challenge to the system of old definitions and consumer mentalities':

> Whitehead was really an innocent harkening us back to the world's first order of survival and primal love . . . It was not so much that she wanted to sell her baby, after all that is the American way — you have a product, you put a price on it, you sign a contract and then you deliver it. Whitehead's problem was not that she did not follow the process, it was that she reneged, she pulled her product out of the marketplace — she did not deliver, she dissented!

A year later the New Jersey Supreme Court handed down its decision on appeal. The first court had granted custody to the Sterns, denied any 'visitation' (access) rights to Whitehead, and ruled that Ms. Stern had a right to adopt the child. Seven to nil the Supreme Court upheld the custody decision. But again seven to nil the Supreme Court of New Jersey overturned all other aspects of the ruling in the case by the court below. On 5 February 1988 *The Age* reported:

> The ruling restored the parental rights of Mrs. Whitehead-Gould, meaning that she can seek a new custody hearing. The justices also threw out Judge Sorkow's order . . . allowing Elizabeth Stern to adopt the baby, who is now 22 months old.
> And having restored Mrs. Whitehead-Gould's parental rights, they also ordered a new court hearing to set rules for her visits with Melissa. She is now permitted to see the girl two hours a week in a Bergen County youth shelter in Hackensack [New Jersey].

In allowing Mr. Stern to retain custody of the child, the Supreme Court said that the Sterns promised 'a secure home, with an understanding relationship that allows nurturing and independent growth to develop together'.

Mary Beth Whitehead (who, the court noted, had become pregnant out of marriage in 1987; was divorced in mid-November 1987 by her husband of 13 years; remarried two weeks later to Dean Gould, a 26 year old accountant; and was to give birth to the coming child in late May or early June 1988, the child's father being Mr. Gould) said she would not appeal the case to the federal Supreme Court. She 'tearfully told a news conference she was satisfied with the ruling because it granted her visiting rights'. The

Sterns said, through a spokesperson, that they were 'thrilled to retain custody of Melissa [Sara to Whitehead]. But they felt that granting visiting rights to the mother was not in the best interests of the child'.

As for the general implications of the 'Baby M' case, in strict law the decision is limited to New Jersey. However, it may well have implications for other American states which have no surrogacy laws. It is likely that the decision may have persuasive value at least at the level of lawyers giving advice to persons seeking to enter into surrogacy contracts, and agencies operating in the field or newly entering it. The court based its decision not on any surrogacy contract or the idea that the 'agreement' drawn up between Mr. Stern and Ms. Whitehead should have any legal force or effect, but on Ms. Whitehead and Mr. Stern's biological parentage of the child, and the question of what was in the child's best interests as to custody with which parent. Effectively, the legal principles applied are those pertaining to custody and access (or visitation) in the case of marital breakdown and divorce where a child is a child of the marriage of two parties. Here, there was no marriage between Stern and Whitehead, but just as in divorce, wife and husband, mother and father of the children must decide on custody and access or have a court decide for them, the mother and father of the child, being unable to settle the matter between them, were held by the court to require a courtroom determination.

It is surely ironic that a woman who gives birth to a child fathered by a man with whom she has never had a marriage or *de facto* relationship is required to 'fight out' the question of custody, where the father seeks to enforce it, through a court. Traditionally the common law has held the mother of an illegitimate child (who might well be born to a woman who has had a close intimate relationship with the biological father) has full parental rights precluding the father from any rights. In many jurisdictions the law affecting mothers and illegitimate children is changing to grant rights to *de facto* husbands and fathers of those children. But are those laws changing, and was the 'Baby M' decision made, because courts and legislatures recognise a social notion of fatherhood? Or is the change based in the notion of 'father-right' arising out of ownership and the perpetuation of a patriarchal line? The *Whitehead-Stern case*, at least at first instance (before Judge Sorkow) supports the latter view. The 'battle' was not one of whether the biological father or the biological mother would provide the better home and the better *parenting*. It was grounded in the acknowledgement that sperm contribution and ova contribution gave an (apparently) equal right to custody, but that *motherhood* was the issue rather than (social) fatherhood or parenting: who was the 'better' mother — Elizabeth Stern (a biological stranger to the child, and almost a social stranger to her) or Mary Beth Whitehead (biological mother and sometime social mother); not who was the better 'parent' — Mary Beth Whitehead or William Stern (biological father and sometime social father). But the end result was the father 'got' the child.

THE CONTINUING FIGHTBACK

The late 1980s have seen no lessening of the push for increased reproductive technologies and genetic engineering. But neither have they seen any diminishing of women's agitation and anger, compassion and concern, and growing awareness on the part of the women going through the programmes. Indeed, as the years go on, and women suffer further indignities and distress, despite more children being born through new reproductive technologies the awareness and anger of women is bound to grow.

And now, some medical practitioners and technologists are recognising the detrimental potential and effects of the technologies. In the Keith Roby Lecture in Community Science Dr. Ditta Bartels reported that in France 'the leading IVF scientist, Professor Jacques Testart, has turned against' the use of IVF for experimentation in genetic makeup, and the eugenicist prospects developing out of this. He calls it 'a perversion of IVF', declaring that he refuses any longer to contribute to the field of IVF. Bartels observed further that Professor Erwin Chargaff, 'a distinguished molecular biologist who contributed to the structure of DNA but then became disillusioned with molecular biology is quite horrified at these latest prospects [in genetic testing and engineering]. He speaks of a "molecular Auschwitz, in which valuable enzymes and hormones will be extracted instead of gold teeth"'.[26] (She added, however, that Testart and Chargaff are exceptions in the world of the technologist.)

It seems that the fightback is being taken seriously. Gena Corea reports that on 18 December 1987 at 4.30pm in West Germany, the Bundeskriminalamt, the German equivalent of the FBI (Federal Bureau of Investigation), or (less aptly compared) the Australian Federal Police, staged 'thirty three simultaneous raids, many of them against feminists, throughout the Federal Republic' (FRD). Corea writes:

Hundreds of heavily armed police (200 in Essen alone) burst into the workplaces of activists. Fifteen to thirty in a group they swept into homes in Cologne, Dortmund and Dusseldorf. *In Essen, Duisburg, Bochum, and Hamburg, the raids were directed overwhelmingly against feminist critics of genetic and reproductive technology,* according to Prozessgruppe Hamburg, a watchdog group.

The targeted critics have written and spoken on such issues as *in vitro* fertilisation, amniocentesis, sex predetermination and genetic engineering. They have actively opposed surrogate motherhood. Many worked together in a massive coalition to stop American Noel Keane's attempt to open a branch of his surrogate business, United Family International, in Frankfurt. (Kean's New York firm arranged the Mary Beth Whitehead surrogate contract.)[27]

The West German women's campaign to 'stop the sale of American women to European men for breeding purposes' ended in success when on 6 January 1987 a West German court ordered Kean's business closed, merely three months after it had opened.

Corea points out that in addition to the lobby against the Kean surrogacy clinic, the groups raided in Germany had given strong support to Mary Beth Whitehead and other women similarly placed who sought to keep the children they had borne under 'surrogacy' contracts. They have also been supporting the efforts of the US group formed in 1987, the National Coalition Against Surrogacy (NCAS), to ban surrogacy in the United States. (NCAS also provided support for the German campaign against exploitation through surrogacy.)

The grounds for the police raids? According to Gena Corea, in many cases the women were given no explanation by police:

But the next day, newspapers reported that the police conducted the searches to ascertain whether any of the individuals were members of a terrorist organisation. They were specifically looking for a group called Revolutionaren Zellen ('Revolutionary Cells') and its feminist wing, Rote Zora ('Red Zora').

The police were operating under the law's Paragraph 129a, 'Support or Membership in a Terrorist Organisation'.

The women raided were forced to undress. All 'non-changeable marks' on their bodies — scars, moles, etc. — were noted down in police records.[28]

Dr. Beate Zimmerman, one of the women raided, said in a telephone interview from Essen to Gena Corea in the United States that she opened the door of her office and 'bluum! They came in like a herd of animals. About 15 of them. They ran into every room and stood there with their guns drawn. I said 'What are you doing here? There is nothing here.' There were two patients sitting and trembling. Nothing else.'

Lest Australian readers adopt a sanguine pose, disbelieving events in Germany consequent upon women's activism in the new reproductive technologies and genetic engineering sphere, or protesting that such raids are remote from the Australian way of life, there are some parallels here. In the early 1970s police raided a clinic in Bondi, New South Wales, for the purpose of instituting legal action for offences against the *Crimes Act* 1900 relating to abortion.[29] The final outcome was the *Levine ruling*, which is the foundation of the legal right to an abortion where the mother's health is at risk, in New South Wales' law. In the mid-1980s police raided clinics in Queensland confiscating records and apparently planning to institute proceedings against medical practitioners for carrying out vasectomies in the clinics. Two doctors were prosecuted for allegedly carrying out an unlawful operation (an abortion) — in contravention of the Queensland *Criminal Code*. In that case, too, it was held that the actions of the doctors was within the law, the decision closely following the *Levine ruling* and the 1968 *Menhennit ruling* in Victoria. The *Menhennit ruling* itself arose out of similar circumstances. Dr. Bertram Wainer's clinic was subjected to a deal of pressure (including police raids) during the 1960s.

In Melbourne in the 1980s it seemed that similar tactics were to be applied when the Action Centre, a centre established for young women under the auspices of the Family Planning Association of Victoria, was subjected to police intrusion and demands for files, which were handed over. The young woman having control of the files was prosecuted for her role at the centre where a person under the age of 16 years had sought and obtained an abortion on legal grounds. (The action was eventually resolved in favour of the Action Centre and its personnel.)

But just as women in other countries who are opposed to the exploitation of and experimentation on women's bodies, women in West Germany continue to circulate information, lobby governments and community bodies and raise the issues to be public level. Immediately following the events in December 1987, women active in the resistance against these technologies planned another major conference to be held in Bonn, in defiance of the police raids. The attacks on women activists in fact appear to have generated a collective outrage and a revived solidarity amongst women in the movement, and within the Women's Movement as a whole.

Women involved in IVF programmes are also increasing their

activism. Many of them are angry at the process, and at those practitioners who forget to treat them as human beings, but rather regard them as 'defective machines to be poked and tampered around with until they produce'.[30] Women are angry at being 'thrown off' a programme when they 'fail' to produce, and are refused further help. When on the programmes they well see the effect of written and unwritten rules governing them. This anger is now being directed into constructive criticism of the programmes and involvement in feminist groups such as the Feminist International Network of Resistance to Reproductive and Genetic Engineering (FINRRAGE) and Feminist Network on Reproductive Technologies (FINNRET). Infertile women are writing about their infertility and their experiences on new reproductive technology programmes, some of their writings appearing in *The Exploitation of Infertility: Women and Reproductive Technology*.[31] Women who have not been on new reproductive technology programmes, but understand that these programmes affect the lives of all women, and ultimately the whole community, join the debate in increasing numbers.

In the late 1980s and into the 1990s, women's activism in this area, as in other areas of women's lives, is bound to increase. Although there has been a view that the late 1960s, through the 1970s, saw a 'high' in women's activism and involvement, and that the 1980s is a decade of selfishness, greed, and mindless obeisance to the money god which affects women like men, there are strong indications that women are not 'becoming more like men', that women continue to work toward feminist aims. Evidence abounds that young women are equally aware, or growing aware, of feminist issues, values and goals.[32] As long as any women are used as experimental objects, all women must resist the exploitation of the new reproductive technologies and genetic engineering. This resistance must continue and grow, until there is no woman who, in talking of her 'role' in any IVF programme, anywhere in the world, is bound to say:

> I felt like a baby machine; no one was interested in me as a person. I was just a chook with growing eggs inside — and if they didn't grow properly, then it was my own fault.

End notes

1. Ditta Bartels, "High Failure Rates in In-Vitro Fertilization Treatments" 147 *Medical Journal of Australia,* 1987 pp. 474-475 (cited herein as Bartels, 1987). The following quotations attributed to Bartels come from the same source, unless otherwise indicated.

2. R.P. Jansen, "The Clinical Impact of In-Vitro Fertilization, Part 1. Results and Limitations of Conventional Reproductive Medicine" 146 *Medical Journal of Australia,* 1987, pp. 342-353. See also Peter Paterson and Clement Chan, 'What Proportion of Couples Undergoing Unrestricted in Vitro Fertilization Treatments Can Expect to Bear a Child?' *Journal of In Vitro Fertilization and Embryo Transfer,* 1987, Vol 4, No. 6, pp. 334-337. Astonishingly, although a longitudinal study, this research shows no evidence, in the publication, of concern about possible detrimental longterm effects for women of being on IVF programmes, and advocates that women undergo more treatments, more often, to raise the possibilities of "viable pregnancies" being created on the programmes. The abstract states:

   A 200-patient cohort has been established so that longitudinal analysis can determine the likelihood of an individual in vitro fertilization (IVF) entrant achieving a viable uterine pregnancy or a live baby. After a minimum of 39 months of access to repeated treatment cycles, 24% have achieved at least one viable pregnancy by undergoing an average of 2.48 treatment cycles per cohort member. Life-table analysis shows that most of these pregnancies have occurred in the first year after entering the program. Many members have undergone only one or two treatment cycles. In the future greater emphasis will need to be placed on factors which encourage *couples* to undergo additional cycles of treatment. This, as much as technical advances, may increase outcome figures. (Emphasis added.)

   Notably, the reality is that it is *women,* not 'couples,' who are required on IVF programmes to undergo surgery and hormonal stimulation, with their inevitable (and also unknown) side effects. Further, what alone seems to be of concern is the raising of percentages of 'viable pregnancies'. What of live birth outcome? What is included in the definition of 'viable' pregnancy?

3. Renate Klein, "When Medicalisation Equals Experimentation and Creates Illness: The Impact of the New Reproductive Technologies on Women", *Conference Proceedings of the Forum International Sur les Nouvelles Technologies de la Reproduction Humaine* organised by the Office of the Status of Women, 1988, Universite Concordia, Montreal, Canada (cited herein as Klein, 1988a).

4. See Marian E. Carter, 'Ovarian Carcinoma in a Patient Hyperstimulated by Gonadotropin Therapy for in Vitro Fertilization: A Case Report' *Journal of in Vitro Fertilization and Embryo Transfer,* 1987 Vol 4, No. 2, pp. 126-128; cited Klein, 1988a.

5. See Klein, 1988a; also Renate D. Klein, "Genetic and Reproductive Engineering: The Global View", this volume.

6. See Klein, 1988a.

7. Klein, 1988a. The quotations immediately following come from the same source.

8. Bartels, 1987a.

9. Women who have been outspoken in Australia on new reproductive technology issues, including in particular Dr. Robyn Rowland, Ramona Koval, and in more recent years Dr. Renate Klein, have been met with repeated attempts on the part of some proponents of IVF and other reproductive technologies

to discount or discredit their concerns and presentations of many women's realities of these programmes. A number of journalists have informed these spokespeople of this and, during the initial years of the IVF debate, participation in seminars and conferences resulted in a more direct awareness.

10. Ditta Bartels, "The Engineering of Reproduction: Is it heading off the rails?" *The Fifth Keith Roby Lecture in Community Science*, 14 October 1987, monograph published by Murdoch University (cited herein as Bartels, 1987b). The immediately following quotations come from the same source.

11. S. Fabro, "The Etiology of Birth Defects" in *Ob/Gyn News*, 1985, p. 4.

12. Klein, 1988a. Following quotations from Klein, 1988a unless otherwise indicated.

13. Voluntary Licensing Authority for Human in Vitro Fertilisation and Embryology, *Second Report*, April 1987, London; cited Klein, 1988a.

14. See Jocelynne A. Scutt, "Women's Bodies, Patriarchal Principles — Genetic and Reproductive Engineering and the Law", this volume.

15. See Jocelynne A. Scutt, "Disturbing Connections — Natural and Artificial Conception and the Right to Choose", this volume.

16. See Attorney General's Department, *Report on Maintenance Arrangements*, 1984, Canberra, ACT; Jocelynne A. Scutt, 'Who's Right; Whose Responsibility?' *Labor Forum*, 1986, Vol 9, No. I, pp. 1-5.

17. See further Jocelynne A. Scutt, "Disturbing Connections — Natural and Artificial Conception and the Right to Choose", this volume and Renate D. Klein, "Genetic and Reproductive Engineering — The Global View", this volume.

18. See further Jocelynne A. Scutt, "Disturbing Connections — Natural and Artificial Conception and the Right to Choose", this volume.

19. Klein, 1988a. The following quotation is from the same source.

20. The length of deliberations was widely reported on in the media at the time, with a deal of speculation about the way the numbers on the committee "lined up".

   Discussions with Ramona Koval in relation to the effect of this section of the *Infertility (Medical Procedures) Act* 1984, the committee's proposed amendment, a critique of that proposal, and an alternative position were central to the formulation of ideas in this section.

21. See *The Warnock Report on Human Fertilisation and Embryology — A Question of Life*, 1984, HMSO, London; reprinted 1985, Basil Blackwell, Oxford; at paras 11.19-11.22, pp. 64-66.

22. An Austrian medical student who participated in a course on IVF gives a disturbing picture of the "harvesting process" in one IVF programme:
   Lying on the gynaecologist's chair, legs apart, an object for the spectators, the woman was shaking with shame and fear . . . Dr. X, sitting between her legs, introduces the vaginal scanner. Free-handed he punctures the follicles by each time thrusting the needle into the woman, analogous to the desire to penetrate. All the students present stare at her genitals. After harvesting five follicles the woman wants to stop the torture because it hurts so much. 'But,' Dr. X says soothingly, 'there are still such beautiful follicles', and against her will follicle six and seven are punctured as well. Each time, with each thrusting of the needle she shakes with pain but Dr. X insists on continuing even to the point where only a black follicle which looks like a bubble remains. It turns out to be a cyst.

   And all of this is considered routine despite the fact that while puncturing a follicle, Dr. X injured the iliac vein. Such life-threatening injuries are diminished and cast aside with jokes: when he had finished, the doctor suggested the patient have breakfast with her husband and go shopping.

Quoted Klein, 1988a; from an article in *The Exploitation of Infertility: Women and Reproductive Technology*, Renate Klein, editor, 1988 (cited herein as Klein, 1988b).

23. Klein, 1988a. The immediately following quotations come from the same source.

24. Merle Hoffman, *On the Issues — The Journal of Substance for Progressive Women*, 1987, VIII, pp. 3, 22-24. The immediately following quotations are from the same source.

25. Phyllis Chesler, *Mothers on Trial — The Battle for Children and Custody*, 1986, McGraw-Hill; 1987, Seal Press, Seattle, Washington.

26. Bartels, 1987b.

27. Personal communication, January 1988. The immediately following quotations are from the same source. See also "Kriminalisierung von Gentechnologie-Kritikern — Nach BKA-Razzia stieg Interesse an Bio-Technologien/1000 Interessiert bei 'Fabrik' — Veranstaltung", *Taz* 7 January 1988, p. 19.

The present author holds a number of documents written by women involved in these raids and in support of those arrested, including *Der Stoff aus dem Terroristinnen gemacht werden — Veranstaltung zur Verbreitung unterbliebener Nachrichten — Widerstand am Beispiel Gentechnoloige & Bevölkerungspolitik, Zur Situation nach den Durchsuchungen vom 18 Dezember 1987*, printed pamphlet, 5 January 1988.

My thanks to Dr. R. Klein for this information.

28. This body search and noting of body marks has echoes of connections made in times past by those in authority between physical appearance and 'terrorist' activity. On this issue see for example Cesare Lombroso, *The Female Offender*, 1898, London; Heinrich Kramer and James Sprenger, *The Malleus Maleficarum* ("The Hammer of Witches"), first English edition with introduction by Montague Summers published 1928, John Rodker, London; reprint 1971, Dover Publications, New York. (It is uncertain when the first edition of the *Malleus Maleficarum* was published, but Summers puts the likeliest year as 1486; fourteen editions were published between 1487 and 1520, with at least a further sixteen editions between 1574 and 1669. All were issued by leading German, French and Italian presses.) See also William Renwick Riddell, "Sir Matthew Hale and Witchcraft" 1926-1927; *Journal of Criminal Law, Criminology and Police Science* Vol 17, pp. 5-12; William Renwick Riddell, 'The Trial of Witches' 1930-1931; *Journal of Criminal Law, Criminology and Police Science*, Vol 21, pp. 257-260; Elaine Showalter, *The Female Malady — Women, Madness and English Culture 1830-1980*, 1987, Virago Press, London; Jocelynne A. Scutt, "Schemers, Dragons and Witches: Criminal 'Justice' and the Fairer Sex" in *Domineering Dowagers and Scheming Concubines*, Suzanne Dixon and Barbara Garlick, editors, forthcoming.

29. See Ian Edwards, "The History of Preterm", *Preterm Sydney Australia Newsletter, 10 years 1974-1984*, 1984, p. 2, and that newsletter issue generally; also personal communication on the circumstances surrounding the raid and women's activism in relation thereto, Julia Truebridge, 15 February 1988. On the *Levine ruling* and *Menhennit ruling* and the law relating thereto, see Jocelynne A. Scutt, "Disturbing Connections — Natural and Artificial Conception and the Right to Choose", this volume.

30. See for example Christine Crowe, "Bearing the Consequences — Women Experiencing IVF", this volume; Gena Corea, "Women, Class and Reproductive and Genetic Engineering — The Effect of New Reproductive Technologies on All Women", this volume; Renate D. Klein, "Genetic and

Reproductive Engineering — The Global View", this volume; Jocelynne A. Scutt, "Women's Bodies, Patriarchal Principles — Genetic and Reproductive Engineering and the Law", this volume: Renate Klein, 1988b.

31. Klein, 1988b. The final quotation comes from the same source.
32. See for example Glenys Bell, "What More Can Women Want Now?" *The Bulletin* 23 February 1988, pp. 54-60; Jocelynne A. Scutt, *Growing Up Feminist — The New Generation of Australian Women*, 1985, Angus and Robertson, Sydney; Jocelynne A. Scutt, *Different Lives — Reflections on the Women's Movement and Visions of its Future*, 1987, Penguin Books Australia, Ringwood, Victoria.

Index

ABBREVIATIONS

FINRRAGE — Feminist International Network of Resistance to Reproductive and Genetic Engineering; FINNRET — Feminist International Network on the New Reproductive Technologies; IVF — *In vitro* fertilisation; NRTs — New Reproductive Technologies

CONTRIBUTORS

Marion Brown

Marion Brown is a feminist lawyer who worked for a number of years as founding lawyer of the Women's Legal Resources Centre in Lidcombe, a suburb of Sydney, New South Wales. She has written and lectured on the effect of the new reproductive technologies on women, and other medico-legal issues affecting women, and particularly in the area of criminal assault at home. Marion Brown works with the Women's Co-ordination Unit, formerly in the Department of the Premier and Cabinet and now in the Department of Family and Community Services, New South Wales, Australia.

Gena Corea

In 1977 Gena Corea's book *The Hidden Malpractice — How American Medicine Mistreats Women* was published in the USA and England. Before and since, Gena Corea, a United States' journalist, has published many articles and contributed to a number of books on women and medicine. She is author of *The Mother Machine: Reproductive Technologies from Artificial Insemination to Artificial Wombs*, published in 1985, and co-editor/contributor to *Man-Made Women — How New Reproductive Technologies Affect Women*, published in the same year. In 1986 she visited Australia at the invitation of the Law Reform Commission, Victoria, to conduct a seminar on the topic 'Determining Priorities in Health Resources — The Allocation of Scarce Medical Resources'.

Christine Crowe

Christine Crowe is completing her Ph.D. with the University of New South Wales, Australia, on the personal politics of women's involvement in new reproductive technologies, in particular as recipients in IVF programmes. She has studied and researched for her doctorate in Australia, France and Scotland, and has published and presented papers at conferences on IVF, in particular at the Emergency Conference on the New Reproductive Technologies in Vallinge, Sweden, in July 1985.

Kay Fielden

Kay Fielden holds the degrees of Bachelor of Arts and Bachelor of Laws from Macquarie University in New South Wales. She has practised as a nursing sister, and as a mediator in community justice, and is active in community affairs. A member of the NSW Women Lawyers Association, she has been a member of the Association's Research Committee since 1987. She is also an active member of the Migrant Women's Network, the Feminist Legal Issues Group and the Feminist Legal Action Group (FLAG). Her special interests include women's issues, current affairs, sociology, anthropology, politics, art and literature.

Joanne Finkelstein

Born in Melbourne, Australia, before accepting a scholarship to the United States of America where she gained a Ph.D. in sociology from the University of Illinois, Urbana, Joanne Finkelstein took out a BA (Hons) in sociology from La Trobe University and a Master of Education in sociology from Monash University, Victoria. Remaining in the USA for eight years, Joanne Finkelstein taught cultural studies and the sociology of medicine at several universities. She has published articles on medicine and its consequences for women, particularly in the area of high technology medicine. She participated in, and presented a paper to, the First National Conference on New Reproductive Technologies held at the Australian National University (ANU) in Canberra in May 1986. Joanne Finkelstein currently lives in Melbourne where she teaches in the Department of Anthropology and Sociology at Monash University.

Renate D. Klein

A Swiss-born neurobiologist and co-editor of *Test-Tube Women: What Future for Motherhood?* Renate Klein is co-editor of the Athene Series with Pergamon Press, and European editor of *Women's Studies International Forum*. She is also a member (together with Gena Corea and others) of the editorial board of *Reproductive and Genetic Engineering — Journal of International Feminist Analysis*, established by Pergamon Press in 1987 to recognise the use and abuse of women as central to the development of reproductive technologies and genetic engineering, and to highlight the relevance of the application of these technologies to the past, present, and emerging social and political conditions of women. In 1987 Renate D. Klein was awarded a Federation of University Women scholarship to study and research in Australia. She is currently Post-Doctoral Research Fellow at Deakin University, Victoria, Australia. In 1987 she was awarded her doctorate in women's studies from the University of London.

Ramona Koval

Ramona Koval formerly lectured in the Environment and Technology Policy Unit, Department of Planning, Policy and Landscape, at the Royal Melbourne Institute of Technology (RMIT) in Victoria, Australia. Trained in genetics and micro-biology, for a number of years she worked as a freelance journalist for ABC radio and the press, writing on issues of medicine, science and society. She is undertaking further research at Melbourne University in the trial studies of science. Her book, *Eating Your Heart Out*, analysing food, shape and the body industry, was published by Penguin Books Australia in 1986. In 1985 Ramona Koval presented a paper at the Emergency Conference on the New Reproductive Technologies in Sweden. She is currently Australian Broadcasting Corporation (ABC) presenter on the morning radio programme from Monday to Friday, covering political, economic, health and legal issues, and general current affairs.

Terese McFadden

As mother of a large and happy family, Terese McFadden is well qualified to write on the issue of surrogate motherhood and how it affects the lives of those involved. She is currently pursuing studies in arts at the University of New England in New South Wales, and in 1984 presented a paper on "Issues in Surrogacy" to the Australian and New Zealand Association for the Advancement of Science (ANZAAS) Congress held at Monash University in Melbourne, Victoria, as a participant invited and sponsored by ANZAAS.

Anna Murdoch

A journalist with the Melbourne, Australia, daily newspaper, *The Age*, Anna Murdoch has written numerous articles on social, political, economic and arts issues as they affect women and women's lives. She also writes regularly as a journalist covering social, political, economic and arts generally. Anna Murdoch has been a frequent contributor to 'Accent Age', the twice weekly page included in *The Age*, which deals with feminist and women's issues. She is currently living in Melbourne, Victoria.

Jocelynne A. Scutt

Jocelynne A. Scutt is a feminist lawyer who has written and edited a number of books on women, law and feminist theory, including *Growing Up Feminist — The New Generation of Australian Women; Different Lives — Reflections on the Women's Movement and Visions of its Future; Women and Crime* (with S.K. Mukherjee): *Even in the Best of Homes — Violence in the Family*; and (with Di Graham) *For Richer, For Poorer — Money, Marriage and Property Rights*. She has studied law in Australia, the USA, England and West Germany. From 1984-1986 she was Commissioner and Deputy Chairperson of the Law Reform Commission, Victoria, and is now in private practice in Melbourne, Australia.